MAN'S BOOK

SAFARI
Doug Allan

★

BIRTH OF THUNDER
Robin Cranford

★

THE BOAT
Walter Gibson

★

THE CHASE
Richard Unekis

ODHAMS BOOKS LIMITED
LONG ACRE, LONDON

MADE AND PRINTED IN
GREAT BRITAIN BY ODHAMS (WATFORD) LTD.,
WATFORD, HERTS.
S.964.RA

CONTENTS

SAFARI

Doug Allan

Introduction by LOWELL THOMAS, JR.

"Safari" is published by
Rolton House Inc., New York

The Author

For many years Doug Allan, a pioneer in TV,
has been producing programmes of action.
He also has had a passion for exploration,
and has become personally acquainted
with every explorer of note. Mr. Allan has
collaborated with these fearless men and
women and has combined their exciting true
adventures into this volume. He has written
four other books, entitled *Building Careers,
How To Write For Television, Lightning
Strikes Once,* and *Gamblers With Fate,* which
has been likened to Moby Dick. Doug Allan
believes this book to be more dramatic and
spell-binding than any of his former works.

DEDICATION

*It is a privilege to dedicate this book to
the three lovely ladies in my life: my
wife, Margaret, my daughter, Judy, and
my Mother.*

INTRODUCTION

SINCE the days of Marco Polo and long before, too, men have been curious to know what lay beyond those distant mountain ranges, or what mysteries might be hidden beyond the wide horizons of those expansive seas. Surely, there must be strange lands, inhabited by strange people, with weird tongues and strange customs.

Man's curiosity has led him to sacrifice comparative comforts of civilization to venture off with the prospects of ever prevalent hardships in search of that vision which has beckoned him to hack his way through the gnarled underbrush of the tense, silent jungles of the Belgian Congo; to trek on long, weary, exhausting safaris across the wind-swept sands of the endless Sahara; to face almost constant dangers in his hunt for the prowling beasts of the African wilds; to scale the pinnacles of the snow-capped mountains and to descend to the shadowless depths beneath the sea.

Never fully satisfied, man kept moving on in search of that elusive something which we call—Adventure.

It has been my good fortune to satisfy my urge for adventure in my constant searching for men and women who have personally experienced the varied forms of exploration, and then, to hear them relate their dramatic experiences to the world during my interviews with them, and, also, to present the brilliant color motion pictures of their adventures on television.

Nearly every man and woman of any consequence in the world of exploration has, at some time or another, related their rare experiences to me.

In a sense, I have re-lived so many of their adventures with them, almost as vividly as if I were present on their safaris, that I feel pretty much as though my experiences constituted a composite of all of theirs.

During my interview with adventurers, I have always liked to feel that we were traveling together through the jungles or the deserts, in the treks across the ice-packs of the Polar regions, or scaling the sides of lofty mountains, or even donning fins and aqualungs to descend in search of undersea creatures or sunken hulks in the ancient sea lanes.

So, in order to grasp the richness, to get the full impact of the stirring adventures recorded in this volume, let us visualize our selves as being members of each thrilling safari as we now proceed to re-live each explorer's experience.

In *Safari* Doug Allan writes about the perils of the hunt and of life among strange peoples. He is well qualified to do so, having known most of the American and many of the British explorers and adventurers who have made that continent their beat, and having been an avid follower of their stories.

Some of us who have roamed the deserts and rain forests of Africa have felt that the greatest danger to human life on that enormous continent is the simple mosquito—the variety that carries malaria! Others, however, have singled out the leopard or the rogue elephant. There's nothing very exciting about the mosquito, so perhaps it is fortunate for those who like a good yarn that Doug Allan has gathered together in this book stories, mostly of Man against Beast—accounts of mighty hunters and adventurers on safari.

Of the thrilling yarns here gathered I think my favorite is the one about the Nile—kayaks, cataracts and angry hippos. Which, I wonder, will be your favorite?

Lowell Thomas, Jr.

Anchorage, Alaska

ACKNOWLEDGMENTS

Acknowledgment is made to the following for permission to use material in this anthology:

SEVEN-TON SPOOK, by Russell B. Aitken, and ELEPHANT SEPULCHER, by Brian O'Brien, both published in Field and Stream by Henry Holt and Company, Inc.

ZANZABUKU (dangerous safari), by Lewis Cotlow, published by Rinehart & Company, Incorporated.

CAMERA SAFARI and SIX-TON CHARGE, by Robert Halmi, and BLACK RHINO OF KILIMANJARO, by Doug Kennedy, courtesy True— The Man's Magazine, Fawcett Publications, Inc.

MY STRUGGLE TO REACH THE ROOF OF AFRICA, from Safari Magazine, by Weider Barbell Co., Inc.

GORILLA WARFARE, by Hal Hennesey, and NIGHT WATCH, by Brian O'Brien, both published in Real. Copyright by Popular Library, Inc.

GORILLAS CAN'T HOLD THEIR LIQUOR, by Brian O'Brien, published in Stag. Copyright by Magazine Management Company. For permission to use maps, acknowledgment is made to the following:

Belgian Government Information Center, Belgium and Belgium Congo.

British Information Services, an Agency of the British Government.

East Africa Tourist Travel Assn.

Victor Bennett, Ltd.

French Embassy Press & Information Division.

CHAPTER ONE

THE RAMPAGING SPOOK

"GROGGY from lack of sleep, I was so busy scanning the ground for spoor that I almost bumped head-on into the wrinkled gray bark of the Baobab. Only this wasn't a tree. It was the front leg of a murderous old rogue elephant, waiting to make me his fourteenth victim," related Russell B. Aitken, past president of the New York Adventurers Club, a Fellow of the Royal Geographical Society, a noted writer and big-game hunter, who makes Africa his favorite stamping grounds.

"We were jolting across Sichifuru bush in Northern Rhodesia," continued Russ Aitken, "when the game ranger suddenly slammed on the brakes. For a moment I thought he'd spotted a reedbuck or an oribi for camp meat, but I was wrong. I've something to show you," he said. "Come along." And we headed over toward the bush.

Climbing out of the Land Rover, I followed him, with Jacob, my Kaonde Ila skinner-tracker, bringing up the rear. The last thing I expected to see in that sun-baked corner of nothingness was a grave. But here was one—or what was left of one. The headstone had been pushed over to a crazy angle and the mound rooted up as if by vandals. Some old dried-up flowers lay scattered among the pieces of a broken clay pot.

The ranger let out a string of curses in assorted English and kitchen Kaffir. "The ruddy beggar!" he growled. "He's done it again."

"Oh?" I said blankly.

"Shajetemo, I mean."

I was still in the dark. "Who the heck is Shajetemo?" I asked.

The ranger squinted at me, a pained expression etched on his leathery face. "My sainted aunt!" he grunted. "I would have bet a quid that there wasn't a bloke in this half of Africa who hadn't heard of Shajetemo. It's like saying you never heard of the Man Eaters of Tsavo."

"Don't tell me a lion ripped up that tombstone," I said coldly. "I may be gullible, but I won't buy that."

He scratched a match on the seat of his faded khaki shorts and held it to his pipe. "No," he said. "Shajetemo isn't a lion. He's a bloody bull elephant, older than the Baobab tree, if you can believe the wogs—worst rogue we've ever had. So far he's killed twelve people and crippled a lot more."

If he was trying to impress me, he succeeded. I jerked my thumb toward the grave. "Who's buried here?"

"Walker, a hunter from Choma. Got mashed into mincemeat after taking a pot shot at the old beggar. Happened four years ago. And every season that crazy bull comes back to spade up the grave with his tusks and yank out the tombstone."

"Maybe I'm over-simplifying things, but why don't you wait and clobber the critter?"

The ranger snorted. "Don't think we haven't tried, chum. It's like trying to grab a handful of smoke. We've never let up on him, but Shajetemo is strictly a hit-and-run and we can't bribe a local tribesman to track him. They think he's the incarnation of some nasty old witch doctor. Once we even tried locating him from a small plane. My Mashukulumbwi boys claim that we couldn't spot him from the air because he's so big he's got a forest growing on his back."

He walked over to a crater the size of a fifty-gallon garbage can. "Here's his track," he said, "made during the rains." It was the print of a left hind foot, clearly defined. He pointed to a big gap left by a missing toe. "That's how you'll recognize his spoor. Probably nipped off by a croc."

Hauling a tape out of my pocket, I looped it around the impression and whistled through my teeth. Even allowing for the expansion of the flange as it sank into the muck, the print still measured a conservative sixty-nine inches. That would put Shajetemo somewhere in the class of the great Knysna bull in the Capetown Museum.

By now I was really impressed. "I suppose he's tuskless?" I said. Most of the rogues I'd bumped into had either been tuskless or had very small teeth.

"The wogs claim he carries heavy ivory," the ranger replied. "Don't hesitate to pop the old devil if you get the opportunity. But don't take any foolish chances."

Jacob had been listening to our conversation, and now he spoke up. To shoot him is useless, *baa*, for Shajetemo has a great magic that turns bullets into water. The elders of my tribe say that he is like the *fishanguku*, an evil creature that can kill but cannot be killed. He is a bad ghost, *baas*.

I kicked one of the big round biscuits of dung, half the size of a volley ball. "For a ghost," I scoffed, "he leaves some mighty solid souvenirs."

The ranger cut in again. "If you run across his fresh spoor," he wheedled, "the brute needs killing badly. You'd be doing us a big favor."

I shook my head vigorously. "No dice, pal. A little old roan antelope is what I've flown ten thousand miles for, you may recall. And it looks like finding a good one is going to be a full-time job."

He wouldn't give up. "Plenty of roan around. You might luck into a decent one before breakfast tomorrow."

"Fat chance! Anyway, all I've brought on this trip is my .30-06, a weapon you limeys like to call a rook rifle. You couldn't get me near that seven-ton spook of yours with anything smaller than a bazooka."

"Maybe you're right," he conceded. "Of course, old Karamojo Bell killed stacks of jumbos with his little .256, but he knew their anatomy inside out."

"I knew all about Bell and his .256 Mannlicher," I growled. "He was a good friend of mine. Unfortunately, I am not Karamojo Bell. The only anatomy I know is my own and I'm trying hard to keep its inventory intact."

He grinned. "I know what you mean."

Half an hour later he dropped me off at my camp. "Well," he said, "I won't be seeing you again. Monday I'm off to England for my furlough. Good luck."

Jacob and I got back to the business of finding a good roan antelope, a powerful buck with bristling mane and a fast gallop that caused early hunters to nickname him the horse-antelope. Two years earlier in the Sichifuru I'd seen scads of them in the distance while I was chasing that Holy Grail of African big game —the sable antelope. Now, having come back specifically for roan, all I could find was their big, splayed tracks in the mud near the pans. To make matters worse, grass fires had swept across the area. With the new grass not up yet, and the waterholes shrinking to filthy puddles, the game herds were drifting across the Barotse Cattle Cordon.

After a week of fruitless hunting we loaded up the jeep and

joined the migration. Heading westward through mopane scrub, we rattled in and out of pig holes and churned through sand, dust and clouds of acrid ashes. Out beyond Kowetu we cruised across Bamashasha country toward Monkoya where the only game we saw were two scrawny blue wildebeest and a wart hog. The breeze was as hot as the breath of a blast furnace and swarms of tsetse flies attacked us.

Finally, I pointed the radiator cap toward the Luampo River, figuring that's where the buck would be. They were all there, too —except the roan. Discouraged, I was sitting on a campstool opening a can of steak-and-kidney one evening, when Jacob shouted to me. Across the veld a native was approaching at a dogtrot. There was something familiar about him.

And small wonder. It was N'Yambe, the faithful tracker who had guided me to a coveted prize on my earlier safari—a record-busting sable bull. Staggering under the weight of a huge musket, he halted in front of me. His cheetah-skin breechcloth was soggy with perspiration. It was obvious he had come a long way through the sickening heat.

Somehow he managed to draw his slim mahogany body erect, holding both hands high in the royal salute. "*Shangwe! Shangwe,* tall baas!" he gasped. The white-toothed smile I remembered was missing, and N'Yambe's sad face made him seem a stranger. Squatting on his haunches, he clapped his hands several times in the Barotse sign of respect.

I shook him warmly by the hand. "Greetings, N'Yambe, son of Tundala," I said in the vernacular. "Seeing you again makes this a happy day. But what brings you here?"

It took him a couple of minutes to catch his breath. Finally he spoke. "Tall baas, long ago I was your man in the Sichifuru. There, by means of my wonderful tracking, I found you the prize you had sought so long and desired so much—the great black *kwalata.*"

"That is true, N'Yambe. And it was truly the grandfather of all *kwalatas.*"

"At the time, baas," he continued, "although you offered me many pounds as a reward, I took only my daily wage, because it was an honor to serve you."

"And I was proud to have so fine a tracker, N'Yambe," I replied, matching compliment for compliment, as was expected of me, and wondering what the devil was coming.

He drew himself even more erect and stood there like a bronzed Pharaoh. "We Barotse are a proud race, baas, and I am not one to beg. But now, I need your help."

I knew I was on the hook for something, but hadn't a clue as to what it might be. "Is it that your tribe needs meat, N'Yambe?"

"No, tall baas. For such a simple thing I would not bother you. It is much worse. Three days ago, my beautiful *umfazi*, Nyakutemba, daughter of Nyakatoro, was herding our cattle to pasture. By evening, when she had not returned to my kraal, I set out to find her."

"I hope she is not lost, N'Yambe."

"I found her, baas, but she was no longer beautiful. She was dead, tall baas."

I remembered his speaking of his Nyakutemba as an avid art collector speaks of some rare treasures he yearns after. In the Sichifuru, on the other safari, he had planned to use his wages to buy enough cattle to meet the bride price.

"It is no longer a happy day, N'Yambe. Was it a lion or a leopard that did this terrible thing?"

"No, baas. It was Shajetemo." He spat the name out as if it had a foul taste. "Near her was found his spoor. He had squashed my Nyakutemba beneath his foot as a baboon crushes a beetle."

"My heart aches for you, N'Yambe," I said, and I meant it.

"You are my friend," he said simply. "That is why I have come to ask you to help me slay the mad one, for I have sworn a great oath that I will not rest until he too lays in the dust."

I had to think fast. My time was limited, and I still hadn't found the record-class roan bull I'd come for. Stalling, I asked, "How is it, N'Yambe, that you dare to take up the trail of Shajetemo, the ghost elephant. And what makes you think that I would take such a risk?"

"Tall baas," he said, "it was you who killed the lion of Kachereko, the man-eater, when no native would lift his hand against him because the witch doctors swore that he was a fisanguku. It was you who said that it was only an old and hungry animal, too slow to catch the fleet zebra. And you proved it, baas, with a bullet from your magic rifle."

"I have no magic rifle, N'Yambe. Nor have I even the big .375 I used on that lion." I pointed out the little Winchester bolt-action propped against the tree.

"It does not matter," he said excitedly. "I, myself, now own a powerful gun for which I traded most of my cattle."

He flourished the mighty musket with pride. A real relic, it was a muzzle-loading 4-bore "roer", a percussion piece that ought to have been in the museum at Livingstone. Its worm-eaten stock was held together by the inside skin of an elephant's ear that had been put on green a century earlier.

He saw me eyeing the gadget. "It is a powerful charm, baas, to keep Shajetemo from hearing or smelling me. And I will give the witch doctors my last heier so that you will also be covered by its wonderful magic."

It was up to me. If I ignored my friend's plea, every native within a hundred miles would turn his face from me. And I wouldn't blame them much.

Stashed away in one of the chop boxes were twenty rounds of special .30-06 solids that Bert Shay had loaded for me. Fitted up with old Krag bullets, they had enough powder behind them to push through five feet of oak at good velocity. But I hadn't had an opportunity to try them on a tusker and didn't cherish the idea of using Shajetemo as a guinea pig. Yet, gazing at the sad, trustful face of N'Yambe, I knew I had but one choice.

"A man can only die once, N'Yambe," I grunted. "In the morning, I will go with you."

Jacob looked glum, but the Barotse leaped high into the air, yelled *"Shangwe!"* as loudly as a hog caller and clapped me on the back.

Unrolling his reed mat, he brought forth his *chiapaupau* sack and extracted some chunks of manioc and twists of *dakka,* native tobacco, which he placed in the branches of a nearby tree. Hoisting the heavy musket into a fork, he hung the polished skull of a tiny steinbok over the muzzle. N'Yambe, son of Tundala, was invoking his gods.

It seemed I had hardly closed my eyes that night when Jacob was thrusting the inevitable cup of hot tea at me, which meant that it was 5 a.m. "What this country needs," I grumbled, "is longer nights and more of them."

When he hadn't responded with his usual grin, I knew he was still worried about that prospect of messing around with a killer elephant. "Relax, Jacob," I said, "I promise that you will not have to go after Shajetemo. Once we cut a fresh track, N'Yambe and I will go on foot while you guard the car." He blossomed

into a wide smile, his sharp-filed teeth making his mouth look
like a small white-painted bear trap.

Outside my tent flap, N'Yambe was squatting on his hunkers.
His eyes were shining. "Look, baas! The gods are with us."
He pointed to his private juju tree. "Last night, they accepted
my offerings."

The manioc and dakka were gone, all right, which didn't
surprise me. I figured that monkeys had probably carried off
the manioc, and I wouldn't have put it past Jacob to swipe the
tobacco.

It didn't take long to strike camp and head for N'Yambe's
kraal. Shajetemo, we learned, was lumbering due west with a
three-day headstart. His spoor was too cold to do us much good,
but we got plenty of information from the Barotse. The mad bull
had invaded two villages in broad daylight, crippling an old man
and smashing down reed huts. Two raids in a row gave us a fix
on his general direction, and the jeep had enough speed to reach
the scene of his third attack while his trail was only three hours
old.

Leaving Jacob to set up camp, I stuffed some grub and a small
teakettle into a knapsack and doled out as much mealie meal as
N'Yambe could carry. Then we were off. Within two hours we
had come upon a pyramid of droppings which N'Yambe probed
with his big toe and pronounced warm.

From that moment on we examined every thicket with a
jaundiced eye. N'Yambe, excited now and tracking with the
fervor of a beagle, set off at a brisk trot. Several times we came
upon balls of sansevieria that the bull had spit out after extracting the juice. An hour later, having smelled the familiar stench
of elephant urine on the breeze, we located a big wet patch of
sand still frothy and bubbling. That meant our quarry was a
scant half hour ahead. I began to get the feeling that proximity
to a tusker always brings, a heady mixture of exhilaration and
sheer fear.

I needn't have got into a lather about it. Swift as was our
pursuit, Shajetemo's long-legged amble was even faster. And
we were badly handicapped by having to claw our way through
thickets that to him were mere cobwebs.

Even though Shajetemo was hotfooting it upwind, he seemed
to sense that we were on his trail. Avoiding the open, he plowed
through patches of stuff that slowed us down to a shuffle,

blistered my heels and frazzled my nerves. Several times we were close enough to catch a whiff of his pungent, circusy odor, but never had even a fleeting glimpse of the rogue.

Four days on the trail can seem like four months when you have the hard earth as a pillow and the nights chill you to the bone. On the fifth day, when we were down to short rations and a swallow of water apiece, we suddenly made contact. And I mean suddenly.

Groggy from lack of sleep, I was so busy scanning the ground for spoor in a gloomy thicket that I almost bumped into the wrinkled gray bark of a Baobab. Except that this was not a tree. It was one of Shajetemo's front legs. Purely by reflex, I hurled myself sideways just as his rolled-up trunk came smashing down on the spot I'd just vacated. A mobile mountain of violence and hate towered twelve feet above me, solid as a mountain. Then he let out a locomotive-whistle scream, and I thought for sure I had reached the end of the line.

Almost paralysed with fright, I quieted the knocking of my knees long enough to aim fast at the bottom of the V in the middle of his chest, the spot where the windpipe enters the body. My gun was wobbling crazily. For one mad moment I felt sure I'd never be able to pull the trigger—at least, not to have it aim where it would really do any good. I had no time to think! He was hovering over me, about to land in a split-second. I couldn't duck out of his way. I had to face him! My gun was still waving nervously toward him. I couldn't seem to pull the trigger. Finally, somehow I managed to squeeze it. If Shajetemo was hard hit, he kept it a secret. Just as he started to rip up a tree to toss my way, I tried to slam a fresh cartridge into the chamber and couldn't. A twig had jammed between face and receiver.

Then I panicked! In my blind flight I almost collided with N'Yambe, who was standing stupefied, holding a hand over his eyes. Still clawing frantically at the bolt, I glanced over my shoulder. The mad bull was bearing down on us under a full head of steam. His great ears, ballooned out sail-fashion, were flapping as he came and his snaky trunk was curled in a tight spiral against his chest.

I made a little headway in unjamming the bolt, but not enough; so as I sailed past N'Yambe, I gave him a whack. "The knee!" I bellowed. "Hit him in the knee!"

The lumbering leviathan was almost on top of us before the

Barotse came out of his trance and fired. There was a blast which nearly ruptured my ear-drums and an incredible cloud of black smoke as N'Yambe was catapulted backward. I chanced a glance over my shoulder. Dimly visible through the smoke screen, Shajetemo had halted, riveted in his tracks by a great gory hole in his leg. I finally managed to horse a fresh cartridge into place, then sprinted up alongside the rogue, just out of reach of his lashing trunk.

It took only a split second to clobber him with a slug through the spine. As his crippled knee collapsed under him, he sank to the ground with the impressiveness of a proud old castle collapsing into rubble. All the fury was drained out of him; now, he was just a helpless old animal, and I gave him a finisher through the brain from behind. I'm six foot three inches but, standing next to that gigantic hulk, I knew how a germ must feel when it has just killed a man.

Helping N'Yambe to his feet, I tore a piece off my shirt-tail to stanch the blood from a cheek that had been chopped into hamburg by the recoil of the musket. Still in a state of shock, he stood there gaping at Shajetemo in dazed disbelief. *"Ena fili!"* he kept muttering. "He is dead! He is dead!"

It was true. We had exorcised the old spook for keeps. There wasn't any forest growing on his back, and my bullets hadn't turned to water as the native had fearfully believed they would. The slugs through the chest and spine had stayed inside him. The .30-06 to the brain had drilled fore and aft through seven inches of cellular-bone skull wall. In sundry parts of his anatomy we found a number of old musket balls.

Within two hours, half the population of Barotseland were on hand doing a wacky snake dance around their defunct foe, pummeling me black and blue and squeezing my hand until it squeaked. They'd already given N'Yambe the full hero treatment.

The elephant, unfortunately, was not my trophy. By law, the paramount chief of the district would get one tusk, the government the other. As far as I was concerned, virtue was going to have to be its own reward.

It didn't work out that way. Picking up Jacob and heading back to the Sichifuru, we returned by a route that brought us to a tiny vlei. And standing there drinking was the grandpaw of all roan antelope—a whopper of a bull with world-record-size horns. He was not only big, he was a bit stupid. He didn't see or hear me as I sneaked up to within a hundred yards and dropped him with a high spine shot.

He was deader than Shajetemo when I reached him, and one hell of a trophy. Jacob came up at a lope and took a look, his eyes widening. *"Baas,"* he croaked, "this is no ordinary *gwenki*, for he did not smell you, although the wind blew toward him." Since I hadn't had a bath in a week, Jacob had a point.

He bent down to examine the thick annulated arcs of the horns. "This great *gwenki* is surely a gift from the gods," he whispered, "the gods to whom N'Yambe gave fine presents."

He made it sound very romantic. It might have sounded even more so if I hadn't spotted a familiar-looking twist of dakka sticking out of the rascal's pocket. Jacob had been out of tobacco when we'd left the Sichifuru. But that was his business. With my seven-ton spook dead, and me still alive, I was in no mood to look a gift horse-antelope in the mouth.

CHAPTER TWO

ITURI FOREST PYGMIES

AT first glance, Pygmies are caricatures of human beings, miniature imitations in fact. When I first set eyes on them, I caught myself staring as I might at circus freaks until checked by the thought, "How do I look to them?", prompted by Lewis Cotlow, who, on several occasions, has lived with the Bambuti Pygmies of the Great Ituri Forest of the Belgian Congo.

"You must first try to understand them," he said. "They're a strange little people."

Lew Cotlow is one of comparatively few explorers who have made a sincere effort. One of his major reasons for adventuring is to understand strange people, whose customs and cultures differ greatly from those of the civilized world. Whenever he sets out on a safari, he winds up living with either the Colorado Indians of the Upper Amazon, the fiber skirted Yaquas or the Jivaro headhunters of the Ecuadorian jungles. Or, if he travels to Africa, you'll find him entering into the primitive tribal life in Equatorial Africa, Kenya, Tanganyika, or Uganda. Lew is one of the few men to plant the New York Explorers Club flag in remote parts of the world. He has won international acclaim for his color motion pictures and books about his safaris.

If a Pygmy looks like a wizened ten-year-old in my eyes, he must see me as an awkward giant, said Lew. My figure must seem unalluringly straight and flat, lacking the many curves that appeal to a Pygmy—balloon-like belly, sway back, and oversize, impudent buttocks. His golden-brown skin no doubt seems just right to him, a proper compromise between the brown-black of his Bantu neighbors on the edge of the Ituri and the pasty pallor of the occasional white visitor. He may suspect that I'm not that color all over, but how can he tell when, instead of wearing a sensible liana G-string with barkcloth apron, I cover all but hands and face with layers of cloth and encase my feet in heavy leather boots?

On several occasions I lived with Pygmies who had rarely seen white men—some of them never had. Once one grew so bold as to rub a finger over the back of my hand, to see if the white came off, like the paint he and other natives sometimes smear on their faces and bodies.

When you first meet a Pygmy, you cannot help staring at him with a kind of disbelief. The true Pygmy, the Bambuti averages four feet in height, and for most of us the only human beings that size are children. Pygmies, however, are obviously not children, in spite of a certain childlike quality, a naïve directness about them. Some have grey kinky hair, chin whiskers and faces wrinkled like a butternut. There are three-foot-nine-inch matrons with babies on their hips, suspended in a kind of sling from the shoulder. The shortness of the mothers is accentuated because Pygmy babies are normal size, as large as ours at the same age. Pygmy children just stop growing when they are about ten years old.

It is confusing to look at a female the size of your niece in the fourth grade and note that she is a toothless old hag with breasts like long empty leather pouches. Or to see a young fellow apparently too young for his first communion and realize that he may have slain fifty elephants by hamstringing their hind legs. Your preconceived notions about values and relationships collapse —which is one good reason for exploring.

If you live and work with Pygmies long enough in their own forest, this first startling impact of their juvenile size diminishes and even disappears. They are so perfectly adapted to their environment, to their work and play and houses and weapons, that they strike you as just about right. If you think of size any more, you think of your own awkward bulk. When that time comes, you finally begin to see the Pygmies with a true un-jaundiced eye, as human beings with a different heritage, back-ground and set of merits and faults.

In the early thirties, a narrow road was cut through a thousand square miles of primitive forest. After the road was built clearings made by the Bantus appeared. These in turn became little villages, adjacent to which are grown plantains, beans and rice.

The Bantus of the villages and the Pygmies have developed a strange interdependence. Only through the Bantu villagers, can one make contact with the Bambuti Pygmies.

If you want to buy a Pygmy bow and arrow, a spear or a head-dress, you cannot buy them from these little folk who seem to own them no matter how much you offer. You must purchase them from the Bantu who "owns" the Pygmy. If you need guides or hunters, you negotiate with the Bantu "masters".

The high point in life among these people is the elephant hunt. Not every male Pygmy is an elephant hunter; this most dangerous chore is reserved for the most alert, courageous and cool-headed. When an elephant hunter's reflexes slow down, he reluctantly gives up the chase for the mammoth and confines his activities to antelopes, pig and okapi.

No Pygmy goes on an elephant hunt casually, as he might for any other beast. The elephant demands preparations, the appease-ment of evil spirits, moral support from the entire village and a little something to bolster courage at the last minute. Some of the prospective hunters consult a medicine man the day before a projected hunt to learn if the signs are propitious.

Actually, the medicine man is not as influential as he is among most primitive tribes. The idea seems to be borrowed from the village Bantu, who lives at the edge of the forest, since few Pygmies themselves act as medicine men. The groups most closely tied to their Bantu owners, which means those who live on the edges of the forest rather than in its depths, are most likely to come under the witch doctor's influence and consult him in case of illness, sterility and a need of good fortune. None of the Pygmies on my second trip bothered to consult a witch doctor before going out elephant hunting.

They made other preparations, however. The day before the

hunt they went into the forest in search of kola nuts, large and pink, which their women boiled, pounded and boiled again. This is the nut from which is extracted the flavoring for all cola drinks, so Pygmies for centuries have enjoyed their pause that refreshes. The men also chew the kola nut for greater virility, they spit the fibres on their arms to advertise the fact to the girls.

First, of course, they must find their elephants. But since the forest is well populated by the big creatures, trackers rarely have much difficulty. By noon they may have located a small herd. The hunt would be much less dangerous if they could find a solitary elephant, of course, but elephants travel in groups most of the time, numbering from four or five and up. The Pygmies must worry not only about the beast they plan to slaughter, but all the others. Elephants show remarkable intelligence and concern for their fellows. I've seen, for example, two elephants support a wounded brother on either side, leading him to safety as two soldiers might carry a wounded comrade from the battlefield.

When the hunters locate their quarry, they study the terrain carefully, compare the elephants and select the one to be killed —usually the one with the largest tusks, for its ivory will bring the greatest rewards. The elephants are unaware of the midgets at this stage, for the hunters not only keep out of the wind but also smear themselves with elephant dung, of which they have found plenty along the trail.

When the lay of the land has been studied sufficiently the hunters retire about a hundred yards, build a small fire, and smoke hemp, or marijuana, to take away their fear. Then they are ready. With the best hunter in the lead, they return to the herd of elephants, who may be asleep in the noonday heat or quietly munching grass. The hunters cautiously approach the animal they have chosen, making certain to keep the wind just right, and circling if necessary to remain out of vision.

At this point the task looks almost ridiculous. A Pygmy is small by any standards, but alongside a huge elephant he looks so tiny, so weak, so ineffectual, that one feels like urging them to call the whole hunt off before they make fools of themselves.

If the elephant lifts its trunk and turns its head as if it heard or smelled something unfamiliar, the approaching Pygmies freeze into immobility. The elephant sniffs only an object that smells like another elephant, lowers its head, and goes on eating. Then the little men close in until two of them stand beside the hind legs of the elephant. The others place themselves to rout the other elephants and take up immediate pursuit of the selected animal.

At a silent signal the two leading hunters reach out with their sharp spears so the blades are just behind the elephant's knee joints. A sudden sharp slash and the tendon is severed in each hing leg. The two then dart away, the wounded elephant whirls to grab them with its trunk, the others shout and jump and bellow to frighten the rest of the herd into a stampede. They rush away, and the wounded animal tries to follow. But it can barely drag itself along, its hind legs being useless.

The beast bellows angrily, tugs itself painfully along the ground, its hind legs dragging. It reaches out with its trunk and grabs a tree to pull itself along, ripping up the tree by its roots. With the other elephants out of the way, the hunters dart in as close as possible, trying to thrust their spears into their victim. But the animal still lashes out at them with its trunk, and makes them keep their place as it tries vainly to escape. Sometimes the elephant manages to go some distance, with the Pygmies following, waiting for their chance to kill it. But in the end it falls to their spears.

Sometimes, of course, the plan goes awry. Perhaps the tendons are not completely severed, and the elephant manages to snatch up one of the hunters and tramples or gores him to death. Perhaps one of the other elephants refuses to panic and run, attacking the hunters instead. William Spees, a friend of mine, tells the story of one Pygmy hunter who was separated from his friends while trailing an elephant which had been wounded but not incapacitated. The animal circled around to fool its pursuer and attacked the hunter from the rear, goring him in the side. The Pygmy dropped to the ground and, although bleeding badly, retained consciousness and his quick wit. He lay completely motionless, as if dead. The beast approached, reached out its trunk and poked the hunter, who remained limp and lifeless. Finally, after a good deal of investigation, the elephant decided the hunter was dead. Like all good elephants, it then proceeded to bury its victim. It dug a hole in the earth with its tusks, pushed the Pygmy into it with its trunk, then began to cover the hunter with dirt, brush and leaves. The Pygmy said later that this was most difficult time—trying to keep his nose free to breathe without moving or showing the elephant that he was still alive.

But he succeeded, although he felt as if he would suffocate any minute. The elephant did not make things any easier for the hunter by going away when burial was completed. The beast must have been suspicious for it stood near by and watched the grave for a few minutes to make sure there was no movement. (African buffalo do the same thing after they have killed a man.) At long last, the elephant moved away and the wounded hunter pushed himself up out of the hole. Within a few minutes, the other hunters came and found him. Fortunately, they carried him to the mission rather than to the Bantu witch doctor. Penicillin, cleanliness and rest healed the patient's wounds and during the time he spent at the mission he became converted to Christianity. Spees thought that in view of this momentous change in his outlook on things, the Pygmy might give up elephant hunting. But the young man just shook his head, "NO".

When Pygmy hunters kill an elephant, the animal is usually many miles from the nearest Bantu village. But the hunters may not touch the animal until the "owner" of the chief Pygmy hunter arrives to oversee the butchering and distribution. So one of the little fellows races to the Bantu village to announce the news, another returns to the village. Within a day, a huge crowd has gathered to watch and participate in the division of spoils. With the heat of the jungle, spoils is a term that can be used in more than one sense. The elephant's big belly begins to puff out like a balloon, bloated with the gases of decomposition.

Much is said about the Bantus owning the Pygmies, but none of these expressions is quite correct, nor do they give the right impression of the relationship of Bantu and Pygmy. The little Bambute Pygmies are not really slaves, they are, on the contrary, fiercely independent and jealous of their rights and prerogatives. A Bantu may say that he "owns" a certain number of Pygmies, and he always refers to them as "my Pygmies", but he does not actually own them. He could not, for instance, remove the Pygmy from his section of the forest if he tried—and he would never dream of trying.

The Bantu is contemptuous of the Pygmy and at the same time afraid of him. He considers himself as far above the forest dwellers as most Americans consider themselves above the village Bantu. He laughs at the Pygmies, and explains to the white man that they are not really human beings; they are animals, perhaps a cut above the chimpanzee, but still animals, because they live in the forest like animals.

Bantu villagers have partially domesticated these wild creatures for the usual purpose—to obtain useful goods and labor. From the Pygmy hunters, the villagers obtain meat to eat and ivory to sell, plus some manual labor in the gardens during the dry season. In return, they have used the good American advertising technique of creating a demand and then satisfying it. For centuries the Pygmies lived completely self-sufficient lives in the forest; then the villagers introduced them to bananas, manioc and sugar cane, to iron for arrow and spear heads, to tobacco and hemp for smoking, and to more salt. The Pygmies succumbed to these luxuries, although they seem to have rejected all others, such as clothing and, in the main, religion.

The Pygmies have mortgaged themselves for the sake of their new appetites. If Bambuti society had been more advanced, both Pygmy and Bantu might have developed their relationship through commercial channels alone, through straight barter and trade. The forest hunters could have brought their meat and ivory to the market and sold to the highest bidder. But the Pygmy had no concept of commerce and could think only in terms of individual relationships. If he gave meat to a village Bantu, that man gave him bananas and arrow heads made of iron. So he dealt with that Bantu alone, and perhaps persuaded his brother and his cousins to do the same. In time, no Pygmy could get along without a close tie-up with a villager, and some villagers found themselves "owning" from three to twenty or more Pygmies.

It was a good arrangement for the villagers, who proceeded to rob the poor Pygmies blind. A hunter might bring in ivory tusks which the villager could sell to the licensed ivory dealer for two hundred dollars; the man who risked his life to kill the elephant might receive the equivalent of ten dollars, while the middleman villager kept the remainder. In a week's time, of course, neither Pygmy nor villager had anything to show, since both are spendthrifts. Tomorrow? They don't think about that.

The Pygmy knows, most of the time, that he is getting a raw deal. He complains, verbally abuses his Bantu overlord, and tries to haggle over the price of the next thing he brings in. But he never contemplates staying away from the village entirely. He could disappear into the forest and no Bantu could go after him and find him. But if he fails to bring in his supposed quota of meat or acts recalcitrant in any way, the Bantu master withdraws his marijuana or beer and that makes the Pygmy knuckle under quickly. He may retaliate by sneaking down to the village in a heavy rain, when all villagers are in their huts, and stealing fruits or vegetables from a garden—usually the garden of another Bantu, not his master. If he is caught, his master must pay for what he stole.

Even though the village Bantus look on Pygmies as animals, they will take Pygmy women as wives readily enough, especially if their Bantu wives are sterile, an increasingly common condition resulting from that early fruit of civilization, venereal disease. Intermarriage works only one way, however, for no Bantu woman ever marries a Pygmy. She could not possibly stand the nomad hunter's life in the forest and no Pygmy male would abandon his natural home for life in the village.

Many Pygmy women who have married Bantus find, in time, that they must return to the forest. They run away from the villages and go back to their families. Once, when I was staying with the Pygmies, two young men from the village came to visit their Pygmy mother who had run away from her Bantu husband. There was a noisy and joyous reunion, then the sons returned to the village. They were thoroughgoing villagers just as their mother was, despite a few years' exile, a forest Pygmy. The husband did not really mind; he had his sons, which was the chief object of taking the Pygmy as wife. Anyway, she was never as good a housekeeper as his Bantu wife.

The unusual symbiosis of Bantu and Pygmy is a fortunate thing for the traveler who wants to meet Pygmies, who trust only those strangers introduced under the auspices of their Bantu masters. At the approach of anyone, the Pygmies simply disappear into a few thousand square miles of forest, a place that even the Arab slave traders of the last century dared not penetrate. A Pygmy can still be a deadly opponent to anyone poaching on his territory without permission.

Stanley found the Pygmies as vicious as any native enemies he encountered in Africa, and even today their Bantu masters maintain a healthy respect for Pygmy bows and arrows. They look like toys, but the twenty-inch bows are accurate in Bambuti hands and the arrows are dipped in poison. Which poison depends upon which book about Pygmies you read; some say it comes from strychnos and euphorbia trees, others from dried snake venom, still others from the roots of swamp orchids or the decayed bodies of insects. The chances are that Pygmies use all of these and perhaps others, depending upon what is available in their part of the forest at the time. In any event, the poison is effective, as are many of the thousand other herbs and plants used as medicines and charms.

I met my first Pygmies in 1937 with the help of Kalumé, chief of a Bantu village on the eastern edge of the Ituri Forest, between Beni and Irumu. The Bantus are made up of scores of different tribes. Those in this region were the Bandande, among whom Kalumé was an important leader, a genuine Sultani with numerous capitas, or subchiefs, beneath him.

Kalumé, a tall and well-muscled man in a long toga, greeted me with friendliness and courtesy. He smiled broadly as I made my speech, which had been written out for me in phonetic Kingwana by Commander Attilio Gatti, who had known Kalumé some years before. The sounds I uttered haltingly meant nothing to me, but much to my surprise they seemed intelligible to Kalumé. It tickled my vanity to have conversed at least once in Kingwana on my first trip to Africa.

Business with Kalumé was easily conducted; a little something for him and the capitas, salt, palm oil and other gifts for the Bambutis that was all. Would we prefer to visit with the Pygmies here in the village or go to them in the forest? There was a Pygmy clearing not too far away, and the path leading to it was well worn for an Ituri forest path.

So we walked a few miles through the forest, after Kalumé had sent a messenger in advance to let the Pygmies know that white men were coming with gifts. I had hoped that the Bandande chief would summon some of his Pygmies by drum, as I knew they did in many places. But in this area, the Pygmy clearing was near the village—only a few miles away—and the path was sufficiently plain for a villager to follow. Later I was to hear plenty of drums—drums deep in the forest that summoned more than five hundred of the Bambuti. They never failed to send a little shiver down my back and transport me a few centuries backward in time. Everyone must carry somewhere in his genes a memory of the primitive life from which he was sprung and drums seem to awaken some of those long dormant memories. It is not a thought or picture that returns at such moments, but rather a feeling foreign to everything else in life, and yet somehow vaguely and disturbingly familiar.

A walk of three or four miles doesn't sound like much of a chore, unless you are speaking of the Ituri Forest. There the jungle seems to resent your intrusion and makes every effort to push you back, trip you up, and hold on to you to prevent further progress. Later, when I followed the Bambuti deep in the forest, I knew that this first path had been an easy one. But at the time it seemed impassable in spots and difficult going all the way. True, our Bantu guides slipped along fairly deftly and, although they were far from expert woodsmen, they made my efforts look laborious and clumsy.

This was one of the first excursions I made into tropical jungles, so I shall never forget it. Thorns reached out and snagged my clothes, holding fast until the tough cloth tore, nettles stung my face and hands, giant ferns slapped my face wetly, looping lianas wound themselves around my body like the tentacles of an octopus. This sort of thing was particularly bad during a detour of only a few hundred yards around a giant mahogany tree that had toppled across the path when lightning struck it.

We saw one huge nest of termites that might do the job. It stood over ten feet high and must have contained billions of the tiny creatures. The sickly white insects live inside, guarding their queen, an immense bloated egg machine, many times larger than her royal guards. The workers, unable to endure the light, never emerge, but toil ceaselessly to cultivate the fungus on which they all feed. When I tapped the mound with a long pole, however, an army of soldiers poured out, searching frantically and pugnaciously for the enemy and squirting streams of viscous liquid from their head-syringes to entangle and trap any insect invader.

As we went deeper into the forest, we began to see a little of its wild life. Splashing across a narrow, crystal-clear stream, I saw a long snake slither into the underbrush, but my glance was too brief to tell me for certain what kind it was. When I described it later as being very thin—only about the width of my thumb—but incredibly long, perhaps eight or nine feet, I learned that it was probably a black mamba, considered one of the deadliest of all African snakes.

I slipped and fell on a rotting log that lay lengthwise in the path and a parrot screeched above my head, as if making fun of my awkwardness. The cry was taken up by other parrots some

distance away and I heard above me the whirring of wings and
the rustling of leaves. But I could see nothing. Then we came to a
space of clear undergrowth and I made an excuse to stop and
catch my breath.

I finally got my second wind and at the same time seemed to
acquire a certain amount of agility and grace in walking through
the forest. Perhaps the Ituri gave up its attempts to keep me out
since I had come so far; at any rate, I stopped stumbling and
managed to evade clutching thorns and embracing lianas more
frequently. By this time the mosquitoes and other insects were
almost unendurable.

Despite the hardships of our little hike, I was excited. I had
wanted to find the primitive, and here I was. The walk was only
three or four miles but it took me back—how many thousands
of years?

Pygmies usually talk the language of their Bantu masters. A
basic rudimentary language called Kilesi, or sometimes Kimbut,
probably derived from the original Pygmy tongue about which
nothing is known but which is spoken by all Pygmy tribes in
their relations with each other.

Aside from a few recent borrowings from the Bantus, the
Bambutis obviously live today as in the Paleolithic Period.
Authorities say that this is the earliest period of man on earth,
extending from the beginning up to about twenty thousand
years ago.

I was mulling over this awe-inspiring thought when a light
almost blinded me. We stepped from the half light of the forest
into a clearing, where shafts of the sun's rays cut the gloom like
a shining sword. I stopped, blinked and looked at a dozen
leafy beehives about four feet high and six feet in diameter—
Pygmy homes.

I stood beside Kalumé and his two capitas, waiting for the
Pygmies to appear. But not a creature stirred. We could hear
nothing but our own breathing.

My eye caught the movement of a leaf on the other side of the
clearing, a glimpse of a coppery face, then nothing but leaves. I
realized that dozens of eyes were staring at us, and it gave me an
uncanny feeling. If we were enemies and the Pygmies had not
wanted us around, what a perfect target we would have made! We
might have had a dozen arrows in us without seeing an assailant.

But Pygmies under the benign influences of approaching

civilization don't kill people any more, except occasionally each other. On the other hand, civilization may find that its influences boomerang. Not long ago two Pygmies were seen selling fresh meat near Mombasa. This was strange, since all Pygmies sell goods only through their Bantu masters.

Then a purchaser of one piece of meat thought that it had a familiar shape, remarkably like his own thigh. The authorities came and arrested the two Pygmies. Yes, they had killed a man, a Bantu of another village and had cut him up to sell the meat. Why? They needed money, money with which to buy metal. One of the Pygmies wanted to get married and the father of the girl was demanding metal goods in payment.

Finally, Kalumé called out, Aputo! Manzaele! Nzala!, crying to the unseen Pygmies that the bwana had brought salt and was a friend. In a moment the leaves parted at several points as three small figures appeared, hesitant, watchful, dignified but shy. They stopped fifteen feet in front of us and stared.

"Ituri bonocha," replied one of the little men, to let Kalumé know that the Pygmies were glad to see him.

At this exchange, other figures emerged slowly from the forests, until a group of about thirty Pygmies, men, women and children, stood in the clearing.

I was looking at Adam's cousin, at a remnant of "dawn man". Just as glaciers have preserved intact examples of mammoths long extinct, so the impenetrable forest had preserved, alive, these fossils from an ancient time. Civilizations had risen and fallen in many quarters of the globe without leaving a mark on these people. Perhaps evolution, too, had passed them by. At any rate I stood face to face with the primitive just as I had wanted and it stared at me wonderingly, then smiled. I smiled back and twenty thousand years began to fade away. If two human beings can smile at each other, they have much in common. I knew that these Pygmies and I were more alike than different.

No one from the outside is capable of entering the depths of the Ituri to live as the Pygmies live, hunting elephants with twenty-inch bows and slim spears, finding their way unerringly and in a straight line from one point in the hostile, cluttered jungle to another many miles away. Getting to know them sometimes seems like trying to understand a creature of a different species, with the unique advantage that this creature can speak.

You might say that you could never understand someone who

voluntarily smears himself with elephant dung. The Pygmy does this to confuse the keen nose of the elephant, which he hunts for food and ivory.

Maybe I can't see things through a Pygmy's eyes, as when he looks at a bat and sees food. Certainly I can't smell things through his nose, as when he sniffs a putrifying elephant dead four days in tropic heat and gleefully hurries to the feast. I eat the meat, not the smell, bwana, he explains. But even if I cannot put myself in his place, I can feel hunger which lies behind his actions and mine.

Feelings are the heart of both of us, the bridge of understanding, the common language. Customs are just the costumes with which emotions clothe themselves to fit environment and heritage. The Pygmy's customs are as well adapted to his world as his dress and when I realized this and I recognized the feelings beneath them, I was at home in the Ituri, visiting friends who put on an amazing show for me just by being themselves.

I did not go with Pygmies on many hunts. For one thing, I'm not a big-game hunter myself; I had neither desire nor weapons for killing animals. I wanted to watch the Pygmies at work, which I did in the course of three hunts for okapi, which we never got, two elephant hunts and one for wild pig. I saw them track, stalk and kill half a dozen different creatures. I heard them use their wooden whistles to attract the game, whistles in three sizes hanging from their necks and I saw the work of their wonderful, if unattractive, dogs.

The dogs are mongrels that look as if a bit of hyena and fox has been grafted on to the family tree with permanently built-in moths, to make their short coats splotchy and full of badly-darned holes. But no canines can beat them at their jobs and I doubt that many can match their courage. When they accompany their masters on the hunt, they can follow the spoor even more surely and swiftly than the Pygmies, unless the prey crosses a good-sized stream and even then they may pick it up on the other side. They never get too far ahead of the hunters so that the men can hear the clop-clop of the little wooden bells tied around each dog's neck. Since the Pygmy dog has no bark, the bell is essential.

No "man's best friend" relationship exists between master and dog, so far as I could see. Never did I witness a pat or other sign of affection. But no Pygmy would underestimate the value of his dog and a dog would give his life for his master, as shown by one experience I heard about, but in which, I am happy to say, I was not a participant.

Three Pygmy hunters were moving swiftly through the forest on the trail of some animal and their dog was just a few feet from the first hunter. Suddenly a leopard sprang from a low branch upon the first Pygmy, who was quick enough to dart beyond the reach of a man-killing first blow but not quick enough to avoid the slashing of his right shoulder and arm. He flung his spear at the mad beast, but his bleeding arm was unable to guide it right. The spear missed its mark and the Pygmy managed to clamber up a small tree. The leopard might have gone after him but its attention was diverted by the charge of the second hunter. The cat-like creature swerved toward him just as he aimed his spear, so that it too missed and broke against a rock.

Luckily for the second hunter, the leopard saw number three and went for him, enabling the second to climb to temporary safety. The third hunter kept hold of his spear and tried to plunge it into the animal as it sprang. The spear merely sliced its leg a bit, serving only to make him angrier than before. Then the leopard and hunter number three battled it out, the hunter struggling to keep the beast's claws from his throat and at the same time maneuvering to get in another thrust with his spear.

He would have been slashed to ribbons if it had not been for the dog. The mongrel rushed at the leopard from the side and from the rear, snapping at the big cat's legs and flank, then racing off as it turned away from the hunter momentarily to get rid of the pesky dog. The two hunters in the trees could do nothing to help; they had no weapons and one was badly wounded and bleeding profusely. All they could do was watch man and leopard struggle, with the dog snarling, rushing in and out. Once he sank his fangs into the leopard's tail and tugged. The beast whirled, howled, and obviously decided to kill the pest once and for all.

That gave the third hunter just the chance he needed. He lunged with his spear, which pierced the leopard's side, cut into its heart and dropped it. But this time the hunter was so badly wounded that he could hardly stand but all three men managed to get back home. As their wounds were cleaned and dressed, they all sang the praises of the dog, giving him full credit for saving their lives. But they did not once pat him or show him any affection.

One thing will divert Pygmies from their hunting, the finding of a bees' nest with honey. Once I watched them scramble up a tall tree where there was a hive hidden in a big hole. They used a heavy liana looped around the trunk to help them in their ascent, much as a telephone linesman uses a wide strap. Once up even with the hive, the first hunter enlarged the hole with his spear as hundreds of bees swarmed about him. Then he plunged in his hand, brought it out full of honey comb dripping with honey and crammed the whole mess into his mouth. One after another, each hunter climbed the tree and ate his fill of honey, and not once did a bee sting a man. I questioned several people about this seeming immunity to bees, but could never learn the reason for it. I was told that in some places, Pygmies smear their skins with honey first and the angry bees will not sting through it.

The Pygmies' tree-climbing agility enables them to rob parrots' nests of eggs and baby parrots, which they sell as pets to the Bantu villagers. Pygmy marksmanship with the tiny bows and arrows is often amazing. One Pygmy was set to guard a banana grove by his Bantu master, who wanted to end the raids of monkeys and baboons. Suddenly a full-grown elephant lumbered from the forest into the grove, confronting the lone Pygmy armed only with his twenty-inch bow and a few arrows. The little hunter knew that his only chance of killing the huge animal with his feeble weapon was a clean shot through the eye into the brain. He would not have a second chance, for the elephant would be on him. He aimed the slender arrow and shot at the right eye— a tiny target in the massive head. It struck its mark and the elephant dropped in his tracks.

The forest is full of hazards and the biggest beasts are not the most dangerous. One night Bill Deans, my missionary friend, and I were sitting at our camp table in the heart of the forest having supper. We looked around at the towering trees and thought how beautiful it was. You might have thought at such a moment that, even though this was the jungle, it was really not so terrible.

But in the Ituri Forest there are many dangers, seen and unseen. There are numerous deadly snakes—including pythons fifteen to twenty feet long. As we sat in front of my tent, a Pygmy suddenly darted up and crashed his spear down right at Bill's feet. We were startled and couldn't believe that he meant to attack. Then he pointed to the viper, now dead from the quick thrust of his spear, whose fangs were only inches from Bill's legs.

Another menace is the ant. Safari ants travel in solid columns a few inches wide, a more dangerous enemy than many wild beasts of the forest and much more difficult to dispose of. Their bite is like the prick of a red-hot needle which burns for hours afterwards. And no matter how many ants you kill, there are ten times as many ready to take their place.

A doctor's assistant in a nearby camp had a pet monkey. One night the monkey, which had been chained to a stump on which it slept, suddenly let out the most piercing shriek. By the time the assistant got to the monkey, it was struggling to pull away from the stump but it could scarcely be recognized as a monkey. It was a writhing mass of ants. The chain became a thick rope of ants, and the stump was alive with them. The monkey's owner put the little creature beyond torture with one merciful shot. By that time there was not much flesh left on the monkey.

The men wasted no time in trying to repel the ant invasion, for within a few hours the horde would have attacked everyone and everything in the camp.

During my second trip, I was most eager to get motion pictures of the elephant hunt. I soon learned, however, that it was almost impossible to film because there was never enough light in the forest for picture taking. I was beginning to despair of success in this project as the end of my visit approached. But then luck, which has so frequently seemed to balance things out for me, came to the rescue. One group of Pygmy hunters killed an elephant in a clearing close to the edge of the forest, near the village of a Bantu chief named Pawanzas, who was a member of the Walese tribe. They sent a runner to bring me the news and guide me back to the clearing. Never did I travel through the forest so quickly, for this was an opportunity that would never come twice. According to my guide, the hunters had tracked the elephant for miles after wounding him, and had finally dispatched him in a large clearing where sunlight abounded. The only growth was tall elephant grass, which would soon be trampled down by the crowds.

As we hurried through the forest to the clearing, I hoped that the Pygmy was not just saying things he knew I would like to hear but, when we came to the clearing, I saw that he was right. Plenty of sunlight, a little late in the day but good enough. The only factor that dismayed me was the big crowd that had gathered, between three and four hundred men and

women, about equally divided between Bantu villagers and
Pygmies. They were all relatives—some rather distant, I gathered
—of the Pygmy hunters or the Bantu overlord of the chief hunter.
Luckily, the butchering had not yet started, as everything had
to wait for the arrival of the Walese chief of that area and the
headman of the village in which the Bantu owner lived.

While waiting for them I was able to clear a little space for
good camera shots. When the important personages arrived,
everyone turned to the Bantu in charge. He glanced around to
see that everyone who might claim a share of the elephant was
present, then lifted his hand in signal to the four Pygmies who
had made the kill. They scrambled up on top of the big beast
and stood on the bloated belly. At a second signal, the chief
hunter plunged his spear into the elephant's side. A geyser of
gas and stomach juices spurted into the air seven or eight feet,
spreading an odor that made my senses reel. But the Pygmy
hunters shouted and pushed their faces into the liquid, gulping
it, bathing in it. This act was supposed to give the Pygmies
some of the elephant's strength to aid them in their next kill.

In some instances, the first act of the hunters, upon making
the kill, is to cut a hole in the abdomen, walk inside, and take
bites two or three inches long and then offer bites to the remaining hunters, teeth to teeth, as a token of victory in the hunt.

When the gassy geyser subsided, the hunters returned to the
ground. Pygmies and villagers then lined up, each with a sharp
knife. Behind each man stood his wife, ready and waiting with
a big basket. At another signal, the Pygmies and villagers raced
for the elephant, clambering up its sides, slipping, clutching for
a firm hold—each one trying to reach the backbone first. The
men yelled, the women shouted encouragingly and the whole
scene became a small riot. But there was organization and plan
behind the bedlam, though I could not see it at first. When a
man reached the spine, he gained the right to cut a strip of
meat down the side from that point. As I learned later, he did
not necessarily get to keep all the meat he cut but each man
no doubt figured that the more he had the more he was likely
to wind up with.

Shoulder to shoulder, Pygmies and villagers lined up along
the crest of the fallen elephant and started hacking away at
the meat. As one man cut a big chunk of flesh away he merely
flung it back over his shoulder. He knew that his wife had her

eyes fixed on him waiting to snatch whatever he threw for deposit in her basket. Soon big chunks of elephant meat were flying through the air, women were rushing forward to grab the pieces, sometimes catching them even before they struck the ground. There was remarkably little bickering for such a confused scene. I suppose it was confusing only to me and not to the Pygmies and villagers.

Finally the meat was cut away from the exposed side and there was a lull in the proceedings while two Pygmies took an axe and chopped a hole through the elephant's ribs into the chest cavity. They then proceeded to take up their sharp spears and hop inside the beast. In a moment I saw two spear points sawing their way along the ribs, as the men worked from the inside out, cutting away more meat and flinging it out through the hole, along with heart, liver and all other prized entrails of the beast.

I could not quite believe that an equitable distribution of meat could be made among so many demanding men and women, but by the end of the forenoon the job was done and no one seemed angry. In fact there was much hilarity among the entire group. The Bantu chief of the area received one huge leg as his share. The headman of the village was given a select piece. The owner of the chief Pygmy hunter kept some entrail delicacies for himself, as well as some solid meat and, perhaps most important to him, the ivory tusks. And he decided just how much meat should go to all the assembled villagers and Pygmies. The Pygmy hunters received most generous portions for their families of course, and other relatives from their village came in for shares. Not a thing was wasted. At the end even the tough skin was cut up so some of the Pygmy women could make soup from it.

When I went to Africa in 1954-55 to make Zanzabuka for Republic Pictures, I had a proper expedition consisting of an assistant and four other cameramen, a Dodge Power Wagon and truck, kindly supplied by the Chrysler Corporation and more time than I had ever taken before. I wanted to visit the Pygmies again to take pictures of one thrilling achievement of these little people which I had never been able to get. This was the building of a liana bridge across a wide river.

It would not be an easy task, I knew. I had to find the right spot on the right river, assemble a group of Pygmies and persuade them to tackle the really difficult job of building a bridge for which they might not see any necessity, and finally arrange to have all this take place where there was sufficient light and proper positions for my cameras.

Lady Luck outdid herself on this occasion. During the better part of a year in Africa, on my third journey, I frequently felt that she had abandoned me altogether, migrated to another continent, crossed me off her list once and forever. There were days, weeks of delay, frustration, rain, accidents and interruptions. But when I returned to the Ituri, this time luck flew back and settled down on my right shoulder.

However, the first spot selected was not right, for the river was narrow and the building of a bridge would not have looked at all difficult. Hollywood demanded the spectacular, so we searched further until we found the ideal stretch of the Ituri River. At this point it was about ninety feet wide and throwing a liana bridge across that distance would make a magnificent spectacle. For a quarter of a mile the river flowed in a straight course instead of twisting and winding. Very tall trees lined each bank, a necessity for the Pygmy method of bridge-building. But the undergrowth was rather sparse, leaving clear spaces from which my cameras could obtain good shots up and down the river.

Most important of all, however, was that here the river flowed from west to east. When the sun rose in the morning, its light would not be cut off by two-hundred foot trees until almost noon. And in the afternoon the sun would set at the western end of the stretch, giving me light until four o'clock at least. Each day would bring three or four hours more of filming time than I had ever enjoyed in the forest. It was almost too good to be true.

The Ituri at this point was as wide as any river the Pygmies had ever spanned. I wanted the task to be difficult because that would make it more dramatic but I hoped it would not be too difficult.

The crux of the problem in bridge building is the first long liana that must be stretched across the river. After that the work is precarious but relatively simple. We selected a tree, tall and straight at the water's edge, from which the first attempt would be launched. Free of low branches, it looked like a double-length telephone pole with another tree on top. Opposite this tree, on the other bank of the river, stood several trees of comparable height with wide-spreading branches.

Looping stout lianas around the trunk of the first tree, one of the more agile Pygmies worked his way up the first big branch, taking one end of a hawser-like vine with him. He climbed out on the branch and tied the long liana securely to it, using smaller vines as tough as wire to reinforce it. A second long liana was attached about two feet away, so that two long and supple wooden ropes fell to the ground. These were simply the ropes for a giant swing to which a small seat was attached. The idea was to place a strong young Pygmy in the seat, set him swinging and hope that he could swing out far enough to reach a branch of a tree on the opposite bank.

The swing did not look quite long enough to me, but I deferred to the judgment of the Pygmies. I was no engineer but I could see that, to reach across ninety feet of river, the swing had to be at least ninety feet long. Allowing for slack and a few extra feet on each side, a hundred and ten feet would be closer to the required length.

None of the Pygmies seemed to be particularly eager to act as the swinger. As the time approached for the first launching, I think they looked at the river's width, at the great height of the swing and found themselves assailed by doubts. But they were very vocal in their insistence that the job could be done and equally vocal in their modesty. We finally settled on a young fellow of about twenty named Meru, who seemed both proud to have been chosen and afraid to get in the swing. When I enumerated the special gifts of dried fish, nuts and palm oil plus several arrows that would go to the man who carried the first liana across the river, Meru appeared more eager for the task.

The Pygmies had cut a clear path through the forest leading straight back from the tall tree, a kind of narrow alley in which the swing could be pulled back to launch Meru on his flying mission over the water. A long liana, tied to the seat of the swing, was led back through this path and passed up to two or three Pygmies perched high in the branches of a tree. The idea was for them to pull Meru back and up as far as possible, then suddenly let him go. He was equipped with a sharply curved piece of hardwood that looked something like a longshoreman's bulky hook. As he swung up close to the branch on the other side of the river, he was supposed to latch his hook over the branch and hold on for dear life. I was afraid that this movement would jerk him right out of the swing seat, but the Pygmies assured me that he would be fastened to it securely and would manage to scramble upon the branch once he caught hold of it.

Looking quite serious, the young man settled himself in the swing, hooked his arms around the supporting liana, grasped his wooden hook and watched carefully while others strapped him to the seat with small tough vines. Then the Pygmies in the tree back at the end of the cleared path began hauling on the long liana, pulling Meru back and up higher and higher. I had one camera on a platform filming this action and another on the river bank to shoot the flight of the swing across the river and I hoped Meru's grasping of the branch on the other side. I stationed myself near the base of the tree with the swing, where I could see in both directions and give the necessary signals.

Slowly and laboriously the Pygmies in the tree hauled Meru up on the back half of the swing's arc, until he was suspended, almost face down, near the far end of the narrow alleyway. Then I gave the signal, "Cut!" and one of the Pygmies in the tree cut the hauling liana. Meru's tiny body hurtled down and out at increasing speed, barely missing the trees beside the cleared area. In a fraction of a second he reached the bottom of the arc at the foot of the tree and sped out over the water and up toward his goal. But something was wrong! He didn't zoom upwards as he should. I heard the groan of a bending branch and looked up to see the branch to which the lianas had been attached bending from the force of the pull that had been exerted on it. Meru's foot touched the top of the water, cut down his speed and prevented him from coming anywhere near the tree on the opposite bank.

The swing arched back toward us, and the Pygmies grabbed it, bringing Meru to a stop. The young fellow was obviously deeply frightened and I did not blame him. If the branch had broken he would have been a goner. Even if it had bent a little more, so that his body struck the water, he would have been killed by the force of the impact.

He stepped from the swing rather shakily and I put my arm around his shoulder in an effort to calm him. He kept shaking his head and muttering to himself something that sounded to me like "Zanzabuku! Zanzabuku!" I had no idea what it meant at first, and neither did anyone else, for it was apparently a word or phrase in the original Pygmy language. But as he gestured at the swing, the branch and the river, shaking his head as if to say "Never again!" I gleaned a fairly good idea of what he meant. He was trying to tell me that this job was too dangerous for him to tackle. Somehow, in spite of the tenseness of that critical moment, I have never forgotten the word and it has come to my mind several times when I suddenly found myself in a hazardous situation. Zanzabuku must mean some perilous task or "dangerous mission".

About ten feet above the branch we had used was another much thicker and stronger. This meant cutting off the first branch and also finding longer lianas for the swing itself. I was pleased, for it seemed to me that they would now be long enough to reach clear across the river, with a bit to spare.

The next day, everything was ready. The branch was obviously sturdy enough and the swing long enough. Still, Meru looked as if he had made a mistake when he sat himself in the swing. He was quickly lashed to the seat, given his hook and started on the backward pull. Higher and higher he rose until I gave the signal for him to be released. Down and out he flashed and this time nothing went wrong. Meru arched out over the river and up toward the branch on the opposite shore. At the top of his swing, his arm darted out with the hook, and missed the branch by inches!

A groan went up from all the Pygmies and from me too. Meru swung to a stop and I walked up to him disconsolately, feeling sure that he would refuse vehemently to try again. But he was not frightened this time. The branch and swing had held firm, so there was nothing to be afraid of. He was truly a courageous little Pygmy!

Meru explained that if the men who hauled him back to start the swing would pull just a few feet farther he felt sure he could then reach the tree across the river. I gave the necessary instructions, installed Meru in the swing again after a brief intermission for a cigarette and started the procedure for the third and, I felt sure, the last time.

Some of the other Pygmies were no help, for they cried out "Utanguka!" (You'll fall!) as Meru was being hauled up in the air. But the young man was so determined that I don't think he heard them. I waited to give the "Cut!" signal until Meru was several feet higher than before, then watched him zoom down and out, looping up gracefully toward the distant branch across the water. At exactly the right moment Meru lunged with his hook and caught the branch. His body jerked so violently that

I felt sure he would lose his grip, but he pulled himself up slowly until he lay panting on his long-sought goal.

Everything after that was anticlimax so far as spine-tingling excitement was concerned, although there were many fascinating shots for the cameras as the main supporting vines were placed lower down on both trees, arching down over the river like the cable of a suspension bridge. The Pygmies built ladder-like approaches up from the ground on either side and set quickly to work enlarging the bridge. More thick lianas passed across the water, a little higher than the first so that they could serve as handrails. Pygmies worked their way out from the tree making a narrow footpath and more vines were woven in and out to form a kind of netting on either side between footpath and handrails. Finally the day came when I ascended the ladder at one end, stepped on to the bridge and made my way across. The bridge swayed and danced under my feet and I looked with a good deal of trepidation at the rushing waters below. But the bridge was strong and would no doubt last a long time.

It had been a long and arduous task but in the end it had turned out so well that I felt like celebrating. When I left the Ituri Forest the third time I felt happy. And somehow, I no longer felt that the Pygmies were strange or unusual human beings. We had been through too much together.

Although the bridge-building was the outstanding incident of my third visit with the Pygmies, there were other events that come back to my mind now. On this trip I finally learned, I believe, the secret of the Pygmy's uncanny ability to find his way through the forest. What has always baffled outsiders is not his marvelous tracking of animals but rather the beeline route he follows without a path in going from any one spot in his jungle to another, even five or ten miles away. There is no mystery involved, no sixth sense. The Pygmy is very observant, but above all he is thoroughly familiar with every single part of his section of the forest. There he has lived his entire life. He has lived a month here and a month there, ranging throughout the whole territory, and has hunted through those woods daily. When he wants to make sure just where he is, he looks up and sees an ironwood or mahogany tree which has stood in this spot for longer than the Pygmy's grandfather can remember. To a forest-dweller's eyes, this particular tree is somewhat different from any other tree in the forest.

It is difficult for me to believe that the Ituri Pygmies will ever be civilized. They reject civilization and everything that it offers with a few exceptions. It is amazing that they have been in contact with the village Bantus for so many decades and have adopted so few of their ways. I believe that Pygmies possess enough intelligence to cope with civilization if it is not thrown at them too rapidly. Converts who have grown up in and around some of the missions have learned to read and write readily, have shown themselves adept at learning new skills if they want to. Most Pygmies don't want to.

Once there were no roads through the Ituri. Now there are two or three. In time there may be dozens, cutting the forest up into smaller and smaller areas. Bantus will cut back the forest along the sides of the roads to make gardens and villages. The Pygmies will be confined to continually smaller regions. This is the inevitable course of civilization on the march in Africa. But if no one finds gold, oil or uranium in the Ituri, perhaps there will be a limit beyond which the constriction of Pygmy country will not go. I hope so. I hope that the government will create for these wonderful wild dwarfs a sanctuary in the Ituri, as it has set aside huge reserves for wild animals.

CHAPTER THREE

WILD ADVANCE OF A MONSTER

WHEN six tons of enraged elephant come charging at you with the thunderous fury of an avalanche, you're bound to cringe. That happened to Robert Halmi on one of his big game hunts in French Equatorial Africa.

"For a frightful moment," Bob recalls, "I wanted to run off and hide in any place out of reach. Instead, and I'm still not sure why, I froze in my steps, as a giant bull elephant came thundering down the trail like a railroad locomotive."

Nothing seems to phase this intrepid photographer. He has a penchant for being right in the middle of anything that smacks of danger.

By profession he is a photographer, but, actually, that is only a springboard for the dare-devil stunts that he conjures up. Anything for a thrill! So long as he can take a picture of it.

As an adventurer, he enjoys using a rifle about as much as a camera. Yet, he has done most of his shooting with a camera.

I recall him telling of an earlier safari into the African jungles, which started at Nairobi, capital of Kenya.

"When we headed for the bush," said Bob, "the outfit looked much like any other one going after big game, but instead of bearers carrying Holland or Mannlicher rifles, they were lugging fiber cases fitted with cameras. We were after game, as any other hunter, but instead of dropping them in their tracks with rifle slugs, we were going to capture them on motion-picture film.

Even seasoned sportsmen are foolhardy to go into open country in Africa on their own, without a professional white hunter in the party for protection and guidance. He is indispensable for a safe and successful safari. The hunter on our own trip was Owen McCallum, a wiry Kenyaite who was born and raised in that country and is as tough as they come. McCallum was to be with us constantly while we were in the bush. We parted only after I left the wilds for a motor journey through three large game preserves, for which a hunter is not needed—only a knowledge of game preserve rules and the ability to handle a vehicle's steering wheel.

While helping to get the expedition organized I managed an afternoon's trip to Nairobi National Park, only four miles from the town, in order to test my equipment for the last time. The park is filled with big game and many fine shots can be made there, although the animals are naturally more docile than the wild ones away from civilization. After this check of my gear and three days' assembling our food, equipment and personnel we were ready to roll.

Our party consisted of McCallum, a chef, a tracker, a gun bearer turned camera-bearer, two natives to act as servants, myself, and two skinners who acted as handymen. Both of the skinners could repair a carburetor as well as they could skin a gazelle. Eight of us and our gear were loaded into one truck and two Land Rovers, the British version of the jeep, always so handy for travel in the bush.

From Nairobi we drove about one hundred miles due south to Arusha, in Tanganyika, and from there some fifty miles south-west to the edge of Lake Manyara where we established a base camp. We made the drive in one day over dusty roads. In the dry season this is normal driving time but my sympathies are with the man making the trip during the rainy season when the dust turns to sticky mud that makes driving all but impossible.

Around Lake Manyara I photographed wildebeest, impala, Thompson's gazelle, grand gazelle and other specie of antelope, often roaming herds of a hundred or more. The country in Tanganyika—as in Kenya—is open plain with gentle, rolling hills boasting only the sparsest of vegetation in the way of tree or bush.

Stealth is the keynote for getting good photographs of animals. There is almost nothing to hide behind and the greatest of patience is required in order to get close enough to the animals to make decent pictures. But, by crawling across the grass with a minimum of noise, I managed to get within fifty yards of the antelope, where I could cover the herd with a 135 mm long-focus lens.

After two days of studying antelopes in the field we decided to try our luck on lions, which are notoriously hard to photograph outside the established game parks. In unprotected country lions are quite spooky and will generally take to flight at the first human scent.

Moving farther from the lake we set a lure for the kingly beasts by using a zebra carcass placed under a tree. We watched from concealment but nary an animal appeared, the sun finally going down without result. The next morning at daybreak we inspected the tree and found that the zebra carcass had disappeared. At least we were satisfied that lions were in the vicinity. Accordingly we strung up a second carcass and sat down to wait from a distance of fifty yards.

The ruse worked. Shortly afterward in the warm, shimmering morning heat, a family of lions stealthily approached the tree and tried to reach the bait suspended there. Silently I began photographing them. Watching the cubs and their protective and devoted mother, I concluded that I preferred to shoot these worthy beasts with a camera rather than the bone-shattering rifle I had used before.

When in the course of a day or two, we had our fill of lions, we left the lake area and hunted buffalo. It wasn't until the next day that we located a herd of nearly two hundred. Stopping the Land Rovers, we jumped out and started crawling to the windward side of the herd. After an hour of circling through the grass, we managed to get to within a hundred yards of the grazing animals. I had been photographing from the cover of an ant-hill for about half an hour before I noticed that the herd had shifted its grazing grounds and was almost on top of me. Looking away from the camera view-finder, I noticed with some alarm that the nearest cow was only ten yards in front of the ant-hill. Suddenly, she caught my scent!

With a bellow, she raised the herd's attention! The buffalos stopped grazing and began nervously shifting and lowing. I had a queasy feeling in my stomach, for if the herd decided to gallop in my direction my ant-hill would be ground to powder and I along with it. Did I stop shooting pictures! My knees knocked together and I was breathing in short, guarded breaths. I felt naked and alone without hope of any future. Then, providentially, without the slightest warning, the herd stampeded!

Had they known that humans were in front of them, they probably would have turned in the other direction, but all they knew was that man was near and, as luck would have it, the entire herd started moving toward me. Feeling another moment of wild panic, I dashed from behind the ant-hill and began yelling and waving my arms at the onrushing herd. At this point my ears were suddenly deafened by two roaring, crackling sounds to my left. McCallum, whom I had forgotten in my overwhelming fear, was standing to my left, calmly shooting over the heads of the buffalo. Reloading quickly, he fired again and again, until the herd turned as if by magic and galloped off to our left, covering us with dust and leaving our nostrils filled with their heavy, unforgettable smell.

Back in camp, we rested from the fatigue, the dust and the smell and, as usual, dinner in the bush was a hearty experience.

After it I slept in a six-man tent which I had all to myself with a private bath attached. I amused myself listening to a small-wave radio and played cards with my neighbors by the light of hurricane lamps. The evenings are very cool and conducive to good sleeping.

After a week around Lake Manyara we broke camp and started searching for rhinoceros and elephant. We headed into the Yaida Valley, below Massi country, where the rhino makes his home. The valley is bordered by steep escarpments of volcanic rock, its floor filled with mudholes and in places heavy vegetation. Not trusting open country, the rhino, due to poor eyesight, likes a lot of cover and the Yaida Valley is one of his favorite haunts.

It was here that I had one of the most thrilling and dangerous moments of the photographic safari.

We had spent two days tracking a rhino across the valley floor, up the rugged escarpment and back down again. The tracker suddenly pointed up at the sky where big birds were circling and we knew we had finally located our animal. Pushing through thorn bush and across rugged rocks, we broke into a clearing and there he was grazing as contentedly as a cow. The wind was coming from the rhino and wasn't very strong. I started to crowd forward, carrying a Leica attached to a gun-stock and mounted with a 300 mm telephoto lens. I was going to try for a head-on view and with this in mind began circling rather closely around him, knowing that a rhino lacks good eyesight, although he more than makes up for this with his keen hearing. McCallum, who was with me, carrying his .465 Holland, laid a restraining hand on my arm, whispering that the wind had changed and that was as far as we had better go. So I started taking pictures. The shutter of a Leica is very quiet but even the slight noise it did make caused the rhino to lift his head and look right at us, and what the rhino had just heard spelled danger to him. Instinctively, and in the twinkling of an eye, he charged. I had taken chances before and was determined to take another. So I kept on winding and shooting with the other camera. Rushing madly with his head lowered, the angry tusker flew at us until it was no longer necessary to use the long lens. McCallum, having the animal covered, shouted for me to keep my camera going. Each fraction of a second the monster loomed bigger in my view-finder, his immense horn the personification of evil. I was held behind my camera by sheer magnetism and excitement, forgetting for the moment the impending disaster. When it seemed inevitable that I would be pulverized beneath his mighty feet, two shots roared in my ear which brought me to my senses just as the enemy dropped in his tracks, so close indeed that I could smell him strongly. Bewitched by this one, I decided that I had enough of rhinos and went back to the pursuit of elephants!

Halmi has had many exciting experiences, but the most frightening occurred on his hunting expedition through French Equatorial Africa, when he came face to face with a mammoth six-ton elephant charging madly at him, catapulting along the trail directly for him.

Our small safari, says Bob, was some 200 miles east of Fort

Archambault, in French Equatorial Africa, when N'Gakoutou, our chief tracker, reported the unmistakable sign of elephants. In moist ground under some shade, were the huge footprints I came to know so well, and close by were the foot-high stacks of dung that are as revealing as a time table. Since boyhood, stories about the intelligent and lovable elephants had stirred my imagination and now at last my chance to meet a few was near. I was anxious to see them up close, to photograph them and if fortune would have it, to get a fair shot at one.

There are several ways to kill an elephant, from long-range shooting with a scope-sighted rifle to the poisoned darts of the Pygmies, but I did not want my elephant that way. Nor did I think for a moment that Jean Gerin, my white hunter, would have countenanced the lethal manner. Like most white hunters I have met, he has great respect for all wild game and an almost affectionate feeling for elephants.

Since we had found the spoor too late that day to consider pursuit, we were up at four the next morning. Breakfast, a last check of guns and equipment and we were off. At dawn we picked up the trail again near the shore of Lake Iro. The herd had evidently gone there in the early hours to drink and was now moving back into the brush to forage and reach shade for its noonday rest. The trail was easy to pick out, for the huge footmarks were sunk deep in the marshy ground.

I wondered why N'Gakoutou seemed to puzzle over the track, for even I could have followed it with ease. He seemed excited and I was sure that we must be near the herd. Instead, he called us to look where the clear outline of a footprint showed through the muck. Jabbering heatedly in French, N'Gakoutou declared that the imprint was the biggest he had ever seen. There's a rule of thumb for measuring the height of an elephant from his track, so we quickly tried it out. Bending a reed around the circumference of the footprint we laid it out flat and measured it. Gerin whistled softly. He was sure the elephant should stand at least twelve feet tall at the shoulder. And, while it could be an old bull without ivory, one thing was certain—it *was* big.

"Quelle chance, Monsieur!" Gerin said. "Your first hunt for the elephant seems promising."

I asked him how far we were behind the herd; he reflected a moment. Judging from the condition of dung heaps on the trail, he reckoned the herd was about five to six miles ahead of us and traveling at about the same rate of speed that we were. Apparently the elephants were moving at their normal pace of two to four miles an hour, leisurely reaching up in the high branches along the route for one of their favorite delicacies—mangoes.

South of the lake we moved into high grass where the six-foot reeds had been bent like arrows, creating a roadway. I had expected elephants to cut a wide swath, but for the most part they amble along in a single file, putting their hind feet down in the same spot as their forefeet.

An interesting thing about elephants on the march is that the young males and babies stay close to the mothers, while the old males form a group of their own. Usually the herd is under the leadership of a huge, powerful bull which can command the obedience of any one of the herd.

Within an hour we had broken out of the reeds and passed into bush country where the ground was baked as hard as stone, and it took all of N'Gakoutou's experiences to search out clues to the trail. Where I could see nothing revealing, he found a freshly snapped twig, a patch of fallen leaves undersides up, or the dim indication of a footfall. Or, glancing at the bush at trunk level, he would detect a place where a vine had been recently broken off. Only when we reached an occasional shady area and were able to make out tracks in the soft ground was it apparent that we were following an actual trail and not just N'Gakoutou's instinct about where elephants should be.

Fortunately, we were downwind of the herd, so there was little chance of their catching our scent and taking flight. Elephants constantly raise their trunks to test the air and one quick whiff of man is enough to put them on guard, even causing them to break into a run that would take them far out of reach.

The sun was now at its zenith—a blazing ball in the sky. Swarms of blood-sucking insects buzzed us from every direction. The heaps of elephant dung we tested were already baked hard by the sun; Gerin said this meant that we were still not close enough to reach the resting place of the herd, where, having finished its midday snooze, it would slowly rouse itself and resume its march to their rendezvous for their nightly council. Elephants do their serious eating and playing at night. They become aggressive at that hour, Gerin said. Their whole character changes and a man is taking a grave risk to pursue them after sundown, even in bright moonlight.

Elephants are voracious eaters, an average bull consuming half a ton of food a day. Eating therefore becomes their major occupation, both day and night. It is their search for food which prompts their constant migrations. They are frequently on the move wandering from heavily forested regions to the open country. The former they avoid during the rainy season because of the dripping of water from the trees. At midday they usually rest, the bulls go sound asleep but the cows merely doze lightly while their youngsters are at play.

Instinct seems to lead them to their favorite feeding ground where leaves and grass are to be had at all periods of the year. Bamboo, young trees and corn are also favored dishes. Their desire for sweets is satisfied by bananas, sugar cane, plums and tropical fruits. They eat directly from the trees, even uprooting them when necessary to satisfy their craving for the foliage.

Few people seem to know how an elephant chews his food. Actually, he grows teeth during his entire life. As one tooth becomes worn down another takes its place. These new sets of molars appear at odd intervals. For instance, at the age of two, six, fifteen, twenty-five and forty, he receives a new group—one on each side of the upper and lower jaws. As each one is larger than those it replaces, starting roughly at two inches in width and from four to six inches in length, they increase to a length of fourteen inches and frequently weigh over ten pounds each. These are all grinders, as cutting teeth are unnecessary since the trunk handles the process of cutting with great efficiency.

Once again our trail led through a broad band of high grass where we could hardly see ten feet ahead. Notwithstanding this we kept going at a good pace throughout the afternoon. Suddenly, N'Gakoutou, who had been watching the trail closely, excitedly gestured for us to look at another heap of elephant droppings, only thinly crusted by the sun. Inside they were still warm, an indication that the elephants were but a short distance ahead.

We pushed on, but tantalizingly the herd kept just beyond our reach. The spoor, still fresh, now led through heavy bush where snarls of vines and creepers of little consequence to the great pachyderms were almost impassable to us and slowed us to a snail's pace. There was nothing for us to do but set up camp and wait for morning.

That night we were so close to the herd that the sound of their movements came clearly to us. The elephant has a huge digestive

machine causing its stomach to rumble unceasingly. This noise
I could identify, but all of the other cadences of the herd were
significant to N'Gakoutou. The soft buzzing, almost like a purr,
he interpreted as a favorable sign for us because it meant that
the elephants were happy with the night's feeding. From a series
of cough-like bellowing, N'Gakoutou guessed that one of the herd
was vexed, probably an old bull who sensed that one of the young
blades was trying to line up his favorite cow for the love play
of the night. As time passed, it seemed to me that the animals must
surely have suspected our presence nearby, for the air continued
to be filled with loud trumpeting.

I mentioned this to Gerin but he only chuckled. The calls come
from the babies in the herd. They want to be fed and, like human
babies, are loudly insistent. An elephant mother lets her calf
complain like this for hours before she feeds him, usually after
she herself has dined amply.

An elephant audibly expresses its various moods. He emits a
shrill cry through his trunk when he is enjoying his meal and
when taking a bath. Anger is expressed by a roar from his throat
or a scream through his trunk. Mature elephants, Gerin added,
seldom trumpet, except in rage or to warn the herd of danger.

As the evening wore on, the sounds of the herd put Gerin in a
reminiscent mood. Though normally taciturn, that night he
talked unreservedly about "man's only formidable foe".

"A hundred years ago," he told me, "vast herds of elephants
roamed Africa from the southern Sahara down to Bechuanaland.
Then came the white man who slaughtered them by the thousands
for their ivory. The elephant soon learned that he could not
conquer the white enemy so he retreated into the jungles and
marshes. The scent of his enemy became a part of his heritage.

"Isn't it difficult to think that a mother could kill her own
child? Whatever the answer, I have seen a cow recapture her
calf after it had been cut off from the herd and led away by a
white man to go in a zoo. Joyfully the calf escaped and came
back to nuzzle against her. But, enraged by the clinging and
hated smell of man, the mother in blind fury trampled her
child to death."

More and more Gerin's thoughts turned to the morbid. A
white-hunter friend of his had grown careless from over-confidence
about his safety. One day he was focusing all his attention on
an elephant before his sights. Absorbed in his task, it was too

late when he heard the cow that charged him from behind.

Contemptuously, he also recounted the story of a man who should never have ventured to hunt the wily elephant. One day, a herd, breaking from thick brush, suddenly loomed ahead of his party. It happened that it was moving rapidly on a wide front, following the hollow-square pattern elephants occasionally adopt. There was not a moment to take cover. Trying to shoot an avalanche of monstrous beasts would have been ridiculous. The guide, sensing the danger, immediately ordered everyone to take cover behind the large trees on the trail. Intending no harm to anything in their path, the elephants were merely on an accustomed march. But as the huge animals advanced, this man couldn't endure the tension. He broke from cover and ran. They buried the remains there.

"Basically," Gerin said, "the elephant is a peaceful beast. He attacks only from fear or provoked anger. But when he does, he is a fearsome sight, his eyes are glazed, his ears stand out stiffly like boards and his trunk is rolled back to bare his tusks."

Gerin asked me if I knew where to aim to kill an elephant.

"In the head," I answered.

"The head, of course," he said, "but what part of it? The elephant's head as a matter of fact is better armored than the French tanks were in 1939. Between the ear and the eyes, or a little above them is the place to aim, or between the ear hole and the eye, if you are shooting from the side. Those are the paths to the brain. There are other alternative shots, but I don't advise you to try them if your life is in immediate danger," he said.

Under my mosquito netting that night I tossed restlessly, seeing visions of great gray ghosts bearing down on me as I frantically fired at them, the bullets ricocheting as if they were striking solid steel. I was up early and after a husky breakfast of dry bread and hot coffee, we set out again on the elephant trail.

The nocturnal tracks of the herd crossed and recrossed as the groups split up to search for food and it took us a while to locate the spoor of the true trail. Gerin judged that the elephants had moved away a mile or so during the night but were still following a southerly course which led to a familiar watering ground. Though the wanderings of a herd seem aimless, they are nearly always premeditated moves to water, forage and shade.

About two hours after sunrise, N'Gakoutou pointed to some droppings with an oily film on top, revealing the fact that they were of very recent origin. Gerin took his rifle from the gun-bearer and we cautiously pushed on through the heavy bush.

"Walk on your toes," Gerin whispered, "with your feet pointed straight ahead. We must walk very quietly."

We had scarcely covered another half-mile when N'Gakoutou touched my shoulder and, in great excitement, pointed at a tree fifty yards away. The foliage was dense and at first I could see nothing unusual, but straining my eyes I finally made out the dark shapes which resembled the giant termite hills of Equatorial Africa. Then I saw them move and my heart jumped. There were the elephants grazing peacefully, their trunks reaching up into the tall branches.

I was close enough to take pictures but the bush partially obscured my subjects. I had to get closer. The giant bull, whose footprint we had measured, must be there and I wanted desperately to take a picture of him, if nothing more.

Slowly, we inched our way forward, circling a bit, being careful at the same time to stay downwind. We reached good cover about twenty-five yards from the herd and I worked swiftly with my camera, fearful momentarily that a false move would give our presence away. Then it happened!

I think I saw the great bull at the moment he sensed danger. There he stood, a magnificent creature, his huge trunk testing the air, its sensitive tip waving to discover the direction and location where danger threatened. His ears fanned out furiously to verify the rustle of our movements and his great gleaming tusks were bared for use.

The most awesome sound I have ever heard blasted deafeningly through the jungle forest. The full lung power of the giant bull was in that trumpet call; then complete silence. Nothing moved. Numb with tension, I froze. He turned his head slightly and started for us.

Quickly, Gerin knocked my camera aside and thrust the .375 magnum at me. "Shoot!" he yelled.

"Head on, between the eyes, but a little above," I repeated to myself as I raised the magnum. I squeezed the trigger. The bull jerked his head, but otherwise stood without motion. Then to my left I heard the thunderous report of Gerin's .500. One second later the earth suddenly began to shake. Six tons of desperate elephant came charging at me at top speed, his trunk raised like the club of Hercules. Running from him would be the height of folly. I was glued to the spot and a hundred thoughts flashed through my mind. I felt so tiny, so insignificant before this greatest of all savage beasts.

Frantically, I again began firing the magnum. Each time a bullet dug into the head of this onrushing bull, he veered a little and shook his head. In spite of it all, massive and implacable, he continued charging until he seemed to tower above me like an avenging demon. Not a moment too soon a spasm went through him and his great forelegs crumpled. Down he dropped with a tempestuous crash. Even in that last vestige of time, his trunk seemed to be reaching out to clutch me, his enemy, only a few yards away.

Dimly, I was aware that N'Gakoutou was still firing. The herd, I saw, was thundering toward us! Following their leader in a cloud of dust, trumpeting as they came to within a menacing distance of us, one of them was stopped by a bullet from the tracker's rifle. Two of their number gone, the herd clumped to a halt, then, quickly turning in retreat, rapidly faded from sight through the dust of their action.

For a while, I shook uncontrollably, unable to speak coherently. It was good to be alive. I looked at Komoon, the monarch of his flock, with a mixture of triumph and compassion, lying dead at my feet.

Gerin and N'Gakoutou, after the first excitement of examining the fallen giant, were now gathering up our gear which was strewn over an acre. Our native packers had a healthy respect for elephants, bordering on the superstitious. At the first rifle report they had taken to wild flight, shedding their loads as they ran and not reporting back for two hours.

We measured the bull as best we could and estimated that he had stood over twelve feet tall at the shoulder. The tusks, which are the real measurement of a trophy, weighed about sixty pounds apiece.

The natives in the surrounding area learned by grape vine telegraph that an elephant was dead and within three or four hours all the tribesmen from three villages, numbering at least 150, had gathered on the spot. Quickly and efficiently they tore into the carcass. In a couple of hours they had stripped the six tons of elephant. What remained would be scanty lickings for the vultures which would presently settle on it.

To my surprise, Gerin told me that I was a local hero, having provided the natives with a supply of meat they seldom get. The tusks belonged to me. I thought they would make a wonderful trophy, but I was destined to be wrong. On my return to Fort Archambault I learned that the French Equatorial government supports itself by a tax on ivory. To take them home with me would have cost me a sum equal to my return ticket, so I made a present of them to Gerin.

That evening we marched back to a nearby village, where I was the guest of honor at a native ceremony, complete with tom-toms, dancing and feasting on the elephant flesh. The chief of the tribe awarded me the hair of the tail of the victim. He strapped it on my wrist as a good-luck charm. I managed to salvage a foreleg of the elephant, which I brought home and made into a wastepaper basket.

This is hardly an exciting trophy to bring back home after such a thrilling safari which brought me face to face with a raging six-ton elephant. I can assure you, however, that that split second looking up into what appeared to be a huge mountain crumbling on top of me was one that super-abounded all other dare-devil assignments I had ever had. It left me with the memory of an experience which was later to prove far more precious to me than any trophy I might have carried back for my collection.

CHAPTER FOUR

BIG GAME OF THE HINTERLANDS

"In that tense moment I suddenly realized the danger that I faced alone beneath the pool's surface with that monstrous bull hippo and two hideous crocodiles. I knew instantly that I had to turn back or press on with my attack. But, which one? Suddenly, the hippo started ponderously toward me!" exclaimed Herman Kitchen, photography director of a twenty-five man safari which ventured into East Africa to film big game.

"Our safari," he continued, "began when I arrived in Nairobi, where I was met by my second cameraman. I had wired ahead for my assistant photographer to select girls in the town to be interviewed for the female lead in the film. I spent that afternoon interviewing eight or ten of them who were eager to go on the safari in the feminine role.

I was agreeably surprised to find so many talented girls in Nairobi, many of whom had been on safaris a number of times, and most of whom could shoot. There were, however, several aspects which had to be considered in their selection—their age, whether they were married or engaged and if, in that event, their fiances or husbands would allow them to be away with a group of eight white men and double as many Africans.

The film's story was about a young American couple who had come to East Africa for a long-desired hunting and photographic safari. The two selected for these roles had to be American in appearance, behavior and compatible to each other. It was three days before I made my choice.

Norman Read, one of our white hunters, now took over some of the preparations for the expedition. He was a strapping fellow who had played parts in several feature films produced in East Africa. He was responsible for signing for guns and ammunition for the safari, obtaining licenses for the rhinos, lions, buffalo and elephants. I learned also that he was a good cook and even a gourmet. Since we would be living off the land for days at a time, particularly for meat, we decided to get agreeable condiments which would make the meals a little more than common fare. So we stocked seasonings, butter and even sherry with which to baste our better meat cuts.

Our party was now complete: the boy and girl appointed for leads in the film: Norman Read, the white hunter who would act as their white hunter and guide, together with his own tracker, skinner and gun bearer; and the three Africans who would appear with him and his two clients—the boy and girl. Besides these who would constitute the cast in the drama, there were added cameramen and a safari master who was a jack of all trades. There were eighteen African natives to do the cooking, haul the water and the wood, carry in the game and generally assist around the camp.

Our equipment—guns, ammunition, cameras, film and the like —were finally loaded and ready to depart after five days of negotiations with the authorities and preparations in Nairobi.

Three two-and-one-half-ton trucks were sent ahead with one of the Land Rovers, a species of jeep, and the second white hunter to prepare the camp located about one hundred and forty miles southeast on the Athi River. The rest of the party left in two Land Rovers for the drive to the camp that evening. Everything seemed quite satisfactory and we settled down to our first evening meal on safari. There were the usual night sounds of the bush babies screaming in the trees, some of the night birds and the weird sounds of animals going down to water in the river.

I outlined the next day's activities which would start off with two reconnaissance parties, Norman and I going in one direction, a white hunter and a cameraman going in the other. The object was to survey the countryside for photogenic hunting areas. The camp fire died down and we all retired to our respective tents. Most of the African boys who did not sleep under cover rolled themselves into blankets around their own fires and talked and chanted until long after I had fallen asleep.

In the morning I was aroused by the chattering of a group of monkeys and the chirping of birds. The boys were up building fires for breakfast, bringing water up from the river and getting the camp awakened for the first day's activities.

After breakfast the two reconnaissance parties set out for their objectives. We decided to go as far as we could by Land Rover, then on foot into the regions which seemed promising for our purpose. Most of the vegetation through which we were passing was quite dead, quite dense and devoid of photogenic character. We saw a few old tracks of elephant and rhino, but nothing of recent origin. The game obviously had moved to a greener location.

Smoke in the air and the burned-over condition of much of the surrounding section was caused by the natives' habit of setting fire to the countryside for the purpose of uncovering the fresh grass springing up for their cattle. The natives in this area, the Wacomba, graze large herds of cattle and goats; more than they actually need but, having a pride of possession and counting their wealth in cattle, wives and corn, instead of in money, they aspire for riches of this kind.

There was a discussion by the entire camp about the condition of the region to which we were assigned by people who were not familiar with the requirements of motion picture production. It might do for hunting but for color photography it was completely unsuitable. Arrangements must be made immediately for another area which would fit our requirements.

However, I determined to make the most of an unsatisfactory situation by having the camp scenes photographed. Meanwhile, I got in touch with distant Nairobi, one hundred and forty miles away, requesting a suitable location. Two days later we received word that the only other region available was on the Tana River, about three hundred and fifty miles east of our present camp.

Three of us left about dark that evening and drove into Nairobi to get permits for the new area. This drive through the dark was a dramatic experience. Much of the wild life being nocturnal, the light of our Land Rover picked up many gleaming pairs of eyes. Now and then a hyena or jackal would race along the side of the road just ahead of us. Every turn in the narrow winding trail through the Makindu country was exciting because of the many lions and black rhinos encountered there.

Early the next morning we got permission to enter new hunting grounds on the Tana River. This section is not too frequently visited being, as it was, three hundred and fifty miles from Nairobi, the entry point for the African game country. We would be east of the Tana River in the Northern Frontier District, not far from the Somaliland border. Travel in that section is not permitted without licenses from Nairobi or the District Commissioner at Garissa.

It was afternoon when we saw that our main safari party had entered the Nairobi-to-Garissa road and was well ahead of us. At this point, we were getting into rocky, hilly country. Tribes of baboons appeared. They inhabit the rocky ledges and cliffs, safe from their arch enemy, the leopards. Here, they are not only safe, but oftentimes in their elfish way will sit on a ledge or rock and mischievously toss stones and sticks down on the leopards.

Near the native villages the baboons are very destructive to the crops. They are smart enough to be wary of hunters who carry guns and elude them uncannily. The natives, who are not allowed to possess guns, have recourse only to cunning strategy for outwitting the troublesome creatures.

It is said that the villagers will rid themselves of a destructive tribe of baboons by building a crib or hut resembling a grainery for storing corn. Built as a slat, pole-like structure with a bushel or two of corn placed inside and a few handfuls sprinkled outside, the leader of the culprits is attracted unsuspectingly to enter the corn crib. As he does, a trap-door is sprung and bang, he is imprisoned.

The natives forthwith gather around to teach the miscreant a lesson. Either they pour paint or lye on the trapped animal or give him a severe thrashing with switches poked through the slats of the enclosure. He is then turned loose and off he will rush to his waiting tribe and chatter a warning to stay away from that neighborhood.

The baboons can be very savage at times, and have been known to attack natives and tear them with their claws and fangs. Their favorite victims, however, are the natives' dogs. They often steal into villages and grab the animals from under the natives' noses, employing the same savagery that the leopard vents on them. As a matter of fact, the baboons in their thieving excursions are best kept under control by the leopards, so much so that in many areas the hunting of leopards is restricted, even though the leopards are not averse at times to attacking natives.

After winding through miles of rock outcroppings and bleak hills, we leveled out on to a wide, sparsely vegetated plane, finally sighting game. We were nearly on our quarry before we saw the ponderous shapes of six cow elephants feeding a few steps from the side of the road. They hardly noticed us, and perhaps didn't see us at all. They simply moved slowly and silently away from the noise of our Land Rover.

Further on other game appeared—several wildebeests, grant gazelles and then the little giraffe-like animal, the garanook—a beautiful fawn-colored creature standing on its hind legs, as is its habit, reaching up to browse on the higher acacia trees.

Then we saw one of the most striking animals of all in the East African plains—the beautiful reticulated giraffe. Five of these dignified aloof creatures, moved slowly, followed by their scrawny-legged young. Giraffes are sought after by some natives, because of the value of their skin, which is very thick and prized for its long-wearing qualities. The flowing hairs of the tail are also excellent trade items among the Arabs and Indians. Other parts of the animal are utilized but the poachers generally kill more of these creatures than they can possibly eat.

As the sun was casting long purple shadows across the road and the sandy parched country through which we were now driving, we caught up with the main safari party. We proceeded to Garissa, the gateway to the Northern Frontier District of Kenya. We arrived at the bridge over the Tana River, which we walked over because the chains had been stretched across for the night. Vehicles are not permitted to pass over after dusk or before daylight. However, we were allowed entry through the guard post and to the home of the District Commissioner, who is the sole local administrator of this large, wild district of Northern Kenya.

The Commissioner granted permission for us to move our entire party across the river next morning. The white hunter and I were alerted to entering this region because of several other hunting parties there. Although this is a large section, a hunting party sometimes covers a vast amount of country, especially if it has located the spoor of a trophy elephant or rhino, which frequently travels twenty or thirty miles from waterhole to feeding grounds. Thus, at times, hunters will cross one another's trails, to the danger of both.

We went back across the river to where our safari party was set up for the night. Later, as the fire died out, the entire party, with the exception of the girl in her private tent, stretched out on bed rolls and listened to the sounds of the darkness on the Tana, over which a full moon was rising. We heard the chimpering, quavering voices of hyenas down the river, while several bush babies started their terrific racket in the trees above our camp. These small, innocent looking creatures with huge eyes and long, bushy tails, have almost the loudest screech of any animal in Africa. Finally a lion began to roar, in the middle of which I fell asleep.

The natives in this Northern Frontier District are primarily the Somalis, a tall, dignified Moslem people, who do little farming but graze huge herds of goats and cattle. These animals are magnificent creatures, their long, ponderous horns sometimes reaching a spread of eight or nine feet from tip to tip.

The Somalis' beasts of burden are mostly donkeys, but we also saw a number of camels staked outside the village, burdened with goods for local trading or to be carried into remote areas of the Northern Frontier District.

We picked up what necessary supplies we needed and set out down a sandy and bumpy road for Bura. The white hunter, the girl and I drove ahead to select the place where we would camp for our three or four weeks' stay in this region.

On our journey we saw our first major game, consisting of eleven massive elephants which moved magnificently across the road in front of us. These great beasts swinging through the wild are fascinating in their behavior. This lordly group seemed to be moving slowly, but actually, they were traveling at a good pace. We came to a stop forty or fifty yards away for fear of

stampeding them and we were sentimental enough to avoid
disturbing what appeared to be a tranquil, good-natured family
of one medium-sized bull, eight cows and two totos or young ones.

Our camp site was an ideal one. Several comfortable bamboo
huts had been erected to accommodate the District Commissioner
when he brought officials to the area. We placed our tents under
the trees and by late afternoon were established in our permanent camp.

This district is one of the largest unmarked areas on the chart
of East Africa. A map of one section, roughly ninety by seventy-
five miles, shows no villages, trails or water courses. For the most
part, it is a great plain covered with thorny acacia, cactus, palms,
grass and occasionally euphorbia and umbrella trees.

During the rainy season, which ends about the middle of May,
the vegetation is green and there are numerous small ponds,
which are really shallow depressions in which run-off water had
been collected during the rains. The game is scattered far and
wide, finding sufficient water at these tanks until the dry season
arrives in July and early August. Here, also, the Somalis graze
their herds of goats and long-horned cattle.

As the dry months approach, a great exodus of wild game and
Somali herds takes place westward towards the Tana River. This
is the best time of year for either photography or hunting big
game. The animals then concentrate around the diminishing
water in the ponds, making tracks to the river and then retracing
their steps to feed in the dry grass.

Here we were then in this ideal area and at an ideal time in
July. In our reconnaissance trips we had seen tracks of small
herds of elephants, rhino spoor and footprints of lions, giraffes,
topi and zebras. In this district is the Grezy zebra, a beautiful,
narrow-striped animal with large, fuzzy-fringed ears, larger than
the Chapman's zebra; also one of the rarest of antelope in Kenya,
the Hunters antelope, which is a sub-species of the hartebeest,
or to give it Kongoni, the Swahili name.

I had set aside the next day for filming several sequences of
our girl bird-shooting, this being a sequence in the script where
the young woman was to hunt birds while her husband was out
on the plain in pursuit of antelope.

There being plenty of grouse, bustards and beautiful guinea
fowl nearby, the bird-shooting episode was simple. In photographing a sequence like this, however, it was almost impossible

to get good shots of the girl flushing fowl, raising the gun, firing, seeing the bird in flight and falling as it was hit. Therefore, it was necessary to shoot this in several parts. This film was edited later into one complete, smooth sequence.

Coincidentally, the other white hunter was out with the trackers to locate a good trophy elephant and a lively rhino.

The next plans were for the photographing of a number of camp sequences, involving the white hunter and his two clients, the male and female leads, and the African boys who would appear in the picture. A film is never shot in the continuity in which it is written. Advantage is taken of situations, photographing what is immediately obtainable and such activities as opportunity offers. We shot the camp scenes, showing the American couple preparing for the day's trek, the checking of guns and cameras, eating meals, and their return from the field with game.

On the third day the second white hunter returned to camp to report that he had discovered the fresh spoor of a lone bull elephant. He estimated the tracks to be only about two hours old and, since the time was mid-morning, the elephant was probably slowly feeding his way back into the heavier vegetation for the rest of the day, where he would be safe from the insects along the river. If the white hunter's judgment was correct we could probably overtake the beast in two or three hours.

Immediately, we reloaded the motion picture cameras, filled our two Land Rovers with our party, and set out after our quarry along an old game trail.

The trackers were sent on ahead to determine the exact direction taken by the elephant, his rate of speed and roughly his size. A good tracker can, after following his prey for several miles, describe the animal he is following; how old, how large, and how far ahead he is. His judgment is based on the size of the track, the depth of foot imprint, length of step, the extent and character of grazing and other lesser details.

In about half an hour, one of the trackers came back to report that the big bull was probably an old one with good-sized tusks, and was moving slowly. We set off immediately in single file, the tracker in the lead.

As had been surmised, the elephant had been feeding leisurely which was evident from the branches he had torn down, then chewed up and spit out. Elephants crunch branches and grass, then eject a mass of fibers. The trackers feel this material to determine by its warmth how old the spoor is. The old fellow we were following was of considerable weight; his tracks were large, his toes were worn, his pads were smooth, his imprint deep—all indications of an old and massive animal.

An hour and a half later, our leading tracker motioned us to stop. He had spotted our quarry a short distance ahead. The first white hunter and I thereupon ventured up with the tracker to within fifty feet, as he stood out in the open feeding contentedly on low shrubs. An elephant's sight is poor; however, his hearing is excellent, and he quickly scents animals or human beings if they are upwind. We circled downwind and thus did not risk frightening him or provoking a charge. The situation was ideal for purposes of photography; we had three cameras, each with an operator.

Now, with our several cameras in position and I behind the stalking party, we made the approach to the animal. Everything went well, strictly as planned. I moved into position for shooting. The bull heard the whirring of my camera. Suddenly becoming alarmed, he threw his trunk up and whipped around in a circle, sensing that danger was near.

We were downwind, however, so he was unable to catch our scent, but was trying to locate the direction of the sound from the camera. Then, in a flash he saw us and charged like an avalanche. As he bounded forward, the client fired, following which the two white hunters, taking no chances, opened up after the client had shot. According to custom, the white hunter allows the client to shoot the game but if a charge is threatened the white hunter automatically fires. This protects the party from the charge of a wounded animal, and prevents it from getting away. Fortunately in this case our bull fell immediately making, all told, good shots for both the rifle and the cameras.

This old fellow never knew what hit him, for he crumpled up, falling on his knees, his tusks bearing on the ground, as though he had just settled down to sleep. We waited a moment and then approached cautiously to make sure the elephant was dead. We checked by opening his eyelids, a positive way of determining whether he was dead or just stunned. The eye will automatically twitch when the lids are opened, should the animal still be alive.

A very good hunting movie was made and we had the effort completed exactly as we had planned. Now came the work of finishing the sequence. It was necessary to take all of the reverse shots—those of the client shooting, of the girl in action taking motion pictures, of the white hunter and of the gun bearers as they had approached the elephant before it fell. From here we now worked backwards and photographed every step of the action leading up to the final drama.

To get back to the elephant, we found upon examination that he had apparently suffered several old bullet wounds, two of which had gone into his mid-section and a third which had furrowed the side of his head.

These may have been caused by the poor marksmanship of natives, or by Arab hunters who poach elephants for their ivory. There is a lively market on the eastern coast of Africa for elephant ivory, rhino horn, wildebeest and giraffe tails. Some of the natives and Arabs do possess rifles, although many of them are of ancient vintage, including flintlocks. A well-placed shot, even with an old firearm, will bring most of these animals down, but frequently they are merely wounded and escape to become a danger to the natives and their habitation. An elephant wounded, as ours had been, apparently four to six weeks previously, will likely become a rogue and roam the countryside alone, wreaking havoc upon whatever disturbs him. We felt that we had accomplished a real service all around, putting an end to the suffering of this old bull, and had probably prevented injury to unsuspecting natives who might have encountered him.

After finishing the filming of this elephant sequence, we had the boys remove the tusks and cut off the feet for use as waste baskets or umbrella stands. The long coarse-haired tail of an elephant is also prized for the making of braided bracelets. There is a tradition that good luck will reward a hunter if he wears a bracelet made from the hairs of the tail of an elephant he has felled. It is a sacrilege to wear a bracelet from an elephant that has not been killed by the wearer.

We reached camp later that afternoon in time to film the successful return of our party with their trophies—the ivory being carried in by the skinners. After a refreshing bath in our individual canvas tubs, it was a light-hearted group that gathered around for the evening meal after a successful day.

That evening another hunting party arrived in camp—a visit made notable because one of its skinners, an old man with a patch over one eye, had been a gun bearer in this game country for Teddy Roosevelt about fifty years ago.

We were not as isolated from civilization as Teddy had been, for at nine o'clock a radio was produced which brought us news from all over the world via the radio station in Nairobi, including the last minute stock quotations!

Our next highlight several days later was brought about by our second white hunter who reported that fresh signs had been found of rhino in the area ten miles south of us. We lost no time in heading there the next morning in three Land Rovers. We traveled slowly over the rough ground through a beautiful sea of grass and short vegetation. There were no landmarks; we had to navigate by compass and time.

Two hours later, one of the gun bearers standing in the back of the car, signaled to me that he had sighted game. We came to a stop and he told us that through the dense growth he had just sighted a rhinoceros walking into the heavy vegetation.

I readied my camera, the white hunter and the client checked their rifles and we slowly stalked the rhino from downwind. In a few minutes we approached the point at which the beast had last been seen. One of our trackers stalked to the left of the thicket, then motioned us to come closer. There the great animal stood oblivious of our presence, in the shade of one of the acacia bushes, his back to us. I was anxious to photograph him from several angles, as the white hunter and the gun bearers led the two clients within close shooting distance.

I got as close as I dared and ran the camera a hundred feet as the rhino, having sensed danger at last, milled around, in an endeavor to catch the scent of something that disturbed him.

I beckoned the white hunter to bring the clients up for the shot, while I kept my camera going to catch the developing action. The rhino finally got the direction of the sound, whirled around, and made several short, false charges in our direction. He could not see well for, like the elephant, the rhino has notoriously bad eyesight and must rely on his high sense of scent and hearing.

We were now in an excellent position, both for the photography and the shooting of this fine trophy. However, our quarry decided to investigate and, as is the habit of their breed, he circled about to get behind his dimly seen antagonist. Suddenly, he picked up our wind and we knew that an instant charge was inevitable. That was something we did not want, so, as he crossed a small open area broadside to us, the client fired, followed by a shot from the white hunter. Dramatically our rhino went down exactly as we had hoped for in the script.

The rhino is a very unpredictable animal. Sometimes he will be easily spooked, or at other times will charge unprovoked. Our first night at Bura, for example, one had charged our camp after dark, upsetting all the native boys, who took to the nearby trees. The rampaging animal had simply charged through blindly, snorting with a fury of noise but without doing any serious damage or returning for another charge.

Various hunters have theories about the rhino's unpredictable nature. Some contend that the ill-tempered monsters are made vicious by acute constipation brought on by feeding on dry boughs, frequently getting too little water, the result being an upset digestion.

After taking several more feet of film we had the boys cut some thorny bushes to cover our rhino to prevent prowling scavengers from eating the carcass during the night. We arranged to come back the next morning with our entire party to photograph the sequence of the stalk and the shooting just as we had done when we killed our elephant.

Having had complete success in filming the elephant and the rhino, we had also photographed sequences of the topi, waterbuck, and the rare oryx, a beautiful animal with long straight horns which looks like a cross between an antelope and a horse. Its long tail is very similar to that of a zebra or a donkey.

Our sole need now was to round up a lion. We made several long treks out through the uncharted areas of the country in the hope of locating one. We heard roaring almost every night, but that did not necessarily mean that there were many lions in this vicinity. There were tracks of them, too, but they were several days old. We shot a few zebras and wart hogs for the deposit of their carcasses in a section where we could approach unseen next morning in the hope there would be a lion on the kill. Occasionally we did get a glimpse of lions, but they were not trophy animals and were quite wild, so we did not try to photograph them.

After several more days of such baiting we had to give up, partly because the Somalis were now bringing their large herds of goats and cattle into the river region, and we did not dare risk shooting in a locality active with people and domestic herds.

We found numerous small antelope and had several chances of stalking small groups of elephants. One of the latter in particular gave us some fine sequences of activity. The white hunter and I, with my second cameraman, followed a group of eleven cows and five calves to within thirty yards. We were downwind in rather heavy vegetation, so were able to approach them quite closely. However, when we drew very near, one of the old cows, apparently the sentinel of the herd, caught the murmur of our cameras running, and whirled around to face us. It was a dramatic sight, this old cow towering high, looking directly at us, her ears out, fanning the air, her trunk in motion, weaving back and forth, trying to pick up our scent. She seemed to be just on the verge of a charge and we knew that we might have to clear out in a rush. One of our number was standing by with his double .470, in case, as a last resort, he had to turn the charge in order for us to scramble for safety.

As we were grinding out the film of this, a small toto not more than four feet high, ambled up to its mother. It had come alongside, and began to mimic the exact motions of its parent, its ears flared out, its trunk up, its head and trunk weaving back and forth in perfect unison. After several minutes of this we decided to leave, because we had shot all the film we wanted of this herd and didn't wish to provoke an unnecessary charge which our hunter would have to stop with his rifle.

The most exciting and hazardous phase of our filming expedition, in my opinion, was at Mzima Springs in East Africa, where I was given the task of photographing the hippos of the region. The spring where they gather is a clear, fresh-water pond about one hundred and fifty yards across richly banked with lush growth. From almost any point on the shore the animals could be seen moving around in the water.

The occupants on our arrival at midday were a cagey old bull with a harem of nine cows and five or six calves; as we approached they were disporting themselves peacefully. At dusk the scene was different; the entire area became alive with activity. Elephants arrived from the surrounding country to water; baboons sauntered down in family groups; lions now and then appeared when their own water holes back in the hills dried up. These visitations were evident by the numerous tracks and the signs of scuffling and activity the next morning.

We decided to take the projected underwater photography

of the hippos the next morning. My equipment consisted of a rollflex in a rolliemarine underwater case, a face mask, snorkle, flippers and a trusty bowie knife with twelve good inches of steel. I don't know what good it would have done me, but there was some feeling of confidence in merely having the latter strapped to my wrist.

In order not to disturb the hippos or other animals that might be at or in the pool, we stopped about two hundred yards short of it where we made our preparations. I changed into swimming trunks, got my underwater gear ready and readied two Askaris with rifles in the event that I needed some outside help. It takes accurate marksmanship to kill a hippo, for the bullet must hit a vital spot in the brain or he will never be stopped. Of course, I was hoping that a kill would not become necessary.

If a hippo is killed in the water, he sinks and remains at the bottom for several hours; then his body fills with gas and rises to the surface. At this point the hunter strips the huge animal of his skin and ivory.

My cameramen had their Leicas and graphics loaded and prepared to photograph my attempts to film the hippos. We circled the spring at a distance to get downwind from the pool, reaching the far side through the bulrushes to a grassy plot at the edge of the water.

As we came to our destination, the Askari ahead of me suddenly stopped. Leaning forward, he pointed toward the pool excitedly, but said nothing; he was afraid to utter a sound; he had seen a slimy crocodile slide into the water with scarcely a ripple—a huge repulsive creature with twelve feet of battle-scarred body. I had spotted the old fellow, too, and frankly, hadn't been alarmed as long as he remained on the bank, but when he disappeared beneath the surface of the water in the very spot I planned to submerge, I shivered with apprehension.

After positioning the two Askaris with rifles on either side of the water I prepared, in spite of everything, to go in myself. I instructed the two cameramen to be ready with their cameras to cover whatever might happen. I donned the flippers, mask and snorkle. With the camera around my neck, I waded out fifteen yards to waist-deep water, and took one final look around. Everything seeming secure, I slipped down into the water and swam beneath the surface in the direction of the hippos. The water was clear and I could see twenty or thirty feet around me.

After swimming several yards, I came up for air and another look around before continuing on my watery journey.

As I broke the surface, I was greeted by the old bull hippo, who had turned and faced in my direction. Apparently he had seen me enter the water and could follow my line of bubbles as I swam toward him. Puzzled as to the identity of this strange creature, he was determined to find out. So he moved out of the center of the ring of cows and calves and focused his eyes on me. Evidently fascinated with curiosity he made no attempt at once to advance closer to investigate, but just lay there in the water and watched my movements.

One of the Askaris on sentry duty suddenly pointed to the left of the spot where I had entered the water. Twenty-five yards distant emerging from a tall growth of bulrushes another croc had slid beneath the surface. Thirty yards from my objective the hippos were in the middle of the pool. I asked the Askaris on the shore if they could still see to the bottom of the water all around them, and they assured me they could.

My moment of decision had come!

Now was the time to retreat or press the attack. I was out of my environment, in a pond which was the stamping ground of a vicious bull hippo and two predatory crocodiles. Here I was invading their privacy! While I pondered a decision, it was unceremoniously made for me. When the aged hippo finally decided that he didn't trust the look of that creature with the glass eye and snorkle, he grunted, snapped his mouth open and closed and started lumbering toward me. There was no motion of swimming, just a quiet surge forward like a gray battleship. Slowly, he moved in an undeviating line. My retreat seemed like descending a steep mountainside after having reached the top, the return being more precarious. Instantly I thought of the crocodile and knew I must get my face under water so that I could keep my eye out for the most dreadful of killers. At the same time I could not for a moment neglect the movements of the old bull.

A few kicks of the flippers put me into waist-deep water again and I stood up to see if any element of danger was between me and safety at the shore. All the while my two cameramen had been shooting pictures of the whole event, so that my challenge to extinction was not in vain.

I crawled up the bank, divested myself of mask and flippers

and sat down for a breather. One of the crocodiles was still lying in the mud by the pool. These repulsive creatures are really a lazy tribe. They love to sun themselves on the banks of pools and rivers, opening their mouths wide, so that the birds can pick the vestiges out from between their teeth, which are filled with parasites.

I had a conference on the bank with my cameramen as to whether several good still pictures of the hippos from the surface would not suffice for the underwater photos scheduled in the script. We decided to try for more. This time I planned to go into the water out of sight of the hippos and swim slowly with only the snorkle protruding above the water, then dive to the proper depth in an endeavor to snap the pictures and return without being seen.

Therefore, I instructed two of our native boys to go a quarter of the way around the pond and distract the attention of the hippos in that direction while I slipped in from the opposite side. This procedure worked satisfactorily until I was half way out, but when there I couldn't resist a peek to get my bearings. As I put my head above the surface I could hear the excited clamor of the boys on the bank. They were looking over to my left and, as I peered in that direction, I saw another ponderous shape swimming toward the middle of the pool. It was another but younger bull hippo, unquestionably planning a raid on the old bull's harem.

Such a raid was a usual occurrence. One of the young romantic bulls would decide to start a harem of his own and the only place for him to get a mate was from the old bull's collection of females, so he raided the harem for that purpose. The aged hippo sensed this intruder and whipped around viciously in the direction of the threat to his happy existence and bellowed out a warning.

Following his thunderous warning the old boy then charged directly towards the young bull, which in turn started a flanking movement to his right. Unfortunately this put me in line with the old hippo's charge to intercept the young bull.

I decided that retreat was the better part of valor and to leave the competition to them. As they seemed determined to destroy each other the idea of being caught in the middle had a dim appeal to me. So in unexampled time I beat it to the bank while the two bulls churned the water into foam in a terrific struggle.

For a time, it seemed as though the senior hippo was about

to relinquish a few members of his harem. Then, suddenly, he reversed the tables in his battle for the integrity of his female charmers. The fight was to the strong. As he convinced the young intruder that he was still the master of the ring his harem was saved. Without visible warning to us, the two monsters ended their tussle and separated as if by mutual agreement.

I was now back at the bank for the second time without pictures and without having reached my objective. I decided on one more approach; this time it was to be underwater, swift and directly towards the center of the pool.

On this third attempt I dropped all discretion and soon found myself getting farther out, closer and closer to the center of the pool. The bottom began falling away, almost completely out of sight. I didn't know how deep it was, but it was eerie looking down into the depths.

Believing I had almost reached my objective I came slowly to the surface for air and for a last look before diving down to take the underwater pictures. Now, above the surface, I saw the backs of several hippos. Apparently they had not noticed my approach. One of the Askaris, standing on the bank with a rifle, started motioning wildly into the water between me and the shore. The second croc had slipped into water and was somewhere in the muddy water between me and the safety of the bank. The cameramen waved frantically for me to come back.

The sudden furor set the hippos in motion again. This was enough! I never scrambled more quickly to get out of anything!

As I swam feverishly back I saw that the water was stirred and muddied up. At such a time crocodiles move out from their lairs unseen in pursuit of their prey and seize their victims in their awful vice-like jaws. I was in a desperate position in the muddy, churning water. The hulks of the hippos were becoming more like huge, vague shadows. A chill went up my spine. It was a frightfully long swim back to the bank—longer than I had realized. Frantically I increased my speed and spontaneously devised tricky strokes to fool my pursuers. Finally, I reached the bank and, with the aid of the Askaris, clambered out and breathed a prayer of thanks for my lucky escape.

From the safety of the bank I was more sure of the foolheartedness of my venture. It was little relief to know that my cameraman's concern was only because the water had become muddy and not because of the crocodile!

My cameraman, in trying to modify my disappointment, said that he had made some wonderful shots of me swimming back to the shore madly pursued by the old hippo and eyed enviously by the expectant crocodile.

Later, from a vantage point overlooking the pool, we watched the scene below us with redoubled interest. The old battle-scarred crocodile crawled back to shore to lie in the sun with his mouth wide open for the birds to pluck at his teeth, and the hippos battled and snorted in the middle of the pond. Now and then the old devil would chase the young bulls from his carefully guarded harem. Every time the old hippo rushed one of the juniors, his furious charges made me realize how foolhardy I had been in attempting to catch him unawares and photograph him in the middle of his circle of admiring women.

CHAPTER FIVE

A SAFARI OF MAD ASCENT

WHAT does it take to reach the rooftop of Africa? Guts, for one thing, and stubbornness, but it takes something more, as Wilf Nussey, a hardened, seasoned big game hunter of the Veld found in his struggle to the peak of Kilimanjaro. Maybe some day he'll know just *what*!

As he put it when this story was told: "A week ago I stood on Kibo peak and looked down into Kilimanjaro's black, yawning crater. My lungs ached with a pain that twin daggers could not duplicate; my head felt weightless and strange; my face was shapeless and swollen, beaten by the eternal winds that tear at the face of Kilimanjaro; my body, tough from years of hunting on the sunny veld, was stiff and aged from the fifty-mile climb through jungle, over rock and ice to the top of Africa's greatest peak.

But I had not conquered Kilimanjaro—I had merely climbed it. Kilimanjaro had thrashed half the life out of me. And I would have it no other way, because to dare such a magnificent natural phenomenon to battle is sheer impudence on the part of any man—he deserves to be whipped. If the mountain allows him to caress her jagged head, that is her business; but she should not give in without a struggle. Kilimanjaro never does. She makes you *work* for her favors!

I suspected it long before I made the actual assault. Every safari I made south of Nairobi would find me gazing at the great mountain in anticipation. I knew some day I'd make the attempt.

My chance came as I sipped a scotch and soda in the bar of Nairobi's Norfolk Hotel. It's a three-day stroll to the summit, a white hunter friend told Johnny Johnson, Ken Angel and me. You don't climb Kilimanjaro, he said, you just keep putting one foot before the other until suddenly you're out on top.

"Sounds easy," said Johnny.

That's what we thought. Because although the hunter had often seen Kilimanjaro's bald peak shining red in the sunset and ghostly silver in the moonlight, he had never climbed it. Therefore he omitted the vital details of the old mountain's powerful army of defences: the crater's deep crevasses vanishing into a blue-black void far below, the treacherous snowdrifts, the glass smooth ice at the brink of sheer 200-foot drops, and the cloud.

Cloud is Kilimanjaro's most dangerous weapon. One minute you're bathed in sunshine, the next blanketed in thick, moist fog and yelling in panic for the guide. You can't see a yard and to blunder about is a short cut to suicide.

But in the warm, comfortable bar of the Norfolk it does sound easy. And so two weeks ago we three were heading for Tanganyika and Kilimanjaro.

I have seen Kilimanjaro many times while on safari in the Serengeti Plains and Amboseli National Park, but always from a distance. Its towering bulk, linked by a long, 15,000-foot high saddle to the ragged and rocky peak, Mawenzi is softened by heat haze and seems to slope gently upward from the vast flats of Tanganyika and neighboring Kenya.

When we crossed the border of the two territories at Longido the old mountain slept behind a soft veil of cloud. We first saw it clearly from Arusha in Tanganyika's Northern Province.

"I can't understand why it takes three days to climb that," commented Ken as we proceeded on to Marangu, south-east of Kilimanjaro and the starting-point of the climb. My first twinges of doubt came as we approached Marangu. The closer we traveled to the mountain the less we could see of it. Over fifty miles away we hit the foothills. They towered above our little car, some of the crests poking into the clouds.

At Marangu Hotel we were 2,000 feet above Tanganyika's veld but still apparently no nearer to our goal. Our real education on Kilimanjaro began in the hotel's four-stool bar.

The local white settlers made quite certain we fully understood what lay ahead. With effective British economy of words they told of the climber who went crazy while negotiating a glacier on the crater rim.

Screaming incoherently he tried to hurl himself over the edge to the lava pit far below. The plucky African guide grabbed him —and found himself battling for his own life. For minutes of agony they grappled on the polished ice in the bitter cold, the demented climber using all his maniac strength to break away and dive into space. One wrong slip and both men would have plunged down the smooth curve of the glacier.

The fellow was quite okay when he got back here. Couldn't understand what happened to him, and was grateful to the guide for saving his life. I hoped we would get the same guide.

Then, over a drink that I bought him, a farmer recalled the climber left on the mountainside by his party when he couldn't make the grade. Foolishly he started walking—in the wrong direction.

Days later they found him almost on the other side of Kilimanjaro, nearly dead from exhaustion and exposure. In his panicked flight through the huge forest, girding the slopes he had bumped into elephants, dodged rhinos and been charged by a buffalo.

A week before we arrived, they continued, one member of a French film production unit almost died up there. Exhausted when the party reached the snowline, he stayed behind to await the return of his companions. Then Kilimanjaro inexorably gripped him. He went mad. When the others returned he had gone.

Only when they descended to the highest hut on the saddle did they realize he must still be somewhere on top of the mountain. Again an African guide with a porter returned to the ice cap to retrieve him.

That night, in my little thatched bungalow, I drastically revised my ideas about Kilimanjaro. This was no ordinary safari.

For so enormous a mountain Kilimanjaro has a comparatively

brief history. It started in 1848 when a tough German missionary pioneered a route on foot from the Tanganyika coast.

Nomadic Masai warriors called the mighty, brooding bulk *Ngaje Ngai*, the House of God. No man could reach the top, they claimed.

When the missionary, Rebmann, returned to Europe and reported his find he was scoffed at. Only a lunatic, said the geographers, could discover a snow-capped mountain so near the Equator where temperatures are often over one hundred degrees.

The man eventually to stand on the roof of Africa was another German, experienced Alpinist Hans Meyer, who was himself beaten several times before he gazed down into the black crater in 1889. The unsuccessful attempts had been expensive; one party lost twenty porters in a blizzard. Since then hundreds of people, including many women, have been up.

We three bravados were far humbler men when they handed out our kit early next morning. Balaclavas, fur-lined mittens, scarves, snow goggles, boots, alpenstocks and a face cream to guard against sunburn where temperatures are way below zero.

The only man who didn't tell us how tough the climb would be was Kimatari, our guide. A tall, wiry WaChagga with the deceptively slow walk of the African, he is one of the finest guides on the mountain. His most striking characteristic is silence. In one hundred miles of hard foot-slogging I doubt whether I exchanged a dozen words with him, yet each of us knew what he had to do. Kimatari was the boss and with each mile my respect for him grew. He knows Kilimanjaro; it is his ally and his life.

Kimatari the Silent took charge the moment he appeared in the hotel garden. Even the chattering porters fell silent. With a jerk of his steel-spiked stick he had them formed into a line, all grinning sheepishly, and waved them on.

The porters are human pack mules. With about ninety pounds of food, bedding and other supplies to bring comfort to the climbers balanced precariously on their stubby heads, they stride with incredible speed always well ahead of the party. Their short muscular legs work like pistons maintaining a mile-eating pace up steep slopes, through bushy valleys and across stony ridges.

The porters are the major factor in the low cost of climbing Kilimanjaro. For five days they lug those packs and are satisfied with a payment of less than a dollar a day each. The guide's pay is twice as much, but the average tip at the end of the safari is never less than three shillings (just under half a dollar) for each porter and twenty shillings for the guide. Most climbers rely on these Africans so much they at least double the tip.

Of the fifty miles to Kibo's dome the first forty is through the jumbled foothills, themselves a pretty severe test of endurance. We traveled through some of Africa's most beautiful bush country, a wonderland of sun-dappled, leafy branches, tall gnarled trees, twisting lianas and moss drapes. We met an African herdsman with a few scrub cattle wandering leisurely through the forest.

Bismarck Hut, at 9,000 feet, is the sort of place honeymooners dream about. Nestling against a frieze of tangled green bush and trees, it is built of stone and has a couple of bunkrooms, a little kitchen with a wood stove that glows red in the cold evenings, and special bunkhouses for the porters and guide.

Its peace and the luxury of a three-course meal on china plates, with neat cloths on the table, dissolve all fears about tomorrow.

The real grind began that second day as we rose steadily to Peter's Hut, 7,000 feet below our goal. Breathing slightly harder now we seemed to climb on and on and on, out of the forest into the wind-swept moorland, where armies of giant heather and lobelia plants stick gaunt out of the swishing grass. It was colder and I soon stopped a porter to unpack a heavy jersey.

As we climbed, Mawenzi peak rose before us, its formidable black canyons and cliffs thrusting into the sky. Parts of Mawenzi have never been climbed and recently it claimed an airways Dakota with the lives of all passengers.

Peter's Hut is actually two small corrugated iron buildings standing close together on a bare rise with a small stream running nearby. We headed straight for the huts and found a fire roaring in the pot-bellied stove as the porters prepared supper—not so luxurious a meal this time. That night the cold began. We huddled in our blankets to snatch a few precious hours of sleep before the next stages to the ice dome waiting for us with all its defences ready.

Kilimanjaro's first weapon, lack of oxygen, began to tell as we followed the porters on the third day. My head throbbed persistently and I dared not count my pulse. My heart already worked overtime to feed oxygen to my blood as we climbed on. To one side Mawenzi towered up, in the distance we could see Kibo clearly now, waiting and watching as the wind whipped thin clouds round its crest.

On the other side lay Tanganyika, stretching like a map far below. Mountains we gazed up at on the first day looked like crinkles in a piece of crushed paper. I told myself: if I can get this far I can go all the way.

As we walked a WaChagga, lagging behind the other porters, told me the story of Kibo and Mawenzi in halting Swahili. You see, *bwana*, Mawenzi is broken and jagged and much smaller than Kibo, he said. It is because many, many generations ago when both had fire in their mouths, Mawenzi was also a fine mountain but a lazy one.

One day he slept and let his fire die. When he awoke he begged a fresh light from Kibo, who gave it to him with good will. But Mawenzi impishly made a joke of this, *bwana*, and kept on letting his fire go out so he could pester Kibo for a light.

Then one day Kibo became very angry, said the WaChagga. He was tired of giving lights to Mawenzi, and he took up his club and gave Mawenzi the beating of his life. He put Mawenzi's fire right out, *bwana*, and smashed his face and mouth, leaving the sharp edges you see now.

And ever since then Mawenzi the *Pumbafu* (Fool) has been ashamed and hides his head and broken face in the clouds.

We soon left Mawenzi behind and descended slightly to the giant saddle between the peaks, surely one of the highest deserts in the world. It stretches far and bleak in all directions, a cold sea of pebbles and sand with great oddly-shaped stones projecting up. There is a distinct path tracking erratically across this windswept waste towards the rugged folds at the base of Kibo where stands the last hut, base for the assault on the mighty peak itself.

Before long I began to feel the upgrade of the saddle. The desert lay seemingly interminable ahead and I wondered how on earth I ever managed to walk thirty miles and more a day on previous safaris. But we could not stop to rest. Solid, malevolent-looking clouds were swirling up the sides of Mawenzi behind us and to get caught in cloud there is inviting trouble.

The guide kept us going. After a few hundred more yards I checked my pulse. It was over 110 a minute—and my normal is 70. A sledgehammer pounded my brain. I started wishing I'd never heard of this damn mountain when the angle of the slope increased and I hit the scree.

Scree. It's an inapt word. I swore unreasonably for several minutes. Scree is a deep mass of stones, pebbles and sand, constantly shifting and the trickiest foothold I've ever walked on. It is formed by centuries of weathering of the mountain rocks and has beaten scores of climbers. I plugged on, my breath laboring, my lungs stung by the cold air.

Time and again I stumbled. The loose, sliding mass scuffed my ankles, rolled from under my feet. Leaning on the alpenstock I progressed snail-like up the twenty-five degree slope.

Kibo Hut appeared round a shoulder of rock, warm and inviting. The chirpy porters were already there, smoke curled in the thin air from a stovepipe. Johnny and the guide were ahead, the guide moving with easy familiarity born of long years of practice. The altitude was now almost 16,000 feet. To hell with the guide! I stopped to rest frequently.

An hour later I stepped from the hut with a hot meal inside me and wrapped in a pair of pajamas, heavy corduroys, three jerseys, two pairs of socks, thick boots, balaclava and a couple of scarves. High above, Kibo's ice crags shone in the moonlight. They appeared to be only a few hundred feet away. Gaze long enough, says the legend, and you may see Menelik the ancient king of Ethiopia, illegitimate son of King Solomon and the Queen of Sheba, silhouetted against the night sky.

Menelik conquered a colossal slice of Africa including Tanganyika. Returning from an expedition, the story tells, his army crossed the saddle. Menelik there decided he was getting old and would leave this world. Followed by his lords and bodyguard he climbed to Kibo and disappeared.

To while away the miserable hours until midnight, when the final climb would begin, I scanned through the visitors' book. There is one in each hut and a fourth kept in a tin box on the ice dome. Entries in the book tell the stories of many dejected climbers and get progressively fewer as you go up.

At Bismarck Hut I saw boastful scrawls: "Going up!" On the way down the same writers entered postscripts: "Never again," and "Going down, thank God."

One amateur climber still had enough strength left to record a poem which aptly describes every climber's feelings on reaching the ice dome:

> God gave us all good things,
> And nothing do we lack.
> He gave us Kilimanjaro
> And now he can have the damn thing back.

I had finally managed to doze when my shoulder was gently shaken. It was the guide, so well wrapped only his eyes and nose showed. Outside it was dark and the porters, who would wait for us to return from the peak, slept soundly. Ken was already dressing. I woke Johnny.

Then we started the most killing physical strain of all my life, a plodding nightmare that will stay with me to my deathbed.

It began simply enough. Fairly fresh from the few hours' rest I just kept my eyes on the legs of the man in front silhouetted against the lantern. We hit the mountain almost immediately. It was still a matter of placing one foot before the other, but no mere walk this time.

This was climbing. Each labored step had to lift the body laden with twenty pounds of clothing upwards. We hadn't been going half an hour when my head throbbed like a Congo drum. I felt the starved blood swish through it with each violent pump of my heart, and the pumps were coming quickly now.

An hour later we stopped in a small cave for a cigarette. I had to suck it to a pulp to keep it burning and the hot smoke scalded my lungs. I threw it away and asked Kimatari how far up we were.

We have hardly started, he said. Maybe it was fear, maybe fatigue but I swore at him openly with words I would never have used down on the plain. The mountain was doing strange things to me.

We plodded on. Suddenly the oxygen-starved lantern flickered out, leaving us in utter darkness. Kimatari wedged the lantern in the scree and we started again. I was scrambling on all fours when the sun rose. A golden rod of light flashed from the ice above, then the sun swelled above the horizon and bathed the crags and clouds in a sheet of flame. I sat on the scree and fumbled with the camera. All I got, I found later, was a shot of the tip of my boot and my alpenstock.

With the sun came mountain sickness, the hardest hitter of them all. It struck suddenly. My brain fogged and the slope canted drunkenly, then the pit of my stomach exploded. Even after I had parted with breakfast the retching continued. All the way up I fought mountain sickness with every ounce of my fading willpower. It left me briefly only to come back worse than before. In these quiet periods I could see the steep slope stretching miles and miles ahead, seemingly through an age of climbing. That's why you leave Kibo Hut at midnight, so you can get as far as possible before daylight comes to break your spirit.

I was determined not to let Kilimanjaro beat me. Ten yards above was a boulder. I stared at it, put my head down and crawled on hands and knees with every muscle straining, stopping only to be sick again. After ten minutes of heaving and panting and retching I looked up. The boulder was still there, no nearer.

This is where you start climbing on spirit. All desire to conquer Kilimanjaro is gone. You just keep going because you can't take back the memory of defeat. For your own sake you must get to the top. You strain until your vision blurs and your lungs threaten to burst.

You reach the boulder and pick out another one ahead. You must rest, and each rest is longer than the last until you realize you are hardly moving at this rate. You force yourself to take deep breaths and more painful paces before your tumbling stomach, dizziness and pounding heart stop you again.

Suddenly I could see the top, the edge of the scree and a lonely cone of rock against the azure sky. Sheer relief gave me strength and I stumbled up the last few yards to the rock and the crisp, cold, white snow. A few more scrambling steps like a Saturday night drunk and I looked down into the crater for a few long minutes before dropping into a crevice alongside Ken and falling fast asleep out of pure fatigue.

Johnny, shivering in the bitterly cold wind, woke me to sign the book. And then I saw one of the most fantastic views in all Africa, a view that made every inch of the struggle worth it.

Far, far below lay the enormous sun-cracked veld and humid forests of the Equator, stretching infinitely into a hazy horizon where sky met earth in a riot of clouds. Nearer, through immense gaps in the fluffy cumulus, I saw the far-flung foothills of Kilimanjaro, with the occasional glint of the sun from a minute lake.

And yet immediately in front sprawled a vast plain of curving snow-fields, great glaciers like suddenly-frozen torrents, tangled ice hummocks and blue caves festooned with hard, glittering icicle drapes—all sloping to the crater rim.

In a stark clash of black rock and dead white snow and ice, the crater plunges hundreds of feet to a pocked lava plug blocking a hole which once spewed thousands of tons of rock and boiling lava over the Tanganyika countryside.

The scene is more than breathtaking. The adjectives to describe it adequately have not yet been invented. It has the majesty of the Zambesi crashing down the Victoria Falls chasm, the infinity of the Great Rift Valley cutting a channel several thousand feet deep down East Africa, the tranquility of the Kalahari Desert lit by the glow of millions of stars, and the utter silence of Death.

I would give a million dollars to be able to preserve that panorama in color. But I could not. I hadn't enough willpower left to raise my camera. I climbed a little higher to Gilman's Point, collapsed on a rock, covered my frosted face with my hands and was out cold. I dreamed of a roaring fire and a quart of mulled brown ale.

About half an hour later I had recovered sufficiently to sign the book and take a weird picture of Ken and Johnny alongside Kimatari.

My body had taken a terrific hammering. I couldn't reason normally but I knew one thing—I wanted to get far out of the cold and sleep for a month. I fought a strong desire to lie down right there and let the others do as they damn well pleased.

Kimatari firmly but gently prodded me up for the return. Once up and moving I headed for the scree like a horse for home. Going down takes about a tenth of the climbing time and in my eagerness to reach a bunk mountain sickness hit me again. This time I let it take me and lay face down on the stones, tired, frozen and dizzy as my stomach tried to tear its lining out.

On the last 2,000 feet of the scree the thicker air gave me new energy and I slid down on my boots, using the alpenstock as a ski-stick. Kimatari knew exactly how we felt at the hut and exactly what we would eat. He produced a mess of canned peaches floating in thick, rich juice.

It was the finest meal I've had on any safari. We wolfed the fruit then tumbled into bunks and slept solidly for an hour until the remorseless Kimatari woke us again.

We reached Peter's Hut in the evening and promptly fell asleep fully clothed. In the morning our faces were grotesquely swollen. It is difficult to account for, probably caused by the combined effects of cold, sun and wind and the lack of oxygen. It did not stop us heading at top speed for Bismarck Hut where the porters produced a large lunch.

While we ate they finished making three wreaths of everlasting flowers, traditional crown for people who reach Kilimanjaro's crown. Chanting sonorous praises, they placed the wreaths on our heads with grave ceremony.

I only just earned the wreath. An hour more of Kilimanjaro's defenses would have utterly defeated me.

Now, on a clear day, I look at Kibo's ice dome shining proud and dominant in the sun down in Tanganyika and find it extremely hard to believe I was up there. Kibo's peak is a world within a world, another facet of incredible Africa.

CHAPTER SIX

THE BRIDGE OF LIFE OR DEATH

"IT was pitch dark in my weather-beaten hut. There was an eerie stillness in the wet dense jungle outside. Suddenly, I became aware that someone or something alive was in the hut with me. I could hear heavy breathing, but could see nothing. Then a flash of lightning, and there it was! I screamed!", exclaimed Mrs. Ava Hamilton, one of the world's most daring women explorers.

As a child in the South, Ava dreamed of exciting adventures. One day she would know what it was really like. Even her schooling was gained abroad, in Switzerland, Belgium, Germany and France. She received a M.A. in Paris and did graduate work at the University of Mexico. Mrs. Hamilton expresses herself fluently in five languages. She has lived in nineteen foreign countries and has traveled extensively in all parts of the world. She is a top rate motion-picture photographer, and lectures throughout the land with superb color motion pictures of the most unusual subjects taken all over the world.

Ava Hamilton's background prepared her admirably for the unusually hazardous life of adventure which was to follow. During my years of experience—over twenty—in associating and writing about the world's outstanding explorers and adventurers, I know of no woman, and few men, whose courage and daring exceeds Ava Hamilton's.

When she was in South Africa a few years ago, planning a lone safari which would take her throughout the length and breadth of that vast continent, she received many warnings about the dangers of traveling through central Africa. Some seasoned explorers would have heeded these warnings and made plans for a less perilous journey.

But, to her, such warnings were a challenge. She set out on what later became the longest and probably one of the most eventful treks ever indulged in by any woman explorer.

Ava Hamilton headed straight for the focal point of adventure, the Congo—and alone! In fact, she drove back and forth across the entire continent of Africa alone, from Capetown to the Mediterranean for four of the most memorable years of her life.

During this time she encountered many dangers, had several narrow escapes, endured hardships that would have completely overcome an average person, suffered from fever and often hunger. But, as she says, "It was all worth it. These were the four most wonderful years of my life." And this after her fantastic escape in the Congo, to top off a life which had already been brimming over with thrilling experiences and dramatic adventure.

Incidents began happening in Ava's African safari soon after she started her trek northward from Capetown, which left vivid impressions on her mind, but the incredible events which followed were far more death-defying.

"Shortly after I crossed the Northern Rhodesian frontier and drove alone into the Congo," said Mrs. Hamilton, "the rainy season broke two weeks earlier than expected. There were but few so-called highways that might be considered at all as roads, and even these became almost untraversable. They were little short of being rivers in themselves, and my car kept skidding back and forth and from side to side. It was impossible to make any progress.

I was forced to keep to the trails which in an African jungle are like a jigsaw puzzle. The trees and brush were so thick I could scarcely distinguish one trail from another, yet I had to keep on moving. All around me was a green and silent world save for an occasional birdcall, the fluttering of a wing, the chattering of a monkey and now and then a faint crackling in the brush— muted sounds of the myriads of unseen, living things around me.

The trail seemed to be narrowing, but I drove on, one half of my mind listening to the small sounds and the comfortable throbbing of the car, the other half listening to the silence—a great enveloping, breathless kind of silence—breathless, as if

waiting to be broken by roars or snarls or shrieks of unseen beasts
stalking their prey.

Suddenly, the trail narrowed down to nothing. I stared into
a wall of green. I was bewildered. There was nothing ahead but
the impenetrable jungle. It was impossible to turn around. It
was all I could do to move the car in one direction. That seemed
to be my answer. Since I could no longer proceed forward, the
only thing left for me was to go backward. I did just that.

With difficulty I continued backing until I reached a fork that
I recalled having passed earlier. Still unable to turn the car
around, I decided to follow the fork, bumping over roots, dodging
trees—a tortuous progress, like struggling through a weird dream.
After a few miles of trying to keep to this track, darkness set in
and I was afraid to go on.

The forest seemed alive with awesome sounds. I closed my car
windows to shut them out. There was a variety of terrifying noise
—screeches, grunts and growls coming from the brush as well as
from the tall trees. There was no silence now in this black world.
A deep sense of aloneness swept over me.

One of my car windows was broken and a piece of the glass
had fallen out. A chill wind stole through the opening, touching
my face. Suddenly, with ghost-like coldness, I heard the familiar
coughing sound characteristic of the leopard. I recognized it at
once and from its loud volume I could tell it was not far from
me. In the distance, I could hear elephants breaking branches,
having their evening meal. Gradually, gradually the sounds
were coming closer. My heart seemed to stand still. Now I could
see a large beast prowling around the car. My eyes pierced the
night. The creature looked to be one of the cat family, probably
a lion! I thought of the broken glass. Suddenly my heart was
beating fast, for I could hear the gentle padding of something
very close.

I looked out into the murky darkness, trying to discern this
moving object, but I could see nothing except inky blackness.
I listened intently. A hundred different sounds seemed to be
coming from varying directions, but not anything to indicate
the nature of the animal that was treading so softly and so near.
I sat in utter silence scarcely daring to breathe. I knew that the
odor of gasoline in a car tends to destroy the human scent. I
hoped with all my heart the animal would not detect a human
in the car and would trek off into the jungle.

It was hours before this was realized. After an endless night with nerves tense and devoid of sleep, morning finally came and with it a keener sense of peace and security for the beast had disappeared.

With a sigh of relief, I started again and continued on the same trail, although it looked for a time as if it, too, would be swallowed up in the dense jungle. Then I came to another fork. Remembering the exhausting effort the evening before, of trying to drive a car in reverse through thick weeded trails. I chose the new branch which looked more promising. After about two miles, it widened and eventually led to the edge of an embankment overlooking a river.

This was the end! This was it! Across the river, there had been constructed a bridge made of large sections of bamboo, lashed together by heavy vines that grow in abundance up and around the trees in the tropical forests of Africa. The bridge was supported also by vines fastened to trees on both sides of the river.

It seemed incredible that a car could cross it safely, even in the hands of an expert driver. It was true that I had driven in reverse, through dense jungle and had achieved a few other seemingly impossible things with the car, but this was the ultimate. No, I could never drive across that flimsy looking structure! But obviously I couldn't remain where I was very long: something had to be done.

I got out of my car and walked across the bridge. It appeared to be surprisingly well made and really strong. It had the usual undulating motion which is very unnerving the first time one crosses this type of bridge, but I had already crossed others by foot, so this did not bother me. However, the thought of driving a car over it, was something else.

I walked back and got into my car. Still a bit wary, I started the motor, took one look at the turbulent, yellow water in the river below and my courage failed me. I turned off the ignition. Yet, what was the alternative? A decision had to be made: I would try again. With the motor started once more, I moved slowly out on to that slender bridge of small branches and vines —and uncertainty! Holding my breath, I continued cautiously, at a snail's pace. Because of the weight of the car, the undulations were greatly accentuated, and once more I was filled with panic.

Just as I had nearly reached the other side, a horrible rending noise resounded in my ears. I looked back horrified to see the long strong vines which held the bridge to the trees on the receding bank slowly breaking. Two or three had already been wrenched apart. Then, I felt something under me give way. I was sliding backward with an alarming sense of helplessness going down, down! In seconds, I was in the bed of the river.

Fortunately the car landed half on one side, wedged between two large boulders. My immediate reaction was one of thankfulness that I was still alive in spite of the fact that I was bleeding from broken glass, and my head seemed to be bursting. Water was seeping in at my feet, but the car had obligingly avoided the deep part of the river. The resiliency of the bamboo crosspieces of the bridge had cushioned the impact and the two huge rocks acting as a cradle and held most of the car above the water level. However, I realized that if another heavy rain came, the river would rise, lifting the car from its secure position and carrying it down stream.

Here I was in probably the most desperate situation I had ever been in. I had often been stuck up in a tree, but had never before been stuck in a river—in a half-drowned car!

With much difficulty of movement, for everything was upside down myself included, I filled a knapsack with my most precious possessions—two of my cameras and exposed film, a first aid kit with snake antidote, a flashlight, matches, a plastic rain cape, ammunition, a cooking utensil and a painfully small amount of food. Inserting a hunting knife in my belt I strapped my two Colt Automatic pistols around my waist. Then slinging a canteen of drinking water over my shoulder, I scrambled out picking my way from rock to rock through the swirling waters until I reached the shore. Now help had to be obtained, but where? I was bruised and bleeding and naturally suffering from shock. I sank on a rock by the river edge and dipping my handkerchief in the cool refreshing water I washed the blood and perspiration from my face, neck and arms. Then folding my saturated handkerchief into a pad, I held it to my forehead, trying to ease the throbbing in my temples.

How long I sat there, I cannot remember, but finally realizing the necessity of obtaining help without delay, I staggered to my feet. Burdened by equipment and dizzy from the blow on my head, I moved slowly down the trail. Where I was going on foot in this lonely jungle world, I had no idea. The light was going fast, the shadows deepening ahead of me. I tried to hurry, but every step was painful. Fear clutched my trembling hands.

After a half mile the trail narrowed to a foot path. The reason was soon evident: I came abruptly upon a deserted village. The huts were in a state of abject decay and the underbrush had closed in on them. I shivered at the very thought of staying in this ghostly hideaway but complete exhaustion ordered otherwise. I chose the best hut I could find, which wasn't saying much. Termites and other creepy insects had taken over well before my arrival.

With much effort, I built a bed of vines and small branches, and in front of the open doorway, I kindled a fire. Since it was now dark in the jungle, the fire was very cheering. It cast a warm glow throughout the hut and even made the spider webs look attractive: indeed, as I thought again how fortunate I was to be alive, they looked as if they were made of threads of gold.

After eating a small portion of the food I had brought with me, I tried to get some sleep, but how I ached all over. And I kept wondering how long it would take me to get help. What would happen to my car and its contents? Finally, fatigue captured my thoughts and I fell asleep.

With an awful suddenliness I awakened! I sat up on my improvised bed with the most horrible fear. Something had struck the back of my neck. Quickly I reached around to determine its cause. It happened again! Then, I realized it was water pouring down my back. My vivid imagination coupled with petrified anxiety made it seem greatly magnified.

It was raining very hard and the water was entering through a break in the roof. It was exceedingly dark, for the rain had extinguished the fire. This worried me since the hut had no door and the fire was a necessary protection against prowling animals.

Silence in a jungle, usually filled with the sounds of nocturnal life, does freakish things to the imagination.

I viewed everything with suspicion. Even the spider webs which earlier had appeared attractive, now, in the light of an occasional streak of lightning, looked grossly distorted and haunted.

Outside, there was an uncanny stillness, broken only by the sound of falling rain and the crashing rumble of thunder. Perhaps the animal life had been stilled by the intensity of the storm.

Oh horrors! Something alive was in the hut. As I became aware of this, terror gripped me until I could not move. Yes! I distinctly could hear heavy breathing. Could it be a ferocious animal? Or was it one of the natives?

Then another vivid flash of lightning! In that instant I caught a glimpse of a huge and shadowy object within arm's length. But, still I could not distinguish whether it was man or beast. The breathing seemed to be close to me now. I instinctively thought of my two Colt Automatics and my flashlight.

Usually I had the habit of sleeping with one automatic under my pillow and the other, together with my flashlight, on a food box alongside of me. Now having no pillow, I had carefully placed both pistols and flashlight on the dirt floor of the hut at the head of my make-shift bed. Luckily, I had folded my rain cape and put it underneath my precious objects to protect them from possible dampness.

From my present position, I could not reach them. In the instant I was torn with conflicting emotions. I hesitated to move. The sound of deep breathing came from my left side, between me and the firearms. If I reached for a pistol, the necessary movement might cause the intruder to attack me. I felt that at any moment someone or something would dash in and seize me.

The breathing grew closer. Then a flash of lightning, and I looked into the wild glowing eyes of a leopard! I let out a most terrified scream! My inmate backed away, snarling, as the darkness swept back again. Even though he was invisible now, I could hear his heavy paws on the dirt floor moving about the hut.

Taking a desperate chance, I lunged forward and grasped one of my pistols, feeling frantically about for my flashlight, not knowing what instant the beast would strike. Another flash of lightning lit the hut for a split second and in that tiny time-span I saw that the leopard was stealing out of the doorway. Perhaps he was only taking shelter from the storm.

Trembling with relief I sprang up and searched for my flashlight. I found it in the corner, where it had rolled just when I needed it most. With its aid I was quick to gather up some of the unburnt logs left from the fire and barricaded the open doorway. Then I lay down on my primitive bed and resolved to relax. After a time, surprisingly, I went back to sleep.

The chattering of baboons in nearby rocks awakened me just before dawn. Still weary from the previous night's horrors, I picked myself up and proceeded to build a fire, a difficult task as the wood was still watersoaked from the downpour. Using the improvised bed that I had slept on, which being indoors was dry, and ripping away some of the interior thatching for added fuel, I soon had a blazing fire.

A cup of black coffee and a fresh start down the trail, filled me with new hope. The sun was shining and after the rain it was a fairy world where everything glistened.

I was now deep in the great tropical forests of the Congo, forests that have a beauty and a majesty that no words can adequately describe. The tall straight trees about me reached into the sky, attaining heights of 180 to 200 ft. before they branched out to form a canopy of dense interlacing foliage, nearly obscuring the light of day.

Intermingled with these forest giants were trees of normal size with wide spreading branches, from which cascaded myriads of trailing vines; and beneath all this was a tangled undergrowth of luxuriant vegetation arising fifteen feet or more above the ground, interspersed here and there by tall tree ferns, giant creepers, orchids and brilliant flowering plants.

The awesome beauty of this vast primeval wilderness was breath-taking, but in all this grandeur of nature, I felt very small and very much alone. The fact most disturbing to me, was the knowledge that there was life all around me, animal and possibly human life; life that I could not see; life that I could not hear; life that was very close to me, much too close, perhaps even within arm's length.

With these thoughts in mind, I quickly covered several miles and, as midday approached, I rested for a bite to eat. I had to be careful with the rations for my food supply was nearly finished and my canteen of boiled water was empty. In the late afternoon, I gathered some bananas and wild honey and boiled more water.

Bananas grow in profusion in the Congo and are the chief source of native diet. Bananas with honey, in fact, constituted my entire diet. I cooked them the native way, I baked them in the ashes of a dying fire and I spread them with honey, as I would a sandwich.

I noticed several small branches along the trail that had been broken recently, which gave me hope that I was coming to an inhabited village. But I saw no other signs to substantiate it and gathered that I must have bypassed it; just when or how far back I could not tell.

Every day I trudged along in complete loneliness, following

first one trail, then another; trails made by wild animals and criss-crossed by large tree roots. The days went by slowly; again it was like walking in a dream. Sometimes when the sun filtered down through the swaying vines, the light trembled through the green around me, and I seemed to be under water. I liked the slivers of sunlight making patterns on my body.

The jungle was so thick and snarled in places that often the foliage on one side of the path merged with the twisted low-lying branches on the other. The ground was wet and slimy, and I kept tripping, slipping and falling.

Occasionally, long hanging vines wrapped themselves around me in the most fantastic entanglements, and the more I tried to free myself, the more I became immeshed. It was frightening! The vines would grip me tighter and tighter, with an enveloping hold like that of an octopus or a python. In mad desperation, I would free my right arm and reach to my belt for my hunting knife. I cut and cut and frantically continued to cut. It was difficult to slash through these tough vines, but after an exhausting struggle, I would somehow manage to free myself. All this was definitely unconducive to a well balanced morale. Actually I expended much effort, but made little progress.

When it rained, as it often did, I protected my camera and film with my rain cape, allowing myself to get drenched through to the skin. Fortunately, in the tropics, getting wet and remaining in wet clothing does not have the dire effects it might have in a more northern climate.

After my night of horror in the deserted village, I decided for safety's sake to sleep up in trees. Each night I made a bed of vines between two branches, interweaving them to form a sort of hammock. Also I wrapped vines around my waist and fastened them to a branch to prevent me from accidentally falling out. Remembering the years of my childhood, I recalled only too well how I was always climbing trees at our summer home and frequently ending in a heap on the ground.

Naturally, therefore, I searched for quite a time before I found one adapted for this purpose. It must have wide horizontal branches, two of which should be in a position to support a vine hammock. It was desirable also that the trunk be well covered with twisting creepers to facilitate climbing and there should be an abundance of hanging vines with which to construct my hammock bed. I had done much outdoor camping in my life and that experience was of immense help to me now. After scouting about, I finally selected a tree that seemed to have the necessary requirements and also an assurance of safety against prowling animals.

With my equipment, I climbed up to my penthouse sleeping quarters and after some wriggling, I succeeded in arranging myself in a comfortable position, but sleep was intermittent.

Suddenly, I was startled by a low growl, right beneath the tree. I looked down from my eerie perch, but the intervening foliage completely screened the ground from my view. Cautiously making my way to a lower branch, I saw to my horror the head of a large black-maned lion. Then, leaning forward to get a better look, I realized that he was not alone: just back of him, lying on the ground, was a lioness and three full grown cubs.

Of course, lions can climb to the lower branches of certain kinds of trees, such as those found on the savanna lands of Africa. However, they rarely do so.

I was quite safe as long as I remained where I was, but how long were they going to remain where they were? I knew that lions spend the night roaming about and hunting for food. They usually sleep during the daytime, preferably in the shade of a tree. A horrible thought came into my mind. What if this were their regular daily sleeping quarters? How would I ever get down? It would be the height of madness to do so at night and still worse, to try to find another tree shelter.

Continuing to watch them, I noted the male lion yawn, stretch and contentedly lick his chops. Then he rolled over on his back and seemed to doze off.

About an hour passed. I decided that I might as well make up my mind to spend another day and night, at least, in my present abode.

At this juncture a little creature about the size of a small gazelle, probably a dik-dik, streaked across the clearing not far off. It went so fast, I was unable to tell exactly what it was. But, quick as lightning, the old male lion shot after it. Apparently, he was not so fast asleep as I thought him to be. Soon the other four lions followed slowly, going down the path that I had come up the afternoon before.

Without waiting for their possible return, I slid down out of that tree, and made off in the opposite direction. I traveled as fast as the weight of my knapsack and the entangled undergrowth

would allow. By sunset I had covered about five miles. I rested for
a while, making a pot of coffee and eating a little more of the
food—bananas and honey—I had with me, all the while scanning
the area for a safe place to put up for the night. There was not
much choice around there, so I decided to risk the only available
tree and promptly climbed up and went to work. The nights were
always filled with horrible noises, but I had become accustomed
to them now. However, the dawn was invariably a joy and an
inspiration to me. The sun seemed like a beacon from heaven,
dispelling the gloom and terror of the darkness and the fearsome
din of the jungle.

I trudged along by day and slept in the trees by night. I did
not know how many days passed, I lost all track of time, but one
evening, just at sunset, I heard the sound of human voices in
the distance. My spirits soared and I hurried on, panting with
excitement.

Finally, I came to a clearing and saw five natives sitting around
a fire. Their clothing consisted of spears and G-strings, and they
looked rather fierce, but I was glad to see human beings.

As I approached, they stared at me, with no change of facial
expression.

Jambo! I said, and continuing in my limited Swahili, together
with the sign language, I tried to explain that I was lost. I asked
them to guide me to a white man's house. As an added induce-
ment, I produced some cigarettes, some salt which the natives
love, and a collection of copper coins. I had brought them with
me for just such an occasion.

Gradually, one by one, they edged toward me, occasionally
looking at one another for approval. I thought I noticed a certain
suspicion toward each other. They moved closer, with their eyes
pinned on the coins. Then in unison, they pounced upon the
coins and started fighting among themselves for possession of
them. Evidently, they knew the meaning of money.

I tried to indicate that they would receive more if they would
help me. The only response was a negative gesture from one of
them, and a sullen attitude on the part of the others.

I wondered if they had been mistreated in some way by another
white person, and this was their reaction. It was rapidly approaching dusk and their hostile manner made me feel that I preferred
the wild animals and the "safety" of the jungle.

With a heavy heart, I picked up the trail again. I was not able to get very far, for darkness in the tropics comes quickly after sunset. I paused to make sure that they had not followed me. After scanning the forest in every direction, all that I was able to ascertain was that none of them was in sight. This I might have known, for they have the most uncanny ways of concealing themselves behind the thick foliage.

In the fast-darkening jungle, I was again confronted with the problem of finding a suitable tree. This was a nightly necessity, if I hoped to arise all in one piece the next morning.

A tree was found, and after a reasonably restful sleep, I awakened the next morning. As the sun began to cast its filtered rays through the dark green foliage my feeling of great discouragement left me. Now, with the advent of another day, I saw the encounter with the natives in a new light. Evidently, I had entered an inhabited area. I would certainly soon come to a village where I might hope to find more co-operation.

I had trekked but a short distance from my tree when I saw a large melon right in the center of the trail. Hastily, I picked it up, as I had not stopped to make breakfast. Eagerly, I cut it open and sliced off a large piece and began eating it. I was very hungry.

Soon after taking a few mouthfuls, I became violently sick. I could not think what might be causing it. I had eaten very little for the past several days. Soon I became so weak I was scarcely able to move, yet I knew that I must try to get to a more desirable place.

I staggered to my feet and managed to trudge on for a short distance until I came to the edge of a cool stream. I collapsed under a tree, pulling my knapsack close to me, propping myself up against the tree trunk, going completely limp for a few minutes.

But an African jungle is no place in which to let down one's guard. I tried to plan what to do. I looked about, everything was swimming dizzily before my eyes. Hazily in the distance, I saw a great tree with its broad branches overhanging a river, affording both sun and shade. I needed both, for I felt that I would be here for some time. With great difficulty I constructed a bed of vines between two of the branches, and with all my strength I managed to climb my way up into this small security. This was to be my home for the next eight nightmare-filled days.

It was not until sometime later that I learned of the native custom of poisoning a melon and putting it in the pathway of someone they did not like. It might not have been intended for me . . . yet so far as I knew there was no one else in the vicinity, except the unfriendly natives that I had approached.

Certainly they had been very hostile to me. They had refused to help me, so obviously they did not like me. They must have followed me, noted my sleeping quarters and knew that I would surely leave by that path. I am convinced that my conclusion was correct and that they had deliberately intended to poison me. They had succeeded in doing just that.

After recovering from the effects of the poisoned melon, I became a victim of an attack of malaria, probably induced by lowered resistance. Being familiar with the treatment for malaria, fortunately, I was able to take care of myself. I had with me in my First Aid kit both quinine and atabrine. I chose the latter. However, as I ran a high temperature for several days, I was left in a much weakened condition.

In due time, with painful effort, I again picked up the trail. I wondered, as I plodded wearily along, what day it was . . . or what month? Time was a negative quantity now. After a day or so, I entered a large clearing, and there at the far edge, I spotted several low structures that were definitely European buildings. I could see people in motion before they saw me. I wanted to shout but found that my voice was not strong enough to be heard. But soon I was within their sight and I could see their surprised faces turned in my direction . . . sunburned *white* faces! They set out for me on the run. My strength at last ebbed. I could only stand immobile clinging to a tree, watching them, tears streaming down my face.

The sign on the low building and the fluttering flag told me this was a Congo Trading Post, with an adjacent Mission Station. Two men supported me and helped me over to the Missionary Home. My clothes were torn; I was starved and ill and must have been a bedraggled sight. I was immediately the center of attraction for people plied me with questions while I drank hot chocolate and ate the food they brought me. I explained what had happened—the trails I had followed, the lions under my hammock in the tree, and the poisoned melon that made me ill, to say nothing of my lost car.

Everyone at the Mission was sympathetic and very kind to me and when, as part of my misadventures, I told them how my car had crashed through the bamboo bridge and was still lodged precariously in the river, they were anxious to start a rescue mission. A native boy was at once sent over to the Trading Post and returned with the East Indian in charge. I talked the situation over with him and he offered his help.

The following morning he came back with an old Model T Ford. He and the Missionary and I and as many of the Mission boys as could be accommodated, scrambled into the car or hung on to the outside and set off for the river. By taking a circuitous route different from my trail we wound our way through the deep jungle byways, eventually locating the broken bridge, and my car still on the rock saddle below. The water since my visit had risen and was still rising, but happily, not enough to carry my car down stream.

Everybody excitedly made suggestions, and out of them came the decision to hitch a rope from my car to the Model T. This was a most difficult and hazardous undertaking, as it compelled at least two boys to leap from rock to rock in the swollen river, attach the rope to the car, push it upright and steady it, while the Ford tugged and pulled on the river bank. Several unsuccessful attempts were made, and finally we were obliged to abandon the effort.

One of the men declared that nothing short of oxen would be able to extricate the car from its wedged position. A ranch some distance away, he said, had a number of oxen, which we might be able to obtain. So a couple of native boys were sent with a note to the owner. While they were gone, several schemes were thought of and tried, but the car was too tightly and too awkwardly pinned in, even to budge it. There was nothing to do but to wait for the return of the boys and hope and pray that they would bring the oxen with them. Every minute counted, for the rising water had now reached the critical stage.

Finally, we heard voices in the distance down the dark jungle trail. It was the native boys returning. We waited breathlessly for the news! Soon the boys came into view, accompanied by the ranch owner driving six oxen. The happiness that spilled from my heart was the loveliest emotion I had felt in months.

Africa is a pioneer country and the European settlers in their spirit of helpfulness and co-operation are reminiscent of America's early days. Under the direction of the rancher the boys cut young saplings and stripped them of their branches to be used as levers to pry the car loose and raise it to an upright position. Then, utilizing a broken piece of the bridge flooring to cover the nearby rocks, and with the boys holding the car on both sides, it was gradually pulled by the oxen over the intervening boulders into shallow water. From there it was an easy matter to get it up on dry land.

Everyone had worked frantically to achieve what seemed to me a miracle. My gratitude to them was profound. I was thankful that everything in the car was just as I had left it. With the exception of a few articles that had been ruined by water, my belongings were all intact. Primitive, savage Africa has not yet learned from "civilization" the art of stealing.

Getting into the driver's seat, I tried to start the car, but the engine refused to turn over. It was then decided to hitch the oxen to the car and pull it back to the Trading Post and I was at the wheel to guide it. The native boys went ahead to cut a way through the brush, so progress was slow.

A short distance further along we came to a stream. A small bridge spanned it, but the oxen refused to make the crossing. We unhitched the oxen and they waded through the water. The native boys pushed the car across the bridge and re-hitched the oxen to it on the opposite bank. This operation was repeated several times. The oxen seemed to have an instinctive fear of the bridges. Nothing would induce them to put a foot on one.

When we had almost reached the Trading Post, we heard an ominous sound in the distance. We stopped to listen for we were very much alarmed.

"Tembo! Tembo!" shrieked several of the native boys, seemingly as if in one voice. By now we could hear the terrifying noise of elephants trumpeting. Presently, right before our very eyes, they were so close we could see and hear them crashing and breaking branches. They were crunching the underbrush beneath their heavy feet as they tramped their way through the jungle. What a large herd of elephants, and how they stampeded!

The sound grew louder and more dangerously close. The herd was heading with all force straight for us. The Missionary and the others all shouted to me to jump out of the car quickly and take cover. As I looked up, the vanguard of the herd rounded the trail a few hundred yards ahead. The warning had come too late.

Just then the oxen, sensing the danger, and suddenly overcome with fear, bolted for safety. They dragged the car along with them —and carried me along with it! I hung on to the steering wheel, too frightened to let go! A couple of the native boys tried to grab the oxen as they whipped by, but the animals were too frantic to be subdued.

Suddenly, and with terrific force, the oxen made an abrupt turn, and my car and I were crashed against the trees. I was thrown free from the car, and luckily, just out of the path of the onrushing elephants. I could only bury my face in my arms and crouch in the brush, as the tornado of force swept by. The wild breaking of branches and uprooting of trees, the high weird trumpeting cries, the ground shaking around me like an earthquake, wrapped me with fear the likes of which I had never known before. Then, like a gray tide of sound and fury, the stampeding herd smashed by.

Then the dust subsided, and the missionary and his friend the rancher, the East Indian and the native boys all rushed to assist me. I was pulled to my feet, covered with dirt, leaves and blood. I seemed to be bleeding from every pore. There was a deep cut in my shoulder, numerous scratches on my face, arms and legs. I could scarcely stand, let alone walk.

The native boys quickly made a litter and carried me hastily to the Mission Station, where the Missionary stopped the bleeding and doctored me with expert care.

I was able to remain at the Mission until I was fit to travel and finally was driven to the nearest airport, from which I was flown back to South Africa.

While recovering from my ordeal in the cooler climate, I ordered a new car to be sent out from the United States. Upon its arrival, and after my complete recovery, I resumed my African Safari again toward the Congo."

For her crossing of the Sahara Desert, alone, Mrs. Ava Hamilton was awarded a decoration by the French Government.

CHAPTER SEVEN

GORILLAS AT WAR

"WHEN the Pygmies opened hostilities on the big apes, we found ourselves right smack in the middle of exciting gorilla warfare," recalled Hal Hennesey, big game hunter and writer, as he related one of his most terrifying experiences in the wilderness.

"When I first trekked into the African jungles, several years ago, I was completely ignorant of how little I knew about the habits of the animals, the natives, or the weird undergrowth of the terrain itself," said Hennesey. "And, it wasn't until I met Harry Durkin, a white hunter, that I really began learning through actual experience—and pretty much the hard way, if I might say so."

When I showed an eager desire to tangle with the gorilla, shortly after my arrival in East Africa, Harry put me in my place in such a profound manner that I felt like worming my way into one of those huge jungle ant-hills.

"Anybody who would shoot a gorilla for sport should be hung, drawn and quartered!" snapped Harry. "A gorilla's the mildest, most inoffensive creature in all Africa." The big Rhodesian, who had been a white hunter for almost half of his forty years, gave me a disgusted glance as he continued to squirt gun oil into the breech of his .375 Magnum. He swabbed it around viciously.

I looked out over the campfire at the black jungle that hid the Mfumbiro volcanoes of southern Uganda. From the jungle came those exciting night sounds that you never quite forget. After three months in the field, I could identify many of them: the cigarette cough of the leopard; the gentlemanly rumble of the lion; the mad-dog barking of over-sexed baboons; the thunderous gurgling of an elephant's guts. At that moment, I found it hard to believe that the wild, bull gorilla was no more dangerous than an organ-grinder's monkey.

I said, "I've read about hunters who had to stop a gorilla's charge with a high-speed slug or be torn apart."

"Those guys," said Harry, ramming a brush through his rifle barrel, "turned chicken. They fired too soon. If they'd waited until the ape got to within ten or so yards of them, he'd have stopped, muttered to himself—and high-tailed it back into the brush. A gorilla's a big bluff."

Two days later, the Bagandas declared war on the Mfumbiro gorillas. Harry and I were caught right in the middle of it. We saw the great long-haired apes kill three of the Bagandas and rip Mbito, the Pygmy scout, in two. A dozen of them charged to within ten yards of Harry and me. Only they didn't turn back. They kept coming.

It started during a hunt for the rare bongo. From the Semliki

Valley on the Congo frontier, Harry and I had waged a two-week search for this most prized of all antelope. Now, far to the south, the trail seemed to be getting hot. It had led us into the dark rain-forests of the Mfumbiro range, which towers 10,000 feet above Lake Kivu. Following our two Baganda trackers, we pushed eagerly through the massed vegetation on the lower slopes. According to Kiibu, the lead boy, a large bongo was feeding no more than ten minutes ahead of us.

So far as I was concerned, the tracks we were on could have been made by a bushbuck, a koodoo, or a kid on a split pogo-stick. During the months that Harry had been trying to make a white hunter out of me, tracking had proved to be my weakest point.

It was Kiibu's strongest. About midday he paused, one hand upraised, the other pointing straight ahead. I slipped the safety off my .375, certain that I was about to sight on a bongo. I strained my eyes to penetrate the forest gloom. All I could see was what looked like an elaborate lair about ten yards away. A mass of underbrush had been pulled down to form a roof over a thick bed of grass.

I should have known right away that no ordinary animal could have constructed such a bed unless it had hands.

"That's a gorilla lair!" Harry's whisper was harsh, his eyes narrowed. Kiibu and his companion, Maseete, looked both surprised and scared.

Kiibu hissed a warning and squatted in his tracks. I felt my adrenal glands give a sudden spurt as I dropped to my haunches.

From the palmetto leaves just beyond the gorilla nest emerged a long shaggy arm. The bushes parted to reveal a shapeless black mass. Then, ghostlike, it was gone. From several points on either side came a series of crackling noises. After that, nothing.

Kiibu turned to us. He held up both hands, eight of his fingers extended. "Maybe more," he said softly.

Harry nodded. "I counted nine altogether."

As we broke into a wide bushy donga, a loud animal noise shattered the day-long stillness. It was a sort of bellowing roar. It came from the huge throat of a great black gorilla. The huge beast was out in the open only thirty yards in front of us. A short distance past him were nearly a dozen others, all headed across the dried stream to the heavy cover beyond.

The one nearest us—a quarter-ton bull with an almost red head—turned and bared a set of teeth like a picket fence. Then, without further warning it rushed headlong in our direction.

The oncoming gorilla approached on all fours for the first thirty feet. Then it rose on its hind legs and spread its fearful arms wide. It was nearly six feet tall, with shoulders a yard across. On its face was the most bestial expression I had ever seen on man or animal. It was that grotesque *human* quality that made the creature appear like something out of a mad-man's nightmare. Now I knew why other hunters had shot at charging gorillas on sight.

I raised my rifle half way to my shoulder. Harry grabbed my arm with his right hand. I could feel my biceps turning to hamburger. "Watch!"

I watched through sweat-filled eyes while the gorilla came on. At fifteen yards he slowed down. At ten, he stopped. Looking like King Kong and twice as deadly, he stood for a moment blinking at us, obviously confused. Then, with a deep rumbling growl, the frustrated monster turned. Hurriedly, yet with a certain elephantine dignity, he shambled back to his vanished companions. A moment later he too disappeared in the forest beyond the *donga*.

I was still shaking. I raged at Harry, "You were willing to get me killed—just to prove a point!"

His answering grin shut me up until we reached camp that evening. It was close to the Baganda kraal where we had hired Kiibu and Maseete. Something told me that our bongo hunt was off for good. I could smell trouble. It lurked in Harry's preoccupied air and in the impassive faces of the boys. After dinner they paid a short visit to the village. When they got back, Harry told me the score.

"The mountain gorilla," he said, "sticks to the high places—up around 10,000 feet. That's why the natives and I were worried to see them on the low hills today. It could only mean one of two things. Either a fire drove them down, or they're on a raid'ng party. And there wasn't any fire." He raised an eyebrow at me.

"I'm a stranger here myself," I said. "What's a raiding party?"

"Most people don't realize it," Harry answered, "but ever since man separated from the ape, the two species have waged a continual war here in central Africa. The natives plant their crops. When the gorillas hit a hungry period, they come down from the hills, glut themselves on plantains and squashes until they've wrecked the area. Usually the natives move away." Harry paused again, his eye on the listening Kiibu and Maseete. "But not this time. The Bagandas are going to fight."

If I had hair on my spine, it would have bristled. I must have looked pretty eager.

Harry shook his head. "It's none of our affair. Besides we don't have a license to kill gorillas."

"We wouldn't have to kill them. We could just sort of look on." Harry had really proved his point that afternoon. I figured the gorilla for a blustering mollycoddle.

Anyway, I talked him into the hunt. That's why I blame myself for what followed.

The battle took shape before sun-up. Upwards of forty of us started out in the pre-dawn gloom that floods all mountain forests. Included were a half-dozen Bakwa Pygmies from the Semliki. Jolly little fellows with monkey-like faces, reddish hair and no clothes whatever, they were to be used as scouts. With their midget bows and poison-tipped arrows, they were the world's best jungle men. I liked them a lot.

What I didn't like was the grim look on Harry's face. Usually good for two or three laughs a mile, he strode along in a dead silence until we reached the scene of our gorilla encounter of the day before. At once the natives' loose talk died down. We paused just south of the *donga*. Everyone sank to his haunches, forming a close-packed group around Harry and me.

My partner reached for my rifle. He opened it and grunted. "Take out those solids and put soft-nosed slugs in it."

My hairless spine prickled again. "But you said we wouldn't——"

"Just in case!" snapped Harry. Then he shrugged an apology. "It's just that I've got a bad feeling about this business. These fellows have never driven gorillas before. Only Kiibu and Maseete have ever killed one. In the rare instances when a gorilla is goaded into an all out attack, he's one of the most dangerous killers in the world. He not only bites like a lion, but he can rip your head off with his hands." The glint of humor returned to his narrow gray eyes. "Thought you'd like to know."

Just then, as though by a pre-arranged signal, half of the assembled natives, including two Pygmies, rose to their feet. I noticed that they were the older, weaker-looking men. Wordlessly, they split into two parties of about a dozen each and slipped into the jungle. Each of them carried an unlit torch or a wooden drum.

"They're the beaters," muttered Harry. "They'll get upwind of the apes and drive them into us. We're the killing party."

My nerves were getting ragged when the first alarm came. From behind the thick green lacework of trees and lianas, we heard the raucous shouts of the beaters, the uneven rumble of their drums. Then, much closer, sounded a frenzied crashing of something through the undergrowth, like the stampeding passage of a buffalo herd.

Every man in our party leaped to his feet. Harry and I stayed where we were while the others spread out in a ragged line. On either side of us stood Kiibu and Maseete, their iron spears ready. A couple of the men were armed with ancient Arab trade guns. I wondered if they meant to beat the gorillas' brains out with them. Only about thirty yards separated us from the lip of the jungle.

An instant later, the gorillas burst through the green wall all at once and closely grouped. I counted a full dozen of them. They came on all fours, their front knuckles brushing the ground, and at an astonishing speed. The distance between us closed rapidly —twenty-five yards, then twenty, now fifteen.

Finally they were within ten yards of us—and not a single spear had been thrown. With a sensation close to horror I realized that every man in that line was staring straight at Harry and me. They were waiting for us to murder the gorillas! All of them.

I shot a glance at Harry. The tension in his face was almost painful, his lipless mouth like a half-healed scar. Deliberately he lowered his rifle and placed the butt end on the ground. Harry didn't intend to fire; the natives knew that now.

Twenty spears hurtled through the air. The ponderous apes were in easy range—only five yards. But these natives were not Massis—the great lion-killers of Kenya. Only three of them hit their targets. One ape struck in his middle by Kiibu's spear collapsed on it, driving the shaft clear through himself. Another, his shoulder pierced, yanked out the offending sliver without pausing. The third stopped in his tracks. He eyed the spear that impaled his arm, curiously, then loped forward again. He didn't seem to feel it.

Only a few feet from us, one of the natives let go with his ancient trade rifle. There was a terrific explosion. The poor fellow dropped without a cry, half concealed by a cloud of black powder smoke. The bolt from the old weapon had been blown back by the heavy charge, and we found it lodged deep in his skull.

With a half-animal wail, the rest of the Bagandas and pygmies turned, unarmed, and fled in terror down the hillside. Behind them rushed the gorillas, their speed unchecked. Two of the great black brutes swept by us on either side, no more than ten feet distant. They hardly glanced at us. A moment later, there were only the vanishing sounds of flight—the shrieks of the natives and the crashing passage of the gorillas.

Glancing down at the Baganda who had blown his face off with the rifle, Harry muttered, "Thank God it wasn't any worse." And not until then did I realize that this really great hunter had had the situation under control every minute. Had we, or any of the men, been in real danger at any time, Harry had five 300-grain bullets to get us out.

The beaters, silent now, came up. They milled about aimlessly trying to work up enthusiasm over the single dead gorilla. Then we headed in the direction of our fleeing companions, just in case, Harry said, "any of them get hurt on the way."

"This isn't the way back to the village," I said.

They went down the steep side of the hill. It's faster. They'll follow the creek back to the village.

I asked him about the gorillas. Where would they go? Harry said they'd run until they calmed down. Then they would turn south to the mountain again. They'd probably stay on the big slopes for the next five years.

Maybe that's what they wanted to do. But we never gave them a chance; we were too close behind them. In less than ten minutes, we reached the bank of the creek, one of the many small streams that flow west to Lake Edwards. The jungle grows almost to the water, leaving about six feet of clearing on the bank.

That's where the gorillas were. They huddled together, peering out over the rushing stream, afraid to cross, afraid to go back. We had broken out of the forest and into their midst before we knew they were there.

I can't describe everything that happened next. The few details I remember were a part of the over-all action that swept around me. I remember the faces of the gorillas as they turned toward us, astonishment and terror making hideous masks of them. For an instant they stood stock still. Then they charged.

The natives panicked. They ran into one another in their efforts to get away, kicking and clawing, the whites of their eyes showing like fried eggs in black skillets. The two pygmies, trusting their size to get them through, made a dash for the water. Only one of them made it. The other ran full tilt into a great bull ape. The beast grabbed both the little man's ankles and swept him off the ground. Then he spread his massive arms with a sudden jerk. It was like a peevish child tearing a rag doll apart. The pygmy was split from his crutch to his chest. The ape dropped the pitiful little body. Then he slumped kicking, as Harry shot him from the hip.

"Aim for the heart!" Harry shouted. "Head's too bony!"

There wasn't time to aim. I pointed my rifle at one of them; when I pulled the trigger he fell forward, arms outstretched. They hit the rifle barrel, knocking it from my hands. As I bent to grab it, Harry's gun went off in my ear. It was like being sandbagged. I turned to see another ape full on his face: he had been right behind me. I could feel no emotion when a huge bull grabbed Kiibu in its arms. It lifted him overhead and hurled him to the ground. Kiibu bounced, his head split open like a ripe melon.

I shot that one in the face. Harry was right—the gorilla didn't go down. As he stumbled toward me blindly, I gave him one in the chest. He dropped to his knees, the black hands fell away from his bleeding face and he looked right at me. We were only six feet apart and I remember noting the grey tips of the reddish fur on his head, an old one. He hit the ground hard; I could hear it because there was no other sound . . . just Harry's deep breathing.

It was all over. From the time we had reached the creek bank, less than a minute had elapsed.

The natives had run away; all except four who would never run again. Five of the gorillas were dead. They looked like piles of hides in a leather factory.

Harry got to his feet, slowly, like an old man. He looked down at the bodies of the dead gorillas. I feel like a murderer, he said.

I knew what he meant. I remembered the look on the old one's face as I shot him. I'll never forget it.

CHAPTER EIGHT

THE STRANGE SAHARA

"From Algiers, looking due southwest across the endless expanse of the Sahara Desert you are aware that there exists the once mysterious city of Timbuctoo. But the urge to visit this mecca of all explorers for many generations past must be strong enough to induce you to trek the 1,500 weary miles across every conceivable kind of desert terrain—mountains, rocks, scrub and sand," said Dr. John Nicholls Booth, who has traveled over all five continents and written six books about his adventures.

Timbuctoo was known for a long time as the mysterious city, because of its amazing past as a former capital of Black Africa and because of the difficulties met by explorers in trying to reach the city. These difficulties were due not only to the cruelty of the tyrannical native chiefs who held power throughout all the region of the Senegal and the Niger rivers, but also to the geographic position of the city.

To the north, Timbuctoo is cut off from the civilized world by the sands of the Sahara; to the west the expeditions, which since the 17th century tried to reach the loop of the Niger, have had to navigate the 1,054 miles of the Senegal River, where navigation was made difficult by large rocks and boulders, and by very great periodic changes in the water level, and then 600 miles on the Niger River.

After my long, arduous journey across the scorched Sahara I finally made my way to this outpost of civilization. The thrill I felt knowing that Timbuctoo lay all around me, was no less strong than the thrill that I had felt upon reaching Tierra del Fuego and Tibet years before.

Since the founding of the new Fifth Republic of France, all French possessions in Africa have been reorganized into twelve different states or self-governing republics. These belong to the Community. This Community replaces the French Union which had been established by the Constitution of the Fourth Republic.

Timbuctoo, a city of eight thousand, is a part of the Sudanese Republic, one of the twelve member states of the Community, of which Bamako, about 600 miles to the southwest, is the capital. Timbuctoo is in a sandy plain dotted with pools, mimosa bushes and palm trees, nine miles north of the Niger River, in what is usually called the loop.

Now, here I was, after my hectic and anxious journey of several months, living without fear or disguise within the once inaccessible confines of the curious old desert city.

The city is triangular with a four-mile perimeter. North and west are numerous ruins, indicating that, in former times, it had covered a much wider area. In the northern sections stands the Mosque of Sankoré. It is pyramid-shaped, with a slight terrace about two-thirds up, and a small, round dome-like projection in the center of a flat top. Seemingly it has scores of guns protruding about two feet out of the walls, at three foot intervals on all four sides from top to bottom. Actually they are for drainage.

In the fourteenth century Timbuctoo was the capital of the Sultan of Mali and a commercial center linking Black Africa to the Sudan. There camel caravans carrying gold and exotic goods from Bambouk met caravans bringing salt from the mines of Taoudenni, 435 miles across the hot sands of the Sahara from the north—ten thousand animals moving in a single rhythmic spectacle.

Timbuctoo was conquered in 1591 by the Moroccans, who occupied the city in a more or less nominal fashion until the French conquest in 1893. Those three centuries of Moroccan domination were a period of insecurity and decadence for Timbuctoo because the Moroccan conquerors were generally incapable of protecting the city from the Tuaregs who pillaged it several times.

Only in my imagination was the golden capital of a Black Empire still alive. For I saw only a disfigured city of mud shrunken with age, fighting for survival against the encroaching sands and the neglect of man.

Timbuctoo is old but not in the sense that Damascus, Cairo or Rome are old. It had been no more than a nomad's camp at an oasis on the Sahara's southern rim until 1100 A.D., when its strategic location for commerce became obvious. Its rise as a once great trade center was so phenomenal that superstitious folk believed the place had been selected by divine decree. From all over Negro-land trade goods arrived upon the broad waters of the mighty Niger, highway to the distant Atlantic. Half of Africa was reputed to have traded through Timbuctoo, unique crossroads for river, desert and jungle commerce.

It held such opportunities and wealth that rich merchants and brilliant men, schemers and plunderers, enslavers and enslaved, descended upon the metropolis. It became a seat of learning and culture. Seven imposing mosques once lifted squat minarets above the sweeping expanse of low buildings. Rumors whispered that heaps of gold were piled high in the various storage houses. And the women! Nowhere in Africa were they so alluring, so full of love, so kindly disposed toward travelers starved by desert loneliness.

Invariably, such glittering prizes of gold, passion and luxury drew their looters. From out of the desert wastes came the fierce, veiled Tuaregs, striking terror into the heart of this Black Paradise. For centuries they periodically persecuted and despoiled its rich populace.

From time to time the brave city sought the protection of various black emperors. There was Kankan-Moussa the magnificent, ruler of one of the world's great kingdoms and hero of a vast pilgrimage to Mecca. Among his successors in dominion over the city was Souleiman, whose orchestra played golden bells and whose guardsmen shouldered golden-tipped spears. Later, Timbuctoo appealed for help from Sonni Ali, an emperor dark of skin and darker in deeds, who executed three hundred virgins for complaining of being tired after they had been dragged across the sands of the desert to his camp.

So sprawling was the city that it stretched to the banks of the Niger, nine miles away. It was the heart of a fabulous kingdom which, reaching from Lake Chad westward to the Atlantic, and from the middle Sahara southward to the territory of Dahomey, required six months to cross.

By the end of the eighteenth century, the old splendor of Timbuctoo had become a memory. Through anarchy, oppression, piracy and bad administration, the city had slowly fallen into a state of embarrassed impoverishment.

Legend and gossip about the remote city drifted into Europe through the centuries, but geographers could not accurately fix its location on the map because no European had been there. Adventurous white men working toward it were fiercely turned back by hostile tribes ranging the metropolis hundreds of miles away. The majority of those who tried to press on met with violent deaths.

The walled city of Timbuctoo was forbidden to all whites.

However, in 1825, an intrepid Scotsman, Major Alexander Gordon Laing, disappeared southwest from Tripoli and one year later became the first white man to pierce the wall of Timbuctoo. But the world didn't know it until later, because he never returned to Europe. He was strangled to death with a turban.

The most famous journey of all was made by a Frenchman named Rene Caillie, who broke through the barrier in the spring of 1828, after a full year of incredible hardships on the way. He found it unsafe to remain more than two weeks in the city, despite a successful disguise.

Only two more venturesome explorers managed to struggle through to the city in the sixty-five years between 1828 and 1893.

Savage depredations by the Tuaregs further increased the poverty and weakness of the trading center, until its opposition to Whites collapsed almost completely. A French garrison of only seven Europeans and twelve Senegalese were able to enter, though not occupy, the city in 1893. This unit was massacred. Within a short time, however, French rule was firmly established in Timbuctoo.

I spent many hours trudging through ankle-deep white sand along twisting lanes wide enough for three or four camels to travel abreast. Mud-walled houses rose fifteen, twenty and thirty feet above my head on either side, punctured every few yards by dark doorways at street level and small windows where second stories had been constructed. Sometimes the quaintly studded doors, heavily built against the Tuareg marauders of other generations, were ajar. In the unlighted gloom beyond, I could see families gossiping as they sat on yellow straw mats which covered the sandy floors of the rooms.

Most of the mud houses faced north or south, so that the prevailing winds blowing from east to west would not waft the evil spirits of the Sahara through the doorways. A more discernible advantage lay in the winds' inability to carry in some annoying sand along with the desert djinns.

The narrow alleys between the buildings were being threaded by as colorful a melange of people as I have looked upon anywhere. The skin of these Bella and Songhoi people was coal black and their features were pure negroid. Women trudged along balancing heavy burdens atop their heads and gaily-colored robes flowed gracefully behind them. The hair of some would be rolled into several large round knobs, producing a striking coiffure as yet undiscovered by the experimental salons of New York, Paris or London. Earrings, necklaces, bracelets, anklets and even toe rings, in a variety of designs that would be the envy of an American jeweler, hung in profusion from the appropriate places.

In its wearing apparel the male population varied from inelegant loincloths and castoff dungarees to resplendent robes of blue, gold or white. Turbans, sun helmets and fezzes were matched by bare feet, sandals and even European tennis shoes. Swarms of children darted about, usually wearing only decorative coats of mud acquired deliberately or in the course of play. To cover their nakedness, some of the more modest little girls wore inch-wide woven belts high up on their waists. More than once, in peering through my camera view finder to evaluate a scene, I would be disconcerted to see a whole row of male and female genitalia suddenly appear, as a crowd of youngsters gleefully tried to rush into the picture.

Within fifteen minutes I could tramp across the city in any direction, always emerging into a vista of endless desert dotted with a few trees and low thornbrush. Here was a population center with an inadequate water supply, impoverished land for food-raising and no enduring building materials, often intolerably hot by day and freezing cold on winter nights. It was incredible to think that despite these handicaps, Timbuctoo had once become inordinately large and rich as one of Africa's greatest trading centers.

Day after day, I had an absorbing time prowling about the small community, always being greeted with courtesy and friendly smiles by its primitive inhabitants. Life in Timbuctoo moves along sleepily with little change and no excitement. Only in the market places is there a hubbub of sound as trading in small goods took place. Behind flat, round baskets, cheap trinkets and chunks of raw salt, sat rows of native women gossiping and waiting for customers.

Until the dawn of the present century, the most beautiful of females and the huskiest of men were sold into slavery by the thousands. When the city was enjoying the full flood of its prosperity, a Timbuctoo slave reputedly lived more abundantly than European farmers of the same period. A surreptitious trade in slaves is still carried on, I was told.

Twice annually Timbuctoo assumes a shadow of its former magnificence when caravans numbering ten thousand camels wind over the scorching sands and camp on the edges of the city. The arrival of the Azalai, or Salt Caravan, as it is also known, is an unforgettable sight. The marketplaces are colorful and the many different types of people—mainly comprising Sourhai, Kountah, Bouna, Peuls, and Tuaregs—are dressed in a variety of costumes.

Immense loads of trade goods and tons of salt from the heart of the desert, 435 miles away, are dumped into the market plaza. Blocks of salt are probably the most valuable luxury in this region because Saharan food is unpalatable without salt. The climate is so hot that the body mechanism must have its quota of salt if health and strength are to be preserved. Thirty bricks, weighing five pounds each, would once buy a fine male slave.

The natives of Timbuctoo are mostly traders, who sell the salt from the mines of Taoudenni; jewelry, leather goods and other products brought from the north by the caravans. From the Sudanese they buy cola, gum, feathers, cane materials and ivory which they sell to the merchants from the north. Though this trading has dwindled, it is still estimated at approximately 50,000 tons yearly.

Shortly after reaching Timbuctoo I discovered that thirst had become a major annoyance. I knew that to drink the undoctored Timbuctoo water was dangerous.

So dehydrating was the climate that I often swallowed in rapid succession the contents of three or four bottles of lemonade and still felt a consuming thirst.

If the night wind had tried to blow any diabolical desert djinns through my always open doorway they would have had several prone human bodies to cross. About ten o'clock each evening, a dozen white-gowned tribesmen, employed by Rene and Etienne, a couple of merchant friends I acquired, would lie down, side by side, and snore away the night hours just outside the door of my room. That first night I awoke about two in the morning to feel a stealthy movement underneath my battered mattress. For a moment I thought that someone under my bed was trying to probe and then drive some object upward into my back. I wondered if all my swarthy associates were actually lying outside the room.

Suddenly I realized that the something alive underneath me had four legs instead of two. It was inside the mattress, either nesting there or chewing its way upward. With my fist I banged several times on the spot where the mattress had been palpitating so that, at least while I was awake, there had been no further disturbances from that geographic center. In the morning, with Rene and Etienne standing by as curiosity-ridden reinforcements, I upended the mattress, found a gaping wound in the ancient

bottom and, exploring inside with a stick, dislodged two pathetic-
ally skinny adult mice.

Apparently I was driving away a good source of food for,
at Segou where I was to fly later, the Barbara tribe makes an
appetizing dish called mouse stew.

The few trees that bravely lifted their foliage toward the
blazing hot sky were usually speckled with hundreds of lazy
storks. Despite the alleged usefulness of these birds in expanding
population statistics, the over-all size of Timbuctoo has remained
about eight thousand souls for some years.

Legend asserts that a woman with a prominent navel was left
to tend goats at an oasis in the desert. In the course of time a
village grew up and it received the curious name of Timbuctoo,
which means the place of the woman with the large navel.

As I wandered toward this very oasis I noticed again that the
majority of the naked children of Timbuctoo possessed bulging
navels. The cruel and primitive method by which the umbilical
cord is cut at birth sometimes leaves protrusions as long as two
inches.

At the edge of the city, surrounded by trees and a few struggling
vegetable gardens, I found the sort of deep pit that a blockbuster
bomb might leave. A continuous thread of men, women and
children, armed with pots, canisters and deflated goatskin bags,
wound its way down a sandy path to the small muddy pond at
the bottom. Sanitation codes must have been non-existent. Men,
women and children strode boldly into the drinking-water, dirty
feet and all, and proceeded to fill their containers.

A herd of goats, trotting nimbly past, smelled this liquid nectar
perfumed by human feet and almost caused a riot as it tried to
plunge en masse down into the precious water hole. Twenty
natives shouting imprecations and hurling sand, chased the
offending beasts back up the slope.

Through the peaceful, winding alley-ways of the city, hand-
craft workers are seen busy at their trade squatting in the dim
coolness of the buildings to escape the sun. Although the community lives almost parasitically off the commerce of river and
desert, a small amount of weaving, sandal making and metal
work is carried on. I could not understand the frantic energy
displayed by some of the men, despite the enveloping heat, until
I discovered that several of them were supporting as many as
four wives.

Rumor had not erred in describing the gentle warmth and inherent beauty of the women of Timbuctoo. Happy smiles wreathe their faces as they walk with that regal posture developed by those who carry burdens atop their heads. Outrageous flirting was not absent either. After photographing and tipping the four grinning wives of a wornout-looking weaver, who wouldn't even interrupt the movements of his shuttle to watch the process, I was followed by the youngest of the group. In a low, beguiling voice she spoke to me in a tongue I could not understand, while her housemates watched and shrieked with laughter.

Besides the carding and spinning of the wool, the women monopolized the pounding of grain and baking of bread. At twilight I could hear dull thuds sounding in every quarter of the city, like so many hollow drums being slowly beaten with an almost sexual rhythm. Bare-chested native women were serenely pounding grain before open-air clay ovens that were shaped like slender beehives.

Rene and I walking along one of the narrow streets glanced upward.

"The weather has been too good for many days," he observed, yet there wasn't a cloud in the sky as he spoke, "but a tornado is brewing."

"Why such a prediction at this time?" I asked.

"Because it is long overdue. One is usually expected at this time of year," he replied. "But I hope it will wait until you have left the city."

"Except that it might maroon me so that I couldn't get out in time to make my plane, I'd like to see one," I told him.

On what I hoped would be my last evening in Timbuctoo, the tornado struck with full force!

The day had been sunny and beautiful, but distressingly hot. At sunset, Rene, Etienne and I pulled chairs and boxes onto the broad, open porchway, beside the campement building, to enjoy dining in the evening coolness. We had just finished drinking one of Cuckoo's nameless delicacies, turning our plates upside down to receive our dessert on the clean bottoms in the interest of avoiding dish washing. Rene happened to look up at the sky.

"Tornado!" was all he said. But with a look that had all the elements of fear.

Moving with appreciable speed up the edge of the horizon, visible over the compound, rose a sharp-edged black form, looking like an enormous opaque lid being drawn by an invisible hand over the earth. Within minutes gusts of wind hurtled with terrific fury through space forcing us to battening down! From the outside we swung shut and tied the crude wooden shutters that hinged to each window opening.

The menacing black mass had already raced across half the sky, cutting the light on earth to complete gloom. The monster storm seemed to be gathering its forces to destroy us. In the midst of it all, there was a pitter-patter of water and hailstones. But the sands remained dry. Dark particles flew through the tempest.

"Grasshoppers," shouted Etienne, scooping up a few.

Driven by the relentless tornado, clouds of these helpless insects whipped past, dropping onto the sands by the thousands. They landed in our hair, crawled into our clothes, crashed into our faces as we hurried inside the building to avoid the onslaught of insects. It became as dark as night. Even the shuttered room in which we sat was full of flopping insects that had been hurled through the cracks in the shutters.

Then rain came in a torrential stream. We dropped iron bars against the shutters for additional support against the tempest and waited.

In America a "tornado" means a twister that fingers the ground with catastrophic effect. But in West Africa, it is a violent electrical storm that rages in the summer season. Since mud buildings are notoriously susceptible to water and the storm seemed unending, I wondered what was keeping the whole city from slowly melting away.

At 9.30, I felt my way into my room and went to sleep in a bed standing in an inch of rain water. Banging shutters, flying drops of water, and crashes of thunder were still under way, when I awakened at 1 a.m. I could hear the ominous sliding of sand and dull thuds as parts of outside walls dropped to the ground. I commiserated with the Timbuctooans on their vulnerability, lacking any better building materials than sand.

In the morning I was scheduled to go through to the airport on the Fort Bonnier truck, unless an emergency intervened. But worrying was useless. I rolled over and went back to sleep, hoping for the best.

A gray sky, emptied momentarily of its rains, hung over a bedraggled city the next morning. One corner of the campement had a gaping hole eroded into it. The decorative wall around

the flat-roof top had broken down in a number of places. Two
natives armed with buckets soon appeared, plastering load after
load of sand into the roof. Etienne pointed to several holes where
walls had sagged, dislodging small rats.

After breakfast, weakened and thinned by my many days of
acute illness, caused by the water, I tramped over to Fort Bonnier.
Small portions of many buildings in Timbuctoo had, indeed,
crumbled to earth. Chameleon-like, even the color of the city had
changed! I found the commandant surveying the damage to his
fort. Several walls had collapsed into desolate hills of sand.

"The worst storm this season," he declared seriously.

Then with a reminiscent smile, he barked; "C'est la vie! You
wonder about the lorry? It will leave shortly. Be ready for the
hardest ride you have ever made."

By eight o'clock, I had reimbursed Cuckoo for his labors,
which, I suspect, may have included serving us at least one mouse
stew, shaken hands with Rene and Etienne, who had gallantly
shaved in honor of my departure, and was seated with two French
soldiers in the weapon carrier which started to churn through
the rain-darkened sands leading out of the city.

I recalled how begrudgingly Timbuctoo had released its first
exploring white visitors when the time for their departure had
come. Major Alexander Gordon Laing; murdered five days after
he marched out. Heinrich Barth; fatally ill with dysentery when
he rode out! Rene Caillie; dead at thirty-nine of stomach ailments contracted in Timbuctoo.

With a certain ironic amusement, I reflected that the city now
seemed almost equally reluctant about loosening its grip on the
latest visitor. Had it not inflicted me with dysentery and tried
to retard me with floods?

I remembered that over the tomb of young Caillie, whose
exploit brought him the highest honours from King Charles X,
leading European geographical societies, and from the populace
of France, a monument had been raised that emphasized one
striking phrase: *"The Only European Who Has Seen and
Described Timbuctoo."* A significant tribute to a brave man
and one which until comparatively recent years held true.

Just before a row of trees closed in around the city, I turned
for one final look with western eyes at the world's foremost
symbol of inhabited remoteness. Two masked Tuaregs, fiercely
armed and mounted on tall, brown camels, were riding toward

the mud-walled town. Atop a low, flat roof, blue robed figures were packing sand as their ancestors had done after each storm for a thousand or more years. A noisy troop of lovable youngsters, with shrieks of recognition, ceased their play near a herd of goats to watch their friend ride out into the desert.

With a subdued feeling of sadness, I realized that the few symbolic Timbuctoos still remaining around the globe are fast disappearing. A universal conformity is settling over the culture and thinking of even the most inaccessible areas.

The existence of the Timbuctoos of history have created heroes like Laing, Caillie and Barth. Curiosity about the strange and faraway lifted them to heights of bravery and achievement. And yet these explorers, by their very discoveries, have inaugurated the process through which the sometimes melancholy changes are begun. With their arrival, isolating walls tumble down and the ways of an outside world begin to flood in.

CHAPTER NINE

KILIMANJARO

"THE rhinoceros, unquestionably, is the most vicious, the most cussed beast that roams the dark continent," said Doug Kennedy, an editorial friend of mine, when we were discussing an account of his experiences in Africa. "And," he continued, "meeting up with one of the worst of the rhinos happened to be my first encounter with African big game."

I have known Doug Kennedy for a number of years as one editor who actually gets right into his subject with all four feet. Yes, he really *lives* Adventure!

He had his first big thrilling adventure when he rescued Eddie Rickenbacker and his friends from floating debris after their twenty-one-day ordeal, following their crash-landing in the Pacific in World War II.

This and many other exciting experiences gave Doug Kennedy a little of what it takes to face the most treacherous beasts of the African wilds.

"But don't get the idea that guns and courage are all it takes (I'm not even sure you could call it courage) to face those dynamos," he pointed out. "It makes all the difference in the world who your white hunters and trackers are. On this particular safari I had a tracker I shall never forget. Mamu was his name."

Mamu is the blackest man I have seen this African side of the Melanesians of the Solomon Islands, Kennedy continued. He wears a blue-black beauty mark, a self-inflicted scar that extends from the tip of his hairline, down straight through his forehead to the bridge of his nose. He also wears a bright-red T-shirt, and a pair of longjohn British shorts. When in the bush, or on the plains, he covers his red T-shirt with a nondescript bush jacket, obviously discarded by an oversized European.

By most standards Mamu is a small man. He would probably make a good flyweight in the U.S. His legs are scrawny but springy. His hands are calloused and work-worn, but when he fondly caresses and cleans a gun, or when he delicately skins an animal or cleans a bird, his hands work with the dexterity and assurance of a Park Avenue surgeon. Mamu has other talents: he is a quick-change artist with a flat-tire; he can produce a cooking or warming fire faster than an Eagle scout; he can foretell weather that would confuse a master meteorologist; he can spot game long before a 20-20 vision white man verifies it with binoculars.

In addition, Mamu is, I am told, a happily married man, deeply devoted to his wife and family. He has one small failing: he is inclined to get stinko drunk once his white hunter or client bags the big game they are after. Mamu stays perfectly sober after a client bags an oryx, kudu or gazelle. It is only the *big* game, like the black rhino, the elephant, or a black-maned lion which sets Mamu off on a three-day tear.

For Mamu is, above all else, a tracker. It is only when he is on the trail of something big that his normally stoic expression, his stiffly correct bearing, breaks down into a broad, toothy grin; down into a posture of sheer animal spirits. For Mamu loves his work and is quietly proud of his ability to tell at a glance that a rhino passed here two days (or two hours) ago.

A piece of bent grass, a nibbled thorn bush, a chunk of bark off an acacia tree, the size and pace of a track, all give Mamu a vivid mental picture of a rhino. He can tell you whether a rhino has eaten well (by its dung); he can tell whether it has been spooked (by the length of its stride); he can tell whether the rhino is angry (by its foot marks when it pauses), whether the rhino is thirsty (by its string-straight path toward a water hole), whether the rhino is happy (by the contented back-scratching against a tree or anthill).

Mamu can tell all this in moments. He tells it in Swahili to his white hunter, Hal Prowse, an American who is a slightly larger and whiter carbon copy of Mamu.

In short, Mamu is a helluva fellow, a man of the Walangulu tribe who, during the Kenya Mau Mau emergency, tracked and fought loyally for his white friends. He is the kind of man who might have inspired Kipling's classic: "You're a better man than I, Gunga Din." Hal Prowse is also a helluva fellow, who has earned his spurs in one of man's most exclusive clubs: the two score licensed white hunters of British Africa.

I was doubly glad to have been along, for the rhino we were after was, in Hal's words, "the maddest damn rhino I've ever seen".

In trying to place a fair appraisal upon a rhino, the most you can possibly say in his favor is that he is an ugly, cantankerous beast who suffers from constant indigestion. And if your diet was the same as his—thorn bushes—you'd probably feel cantankerous, too. He also likes roots, which he digs up with his powerful nose, upon which projects his mighty horn, composed of modified hair and hard, tough skin. Each year his horn gets bigger. It is also used as a terrific weapon. And, worst of all, he has an irresistible urge to demolish with this powerful horn anything or anybody who gets in his way. He has no natural enemies.

The rhino and the elephant are the two most powerful mammals now living, and the elephant is too peaceful and self-sufficient to have any cause to attack the rhino. The hippopotamus somewhat resembles the rhino in his bulky awkwardness, but that is all. He, too, is very peaceful, even timid, except when provoked into action; even then it is more defense on his part than aggression.

All three animals—rhino, hippo and elephant—are the lumbering type. The rhino has very little intelligence, although you could hardly call him stupid and, like the other two, has a very decidedly keen sense of smell. Also, his hearing is keen. Often, when he goes charging at the scent, he keeps right on going for a mile or so after he has passed it. He has severe myopia—can't see ahead much more than a hundred feet.

Rhinos have been known to attack trains, *head-on*; they have overturned and demolished one-ton trucks; they have run rampant through native villages, virtually razing them.

And they attack without provocation—or warning.

Our "maddest damn rhino" had been "spooked" at his early morning grazing by a herd of Masai cattle; his prehistoric pride had been further injured by being driven off his favorite grazing area. He had been tracked and tormented; he was thirsty and hungry and very tired of running. He was in three little words— mad as hell!

But I am getting ahead of my story.

Safari camp life, I learned, is made as easy and comfortable as possible. There is a good reason for this: the hunting is hard, and your white hunter's job is partly to keep you from suffering from cumulative fatigue.

Hal Prowse, our white hunter, chose our first campsite well, some one hundred miles due south of safari headquarters in Nairobi. He picked a spot hard by the banks of the Selengai River, now dry two months after the "small rains" in November. It was deep in the heart of the warrior Masai country, composed of bumpy, semi-mountainous outcroppings.

Far in the background, like a sentinel, stood Mount Kilimanjaro which, as you may or may not know, means Mountain of God, surveying this wonderful natural scene from its 20,000-foot snow-capped eminence.

The campsite was well shaded by the gnarled and spreading branches of a grove of acacias; was well breezed by a gentle prevailing wind which kept the mosquitos at bay. Hal's five-ton truck had preceded us with most of the native boys and by the time we reached the site, tents were being set up with alacrity.

During the hundred mile trip from Nairobi, Hal, driving his hunting car over the backwoods roads at a fifty-mile clip, briefed me on what to expect. Bob Halmi followed in our dust in a Land Rover, lent us by the Rootes group. I met Mamu, who always rides with Hal, on the way down; but since my Swahili is limited to "ndio" (ye) and "hapana" (no), and Mamu's English is limited to yes and no, we hardly had much chance to communicate.

It was still about two hours before sunset when we arrived, so Hal suggested that we all reconnoiter the hunting grounds, some ten miles away. Using a Masai cattle track for a road, we soon arrived at what Hal called "Rhino Hill". I came to know it by the title of "Cardiac Hill". Hal and Mamu hopped out of the car and started trudging upward, heads to the ground like a couple of bird dogs. I started after them, but Hal waved me back, saying that the climb from this angle was sorta sickening. He was right; by the time I reached the top I was panting and blowing like a buffalo, and I had vivid recollection of what I had eaten for lunch.

This climb went on for four solid days, only Hal managed to dream up some sadistic variations. Next morning, for example, I found out that I had to get up at 4.30, swallow a steaming cupful of black *chai* (tea), and drag my butt up that damn hill before dawn. That afternoon Hal thoughtfully called for some rain which mired the car far from the base of the hill and made us trek through the black cotton soil, for two miles before we began to climb. That soil, incidentally, would make fine commercial glue. It clings insistently to your shoes, weighing them down like a pair of lead-lined ski-boots.

After four days of this routine, I was ready to challenge almost anyone to a race up Mount Everest.

Perhaps it might be interesting to recall that at one time the rhino inhabited Europe and North America. That was during the Eocene Age, when mammals became the dominant animals, and the Miocene Age, during the development of the large mountain ranges. Today, these animals are confined to the warmer sections of Asia, India and Africa.

Actually, there are now only three distinct types of rhino. The Indian rhino has but one horn, while each of the African species has two. The black rhino is the smallest. It weighs a little over one ton, and has a pointed prehensile upper lip. It's to be found in Africa, south of Abyssinia, in the wooded, watered districts. The white rhino is the largest land mammal, except for the elephant, and feeds largely on grass. Its flesh is said to be excellent for food, especially in the autumn and winter. He often stands five feet eight inches, at the shoulder, runs to fifteen feet in length and travels with terrific speed.

I should point out, right now, that the only times to get a rhino are at dawn and dusk—unless you are hot on one's trail. He browses all night, mostly on the aptly named wait-a-bit bush which is armed with double prongs of two-inch spikes. Walk into one—and you wait more than a bit before extracting yourself.

During the hot daylight hours the rhino holes up and sleeps. At such a time you could walk to within five feet of him without seeing him.

We may have done just that several times. For we spent four frustrating days trying to locate fresh rhino tracks, and to no avail. I did manage to sharpen up my shooting a bit, particularly around noontime when the chances of bagging a rhino are just about nil. I found that wingshooting in Africa (mainly for sand grouse, guinea hens and francolins) far surpasses anything found in the United States or Canada.

I also learned that knocking off camp meat (zebra for the boys; Thompson's gazelle for us) was relatively easy in this prodigious and profligate country. I was especially pleased to drop a zebra with a 235-yard heart shot, offhand, and was even more pleased to note that I had finally earned the approval of Mamu.

Hal quickly taught me what is commonly termed the Masai stalk. Under the rules of the hunting game in East Africa you cannot shoot unless you are 200 yards away from the hunting car. That means you can drive roughly up to 500 yards, alight and start your stalk. If you belly forward in the short grass, like a lion, the big game is liable to spook for good. But if you walk upright, like a Masai warrior, carrying your gun over your shoulder just as they carry their spears, the game, which is accustomed to the Masai, just eye you carefully and slowly begin moving away. Usually, I found, they will let you get within 200-300 yards (zebras are dumber) before moving away, uncannily, at just about the pace of your approach. If you stop suddenly, they spook; if you slow down, carefully bringing your rifle to your shoulder, they become quickly alert. At that point you have about three seconds to stop and draw a bead before they are long gone out of range.

But I was after rhino. Why? For one thing, simply because our white hunter, who had been practically weaned as an elephant hunter, said that the rhino was the most dangerous of Africa's big game.

Each night, around the campfire, Hal alerted me on what to expect when we got our chance to bag one. He warned me especially of one *inescapable* fact: that a charging rhino can cover 100 yards in eight seconds. He also warned me that a charging rhino offers no heart shot. You have to hit him on that lowered head, hoping to avoid the trophy horn. Hal particularly warned me to stand my ground, since if I made the natural move backward my muzzle blast would nearly knock his head off.

All the talk promised excitement. And I got it.

That fifth day simply failed to dawn. We drove to the foot of

Rhino Hill, then sat miserably cramped, cold and wet in the hunting car. To the south, back toward camp, we could see great masses of rain clouds; to the north was a blanketing fog to rival London's best.

Africa was slowly warming up to a new day. Through wisps of fog I could see zebra and gazelle grazing on the damp grass of the plains. Dead ahead lay rocky Rhino Hill, its crest enveloped in mist.

Hal and I sat in the front seat, huddled and unspeaking; Mamu and Gulu (our other tracker) sat in back, in I guess the same frame of mind.

We sat there—it was pointless to climb in that visibility—for the better part of half an hour until Halmi came roaring up behind us in his landrover, shouting, fresh rhino tracks! Fresh rhino tracks!

It turned out that the rhino had passed across the Masai cattle path we used for a road sometime *between* the time our hunting car had passed and Halmi had driven up.

We all went back down the cattle track and, sure enough, there were the tracks, round, firm, fully packed—and fresh!

Mamu and Hal had a swift Swahili chat; while Gulu, whom we fondly named "laughing boy" because he was constantly clowning for Halmi's camera, jumped up and down in excitement.

Hal decided, since we were upwind, to make a big circle to get downwind of what Mamu had determined was the rhino's probable position. At this point we were only twenty minutes behind him, it was early morning, and the rhino was probably feeding.

We drove to a little rise in the hope that we could follow Hal, Mamu and Gulu with binoculars. But the weather closed in and the thick patches of undergrowth soon swallowed them.

The waiting wasn't easy, but within the hour the hot African sun had burned through the fog.

Somewhere around ten o'clock Gulu came back through the underbrush with the news (in sign language) that the rhino was heading toward the near side of Hal's Rhino Hill. That meant that our best shooting and glassing position would be at the top of the hill.

The climb wasn't so bad this time since we were full of high hopes and excitement. At one point Gulu stopped, eyes bulging, to point out the tracks of a huge lion.

"Simba!" he shouted, stretching the sibilant to a gasp.

Shades of Edgar Rice Burroughs! I thought Burroughs had invented the word just for Tarzan, but Hal later told me that it really is Swahili for lion.

We finally reached the top of the hill and crept across the ridge line, expecting any moment to see Hal and Mamu below us with the rhino somewhere in the middle.

No such luck! We covered that hill for two hours. No sign of our trackers or the rhino.

Finally, Halmi caught sight of Hal trudging across the plain. The rhino, Hal told us, had been heading straight toward the hill at the time he had sent Gulu back. But ten minutes later Masai cattle had spooked it out across the plain, toward the horizon line.

Hal was afraid that we had lost him; a spooked rhino can bee-line thirty miles in three hours. Hal was also worried because Mamu, tracking barefooted in the sticky, clinging soil, had put a thorn halfway through his foot. Hal had left Mamu on the track, hoping we could pick him up later in the cars.

Hal clambered into his gun car, plunged into the lunch basket and announced what was obvious, simply: "My butt is draggin'." Halmi and I were sympathetic but astonished that Hal, still on a hot trail, would take time off to eat. It was now noon. Hal had tracked for six hours. We had spent three hours on Cardiac Hill. The rhino had covered ten miles, maybe more.

"Better eat," said Hal. "We may still have a long day ahead of us."

We ate, hardly tasting it, but getting needed energy from the African hunter's drink; one-third sugar, two-thirds tea.

Then we set out in the hunting and camera cars, fanning out across the plain, sticking to the higher ground, hoping for a glimpse of Mamu. We finally caught up with him about an hour (and five miles) later. Halmi saw him first, frantically waving his bright-red undershirt to attract our attention. As we drove up, he limped toward us, pointing back over his shoulder. The rhino, Mamu explained to Hal, had gone down through a deep, nearby rock ravine about an hour before. He was still traveling fast, obviously unhappy about his spooking, perhaps unhappy because he knew he was being tracked. At any rate, it was way past his nap time; so he was probably ugly on that account alone.

Hal took one look at the ravine, which extended for miles in either direction, and made a flat announcement: "From here on, we go by foot."

Mamu, munching on a piece of dried zebra, took the lead, carrying one of Hal's Jeffery .450 double rifles. Gulu, carrying Hal's other gun, stayed close by, watching for signs of the rhino's turning. Hal was third, binoculars in hand. I followed, toting the Winchester .458 which grew heavier by the mile.

The trail got a lot fresher after three more foot-weary miles. We had stepped up our pace and I could feel the blisters squishing in my shoes, the raw sores breaking out on my shoulders.

Suddenly, Mamu, who had been hurrying along head toward the ground, stopped dead. There, plain to see even for a non-tracker such as I, was a confusion and profusion of rhino tracks all heading uphill on a shallow slope, thick with the wait-a-bit thorn bush, the rhino delicacy. Our excitement mounted with each step up the slope.

At that point we began what turned out to be one of the most agonizing hours of my life. The stalk, the approach and the ultimate climax reminded me, in many ways, of the war. I had fought the war as a torpedo boat skipper where our targets were able, like the rhino, to fight back; where our targets, like the rhino, had built-in radar to detect our approach; where our targets, like the rhino, could kill us.

Tense, pace slowed to a silent shuffle, desperately trying to step in Mamu's sure-footed steps, we headed up the slope. The rifle got heavier by the moment; each wait-a-bit bush seemed determined to poke my eyes out.

Then we had a short reprieve. The profusion of rhino tracks *really* became a confusion—even for Mamu.

At a signal from Hal, we sank wearily against the nearest ant-hill, inhaling with the almost desperate breathing of men who have just finished a marathon.

Mamu and Gulu, almost down on all fours, spread out ahead of us, trying to sort out the fresh rhino tracks from the old.

The tracks were all around us, the familiar triple pug marks.

The respite was broken by Gulu who materialized from the foreground like a sudden shadow. Fingers to his lips, his body tense with excitement, he waved us forward toward a large and apparently impenetrable thicket.

Mamu was already at the thicket's edge, his hand held up in a gesture of warning. At this stage Mamu was the tacit boss of the situation—until the moment that Hal and I reached his side.

Then Mamu relinquished command to Hal at the precise moment we both saw the beast.

The verb "see" is used advisedly, for we could only catch a glimpse, in the dark shadows, of some gray-brown hide in the thicket. He was about ten yards in and I could only marvel at how such a large beast, even with that prehistoric hide, could penetrate the impenetrable.

This was not the moment for marveling, however. Almost unconscious, I stepped back a couple of paces, banging the butt of the Winchester into Halmi's cameras. The noise was muffled by the rubber butt plate. But it was enough.

There was a crashing in the thicket, a deep-throated and angry snort. Gulu streaked off to the right like Jesse Owens on a busman's holiday. Mamu, smarter, slid silently behind Hal and me, holding Hal's other gun in readiness.

The rhino crashed out of the thicket, astigmatic eyes on the moving Gulu, now scrambling up a spindly tree. The rhino stood still for a long moment, just long enough for Halmi to catch him in his lens.

Then he spotted us: closer and fairer game. Head down, breaking pace, he switched targets. All hell broke loose!

All of Hal's warnings came back to me, including one final warning: "*squeeze* the shot."

It was, I thought, much like being hosed by Japanese or German machine-gun tracer fire in night fighting. You watch the scene, detached, in almost morbid fascination. It is, truly, a moment of truth—and yet you have no time to be frightened.

Sighting on the spine—I wanted to protect my trophy—I began squeezing at the fifteen-yard mark. Hal, more aware of our danger, didn't wait. The crack of his Jeffrey beat my Winchester by a fraction of a second. Hal's shot slowed him, spun him off course. Mine finished him.

In agonized slow-motion the rhino, horn down, skidded to a stop and rolled over.

The moment of truth suddenly became a moment of exuberant exultation.

We paced off the distance: six yards. Close enough!

Hal and I, with ritualistic solemnity, shook hands, while Bob Halmi had his moment of exuberance over the pictures he was sure he had taken. I looked at Mamu who was busy putting a tape measure on the horn. He looked up, grinning.

I didn't mind the six-mile hike back to the hunting car in the gathering dusk or the jouncy ride back to camp.

We drank that night to Mamu, to the rhino, to Kilimanjaro— and to any number of other things that I've forgotten now.

CHAPTER TEN

POISON BOW AND ARROW HUNTING

"I WAS perched in the top of a tall tree, camouflaged by the leaves, waiting to film any big game that might appear, when I saw a troop of baboons a couple of hundred yards away, leisurely headed for the water hole. Half an hour later, down through the same clearing in the jungle, one giant baboon made his way straight for me. I knew then that the troop had spotted me and he was their scout. What followed became the most terrorizing incident of my African safari."

This is the way Fred Bear began to relate the tale of the first and probably the most remarkable bowhunting safari in African history.

It is said that he has done more for archery and bowhunting than anyone since Robin Hood. A total of eight bowhunters and three photographers made up this expedition into French Equatorial Africa in April of 1955.

"The purpose of the expedition was not to expose ourselves unnecessarily to death or to pretend that the bow is a suitable weapon for big game, such as elephants, rhinos, lions and buffalo, but to find out just how successful a bowman might be in hunting split-hoof game animals of the African veldt."

There are many species of these animals, all of which are classed as antelope, varying in size from fifteen to fifteen hundred pounds, with the exception of the greater kudu and the giant eland which we found in large herds.

This safari is particularly interesting now because of the popular growth of this ancient art. Almost since the dawn of man, the bow-and-arrow has played an important rôle in his survival. First used as a hunting instrument, then as a deadly weapon of war, the bow has been refined into a pleasurable means of recreation for millions.

After a short stop in North Africa to refuel, we flew to Fort Archambault, a town of 20,000 blacks and 1,000 whites in French Equatorial Africa. There we met our outfitter, Jean Gerin, and his two assistants, Mike and Noa. We had three hunting trucks, each capable of holding four people plus hunting and camping supplies. Added to this was a five-ton Dodge truck and utility trailer. This imposing cavalcade was loaded with supplies as well as fifteen black boys.

Three of these so-called boys, who are really grown men, were trackers, a tracker being a man whose function is not only to discover the tracks of the game for us but who is also highly skilled in the lore of the bush and veldt of the African game country. They serve as gunbearers, too; the best of them are handy with a heavy rifle.

Our party was split up into groups of three or four, and one of the white hunters was assigned to each group. The other boys filled the jobs of cook, laundryman, dishwasher and waiter, and several had charge of skinning, butchering and taking care of the trophies. All these servants are necessary because the extreme heat takes the energy out of a white man who has not been acclimated. The natives, of course, are impervious to the heat.

Fort Archambault, our taking-off place, is located in the Lake Chad district of French Equatorial Africa on the Auk River, approximately 1,000 miles north of the equator and a few hundred miles below the southern border of the Sahara Desert. It is a rather flat area typical African bush country with occasional grassy plains.

We left Fort Archambault at noon on Sunday and crossed the Auk River on a powered ferry, operated by a dozen natives, and drove eighty miles up the river to our destination, the little village of Golongosso. Here the French Government has what is called a government house available for the use of travelers and hunters.

In the afternoon of that day we had sighted some hartebeest and several horse antelope, our first sight of African game.

We left camp at six the next morning and went down river on a faintly marked road used exclusively by hunters. We saw plenty of game, but all indication showed that African game was going to be difficult to approach within a reasonable bow range. We found that it was no job at all to get within 100 to 150 yards, which was an excellent rifle range but not near enough for bowhunting.

The animals of the plains are the prey of lions, leopards and other predatory animals, and are thus continually on the alert against death.

We hunted until ten o'clock, seeing plenty of the antelope family, two wart hogs and a big troop of baboons. Then we headed back for camp because from ten to three the animal kingdom is at rest in shady places.

We broke the midday rule, however, and spent siesta time in visiting the nearby village. The natives were spinning cotton, making grass mats, grinding meal and engaging in various other duties—that is, the women were. The men are immune to work and sit at ease or play simple games.

Clothing is a problem of no significance; the men wear something similar to jockey shorts, the women and girls nothing but a G-string of colorful beads with a narrow cloth flap at front and back.

The village tom-tom drums were all beating during the dinner period. After dinner, wandering up to the village to see what the commotion was all about, we found the natives gathered around in a great circle. The two drums they used for a dance that night keep going until two or three in the morning. This we found is a nightly affair.

These drums, ten inches in diameter and two feet long, are very crudely but strongly made from sections of a hollowed out hardwood tree. Skin is stretched tightly over each end but the drums are played on one end only, by holding them in an upright position between the knees with one end resting on the ground.

The dance seemed meaningless to us. There was absolutely no indication of sex nor was there any rhythm either.

During the first week, most of our hunting was done from our hunting cars. We drove along either through the bush, where there were no roads, or on an animal trail. From advantageous points, we got out and stalked. Even in the bush the game can see the hunter from a much greater distance than it is possible to kill them with an arrow. In open territory, which is normally covered with tall grass and reeds that grow up to ten feet high, it is impossible to see any kind of game except the elephant and giraffe. At this time of the year when the grass has ripened and dried, the natives fire it, their purpose being to clear the area, leaving nothing but dry, hard-baked soil and bunches of roots. From these roots would grow fresh grass to which the wild life would flock for feeding. The animals are easily sighted when they are out in the flat, open country and of course they are equally difficult to approach.

The first kill of our archery safari was an adult reedbuck with horns about eight inches long and a body about the size of a white-tail deer, which fell to my bow on the third day out.

There was game in plenty but, as usual, it was out of bow range. One stalk, however, could have been successful but for a troop of baboons which discovered me just as I was about to take a shot at two kob bucks. Baboons give the hunter a lot of trouble when he is trying to get close to the game.

Several days previously we had discovered a salt lick where water bucks, reedbucks and other types of antelope came to refresh themselves. A hundred yards from this salt lick there was a water-hole and a trail leading from it to the water. We decided to build a blind there and with the help of a number of the black boys we soon had it under construction. Within shooting range of the salt lick and out of sight, we took our stand in this blind underneath a couple of thorn trees. Going there in the evening, we planned to stay all night. The moon was full and the vision was excellent. Nothing happened until one o'clock in the morning when a few reedbuck came through. Then, suddenly, we heard an animal drinking water in the lapping fashion of a cat. Could it possibly be a lion? A few minutes later, the king of beasts strolled quickly across our opening in the foliage thirty or thirty-five yards from our blind. This was our first introduction to the great jungle cat and what a magnificent sight!

At this juncture we remembered that before starting out our white hunter had insisted that we take a .375 magnum rifle with us into the blind for safety's sake—in fact, he would not consent to our spending the night there without it.

I thought, as I looked at the royal beast, that if I could see the sights on my gun in the darkness, I would take a shot at the animal with my bow, even though it would be a dangerous procedure. I picked up the rifle to convert my thought into action but, being under the tree and not in the moonlight, the sights were not visible. A wounded lion is something to be feared.

I took the better part of valor and passed up the opportunity of conquering a lion.

A few minutes after the lion was engulfed in the darkness, a hyena stole through, no doubt following the trail of the king, hoping that a kill had been made and that he would get the leftovers. The lion had great patience waiting for his prey and paced back and forth in the nearby forest until daylight. We could hear him growling and moaning in his displeasure. A water buck came in timorously about dawn but got our wind and made off in a hurry before we could get a shot.

The next two days were spent out in the bush. We went up the river on a more or less exploratory trip and, as so often happened, much game was sighted but always just out of bow shot. We visited several villages on the way and found an excellent salt lick adjacent to a water hole twenty-five miles from camp.

This marked the end of our stay in Golongosso. We packed up and started for a new hunting area.

We found plate-lipped women who I learned were either Ubangi or members of the Chad tribe. In any case, they are the survivors of an era when the Arabs raided this part of French Equatorial Africa in search of young girls to carry off.

Many of these girls, in order to be unattractive to the slave raiders, conceived the idea of disfiguring themselves by splitting their lips and inserting large plates so that they would not be taken captive.

We stopped at one large village and asked the natives to stage a dance for us to photograph. We promised them three antelope and they agreed to put on a full-scale dance for us in the middle of the day, when the light was good, instead of the usual time, at night.

Our route led us to a town named Kyabe. This was a typical small African town: houses made of mud and straw, a market section, where the natives bought vegetables, nuts, flour, baskets, wood and dried fish. Traders displayed their wares, including beads, perfumes, soap, cigarettes and salt.

We arrived at our destination along the upper Auk River late in the afternoon. By the time the camp was made up, darkness had set in, yet some of the men decided to go down to the river for their usual swim. I was late getting started and fortunately, I took my five-cell flashlight to find the way. Arriving on the river bank, I pointed the flashlight on the rest of the party, its members just about to jump in.

By sheer good fortune, something caught my eye on the surface of the water. For a brief moment I froze and could not utter a sound. I kept the flashlight pinned right onto the spot. What I saw that transfixed me were five pairs of fireball eyes! Suddenly, getting hold of my senses, I yelled a warning. How everyone jumped and fled from the river bank! They had caught a glimpse of the same spectacle just as I shouted. One moment longer and they would have been in the water struggling in vain, perhaps, with five hungry crocodiles looking for victims.

This was our first encounter with crocs, and needless to say, swimming in the river was scrupulously avoided thereafter. We took our baths that night by hanging from a tree, buckets which had holes punched in the bottoms.

Each day the members of our three hunting groups shot several species of antelope for food; food, especially for the black boys who were with us and for the villagers near which we hunted. The natives don't have, or are not allowed to have, either guns or bows-and-arrows. Their only weapons are spears and, judging from what I have observed, the carrying of spears is another throwback to tradition.

Actually, I don't believe they can throw their spears very far and hit their targets, although they do secure fish with them. Their main diet seems to be fish; they depend almost entirely upon the white hunters who come to their area for whatever red meat they eat. The missionaries carry rifles and, when they visit a village, their welcome is much more cordial if they have a good fat animal in the rear end of their car.

On our first day hunting from this new camp I found an area in which trails abounded. Coming out of the bush, these trails led towards a nearby lake, along which the animals traveled from the bush down to the water to drink and to feed on the bordering green grass. Here I found an ideal location for a blind. With the help of the black boys a platform was erected six feet up off the ground and only about thirty yards from this trail.

I spent the night and a greater part of the morning at this spot. Before dark I made stalks on various animals in the immediate area. There were water bucks, kob, reedbucks, wart hogs and baboons. The trails showed that buffalo, lions and elephants also used them. There were many hippos in the lake.

The moon at this time did not rise until midnight and while I heard many sounds, before this time I could not identify the origin of any of them.

In the morning just as day was breaking, three natives who came along the trail carrying their spears, immediately noticed our tracks. There was an active discussion among them as to their meaning, but they continued on their way, never spotting me behind my blind, high overhead. Elevated blinds give protection to the hunter, as neither animals nor human beings look upward when on the trail, and the human scent is unlikely to reach the animals.

After the natives had gone, I set out from the blind to try my luck in stalking a herd of six or seven water bucks. These animals were very slowly working their way from the lake and feeding area back into the bush. I maneuvered to keep in front of them so that when they reached the open area I would be within bow shot. When I was twenty yards away in the thick bush and just as the first of them, a doe, stepped out, my white hunter arrived to take me back for the midday rest period at the camp, and of course spoiled the show.

That afternoon was the appointed time to take the three promised antelope and see the natives stage the dance. It was one of the hottest days of the trip but the natives really gave us a good performance—and what a show it was, done in the typical African style, accompanied by a musical instrument called a balafon, but known to us as a xylophone. This instrument, combined with a few resounding tom-tom drums and a blind man blowing a weird whistle, made for a genuine welcome.

The natives had dug up all kinds of curious costumes in great assortment. They danced and sweat, and sweat and smelled, in clouds of dust. Little and big girls, little and big boys, and even some half-dozen plate-lipped women, the Ubangis, took part with fun for all. I took polaroid pictures and passed them around, causing wonderment and greatly varied reactions.

The natives by and large are a friendly lot. But sometimes we entered a village in a remote area to find fires burning and complete evacuation of the inhabitants, who evidently heard us in the distance and sensed danger. We would stand around for half or three-quarters of an hour when the men would begin to filter back from the bush. Finding out that everything was peaceful, the women would follow slowly. They seem to have the intelligence of a child, although they have a good sense of humor and get a laugh out of the simplest things that are not humorous to a white man. The pickaninnies are very cute; it is not at all unusual to see four or five-year-old children carrying babies on their backs, holding them there for hours.

One of the big factors that makes bowhunting difficult in Africa is the impossibilty of getting out in the bush unaccompanied by a black boy or a white hunter. I can understand of course why the hunter, who is responsible for his employer's safety, objects to have him roving around the bush particularly when protected only by a bow. If a mishap should occur, which is not beyond reason, he loses his license and likely his livelihood. He is so cautious it is almost impossible for the hunter to slip out of camp without the black boy who has been assigned to guard him.

The trackers are good woodsmen but they think that hunting with a gun is no different from shooting with a bow, not realizing that the latter is only effective at eighty or ninety yards; a rifle of course carries infinitely farther.

One thing that seems to puzzle the non-archer, or the beginner, is that a slow arrow can be so deadly. It is difficult for them to believe that an arrow which has been shot clear through a huge lion will carry several yards beyond.

One way to demonstrate this seeming impossibility is to hang horizontally a slab of steak several inches thick, hold a sharp knife point down a couple of feet above it, drop the knife, and see it go through the meat easily. On the contrary, in like manner drop a bullet and it merely thumps onto the meat like a dud. The heavy, sharp knife, like the heavy arrow, doesn't need velocity for penetration, whereas the light bullet does.

Most beginning archers confuse bow weight with effectiveness. They think that the heavier or more powerful the bow, the more deadly it is. But the most effective big-game hunting is done with a bow of sixty-five or seventy pounds. The average hunting bow is only about fifty to fifty-five pounds.

The "weight" of a bow is determined by the amount of "pull" in pounds necessary to draw it. Heavy bows are not capable of shooting arrows much faster than light ones. They merely accommodate heavier arrows, which naturally hit harder and penetrate more deeply into big, tough-skinned animals. The limit to bow weight is determined only by the hunter's ability to draw. There are rare instances of archers using up to one-hundred-pound bows.

The problem for the new bowhunter is to know what to look for. He naturally expects to see the whole animal standing clearly in sight, but that is not usually to be expected. He must learn to look for and recognize off-color spots among the trees or brush. A patch of yellow might be part of a lion's body or neck. Or a slender strip of white could be the inside of a leg. An ear or an antler or just the flick of a tail, should command the sharpest attention. Odd shapes should be considered, too. The log that is rounded on one end may be an antelope.

During the first few days in the forest the hunter will be slow to distinguish ordinary objects from those that are actually game. He will lose much time and probably overlook some good opportunities. After a few days, however, he will become more expert and will not often expect an entirely open view of the animal; perhaps nothing more than the highlights of his antlers or the reflection of his shiny hair under certain light conditions.

In hunting big game, three general methods are used: Stillhunting, stalking and standing—that is picking a spot and staying on it.

Stillhunting simply means going silently through the forest and keeping concealed until game is closely approached.

When hunting with a bow, however, one will seldom come upon game within shooting range and is therefore faced with the problem of stalking to within shooting distance. So in hunting with a bow one is really not only stillhunting, but stalking as well and the term stillhunting combines both methods.

Standing consists of taking up a station within shooting distance of a runway, game trail or feeding ground and staying there until animals arrive.

Any large game country has heavier concentrations of animals in some sections than in others. This is due to several things: portions of otherwise good cover may not furnish suitable food, also game that was in one locality last week does not necessarily mean that it will be there this week.

A wise hunter takes advantage of the sun when it is low in the sky. A bright sun in the eyes of an animal is as blinding to him as it is to the hunter and one is definitely in luck when a stalk can be made with the sun at his back and the wind in his face.

One of our group armed with a rifle shot a wart hog, an animal with very beautiful ivory tusks, that weighs 150 to 200 pounds. All in all, so far our party has killed with guns probably thirty head of game weighing fifty to six hundred pounds each—from oribi, which weighs thirty to thiry-five pounds, to good sized hartebeest and damalisque. These animal kills are necessary to provide meat for the safari and for the natives of the area in which we were hunting.

My outfit armed with rifles went after buffalo today. Later in the morning, the disillusioned hunters returned with an elephant's tail.

Going up the trail past the blind where I had spent the previous night they found that eleven elephants had been through this runway thirty yards from my blind at daylight this morning. Following after them to get photographs, they sighted the herd a couple of miles farther on.

Suddenly, one of the elephants got their scent and with mad trumpeting warned the others. Within a moment the herd swung into frenzied action and a mighty avalanche of beasts with wildly swinging trunks charged down the trail straight for them!

Even though the elephants were some distance away a collision, steeped in tragedy, seemed inevitable. The black boys did not stand on the order of their going, but disappeared like magic into the labyrinth of the jungle.

The others, together with the head tracker, scattered, and backed away, bringing their rifles into action to meet the oncoming host, headed by a great bull elephant. By sheer good fortune one of the shots hit the giant leader in a vital spot, dropping him in his tracks. Seeing their leader gone the herd, with instant comprehension, turned swiftly and vanished in the trees. In spite of it all the photographer was able to get the first onrush of the massive pachyderms.

Several villages were notified that an elephant had been killed and that tomorrow the butchering would take place. Sure enough, next morning fifty natives, forming a procession, gathered at the kill, many of them carrying spears across their shoulders on which hung gourds of water. When the hunters arrived at the scene the butchering began. It amazed us to see the enthusiasm with which they went about their task. Darkies swarmed over the carcass, both inside and out, in a feverish endeavor to get their share of the loot and many fingers, feet and legs were damaged from cuts and bruises.

At this point some of us decided that we preferred the hunting area at Golongosso, and we suggested to the white hunter that we go back there and finish out the remainder of the hunt.

Three members of our group decided they would like to hunt the greater kudu with firearms. The remainder of the party and I decided on the Golongosso district. Accordingly, next morning we headed for it and the others started on a hundred-mile trek to reach the kudu area.

We saw much game along the trail to Golongosso—giraffes, ostrich and all species of antelope. As for me, I was finally able to shoot a big baboon with my .44: I had been unable to get close enough to get a clear shot with the bow.

Across the road ahead we saw baboons and I took after them. A shot at the largest through the brush brought him to the ground. He proved to be a difficult animal to dispatch, taking several more shots for the job.

The day following our arrival I took one of the boys on another all-day hunt. At one of the pauses in our journey I was sitting with my back up against a tree between my two aides, Radar and Oscar. The head boy sent Radar, his junior, to bring him a drink of water from a muddy waterhole nearby. Oscar departed to do it and was about to scoop up some water in an empty sardine can, when he started jabbering excitedly in his native tongue. Radar hurriedly got up and ran over into the bush, meanwhile getting a heavy stick to use as a club. He motioned me to join them.

I had no idea what was afoot but gathered from the excitement that something was about to pop. I joined Radar as he began poking around in the grass and finally came to a six-foot tuft. He stood beside it and carefully motioned me to come over. Then he took his club and very cautiously parted the grass and made a little aperture into which we could see. Through this hole I observed what looked like an enormous snake. I thought it was a python, although I wondered how a python could hide in a small tuft of grass. Radar motioned me to shoot, so at a distance of about three or four feet I drew back the bow and shot an arrow into the hole, which hit the object.

Furious action started at once! The object was an iguana, or gigantic lizard. The arrow struck him in the rear of the body and buried itself in the soil beside the water hole, holding him firmly. The reptile thrashed around as Radar beat him on the head with a club. We found that we had captured an iguana five feet long.

The next morning we drove fifteen miles from camp to an area where there were several grassy plains, a mile or two across and ten to fifteen miles long. Just as we were coming out of the bush and into the first plain, which was fairly well covered with groups of antelope, we spied with considerable excitement a lion nonchalantly walking obliquely in front of us 300 yards distant. The sight of course electrified us. None of our party, however, was interested in using a rifle on any game but the white hunter, for some reason, coveted the lion's hide, so he and his head tracker, N'Gokotou, each reached for a gun and began a stalk that would bring them closer to the beast.

At 250 yards one of our party made his first shot, with a .375 magnum, which went high over the lion's back and kicked up the dirt around him. This he ignored except for a brief, scornful look in our direction, after which he slowly turned his head and continued his pacing.

The next shot hit the lion's rear quarter, spinning him around, following which he made for the bush in long bounds. One of us and the tracker went cautiously into the bush after him. In a few minutes we heard a shot and then in three or four minutes a second and third shot. Then the two hunters came out to the edge of the bush and waved us in.

When we arrived the dead lion lay before us. The bullet had entered his open mouth as he charged his adversary and one of the lower fangs was shot off. Still able to travel, he was tracked into the bush where he had lain down. When they came to within seventy-five or eighty yards of him he roared in defiance and charged them. A final killing shot was delivered at forty yards.

During our last days one of our groups reported that one of them had been charged by a leopard. The party of archers, white hunters and native boys were scattered about in the bush adjacent to a plain, looking for a wounded antelope. They heard an animal bleating and moved in believing it to be the wounded animal. About that time growls were heard. One of the archers looked up in terror to find that he was being charged by a leopard. Fortunately he was quicker than the sinewy cat; a split-second leap to the side saved him. The dodging hunter quickly loosed an arrow at him, but it only grazed his side as he disappeared in the distance. One of our last kills, an oribi, a splendid adult buck with horns about five inches long, was brought down by an arrow.

One afternoon I decided to go back to the salt lick. I climbed up to my little platform in the crotch of the tree and an hour later was rewarded by the visit of a reedbuck which came in—another trophy to add to my collection of game shot with an arrow.

The following day we traveled twenty miles over trail roads to a small native settlement where arrangements were made for our trek to a nearby Pygmy village. Arriving at this distant outpost of dwarfs, inhabited by natives of the Babinza tribe, we were greeted by the chief. Making ourselves at home after much handshaking, the natives staged a lively dance for us, with tom-tom accompaniment. The dance, differing from other native dances we had seen, still seemed to lack rhythm. Many of the women danced with babies on their backs, some of the children thus suspended sleeping while the mothers were in action.

For some time we had heard reports that the wife of the Chief of this village was renowned throughout Africa as a supreme dance artist. On the day of our visit a dance was well on its way when she appeared on the dancing enclosure, and the ground was immediately cleared and given over to her.

This ardent wriggler really had it—right out of Egypt, so to speak—with a rhythm and grace equal to the best and without the slightest trace of sex in her performance.

After the Pygmy dance, we arranged a contest between their bow-and-arrow hunters and myself. Quite a spirit of rivalry followed as well as a dispute over who was the winner, but we awarded prizes to everyone in the contest, bringing happiness to all.

In the afternoon we made our way back along the jungle trail. The jungle in its wet state has a very delightful odor; the few small streams crossing it flowed with clear water and many beautiful flowers gave color to the scene. The growth beside the trail was so thick that if an elephant appeared it could not be seen ten feet away. The route was resonant with jungle sounds and the calls of many gaily-colored birds.

In traveling through this section of the country we were annoyed on occasions by some of the chiefs who complained that the elephants were prowling around their banana plantations, wrecking their crops, and we were importuned to stop off and shoot a few. In most cases there were no elephants in their close vicinity! Their real hope was that we would call a halt, kill an elephant or two, and so provide them with plenty of meat.

After some discussion we decided to go back to Golongosso and build a blind at the large salt lick that we had previously discovered.

I spent the next morning at the salt lick. Sitting in a blind in Africa is, of course, infinitely interesting. There is always some kind of big game in sight. Besides other animals the baboons, of course, are often encountered; they are amusingly sharp. In my efforts to stillhunt them they always managed to keep one jump ahead of me. One of their number sits in a tree to watch the intruder and signals back what the visitor has in mind. In addition to guinea hens, quail are found in two sizes, African magpies which differ little from the eastern magpies, pelicans and many kinds of long-legged water birds. Dozens of hawks, eagles and buzzards sat in trees about our camp and flew down to snatch meat from the butchering area.

We also built a platform in a tree adjoining another salt lick. While the boys were finishing the platform, one of us went out and managed to shoot a kob to use for lion bait. It was a crippled animal that had been attacked a day or so before by a leopard. We planned to use this bait between the tree, in which my shooting platform was erected, and the salt lick.

But no lions appeared, in spite of the fact that the carcass of the kob had been dragged over the area for a distance of four or five miles. However, several hours after daybreak a few waterbucks started to come in but, unfortunately, the wind had changed and blew from the kob over the water hole. The result was that before the bucks got within range, they smelled the kob and immediately dashed back into the bushes, not to appear again. The same thing happened a few minutes later with several reedbucks.

The kob had begun to smell and was driving the animals away from the salt lick. A hawk which spotted the antelope flew down and perched on one of the antlers to look the situation over. I took careful aim and brought him down with an arrow. The trees here were full of buzzards but they were too cautious to venture in.

Gerin agreed to take the kob away, supposedly, because of its decayed state and rancid odor, to dump it in bushes remote from the camp. Imagine my amazement when the animal was loaded into the truck and given to the natives of the village. Apparently, the odor and high state of the meat did not detract from the gift because the natives were happy over it.

The next morning I returned to the salt lick. After a couple of restless hours, waiting for game that did not arrive, I started searching for a stalwart wart hog I had sighted the day before in this vicinity. I proceeded carefully upwind and found that the hog was still in residence but my scent reached him and he made off in great agitation. But I did spot an oribi, one of the smaller species of antelope, as he was making his way through the brush, nibbling here and there. Maneuvering myself into his line of direction I took careful aim and sent one of my large broadhead arrows through his hips. With a bound he was off and ran about 400 yards, then collapsed. He weighed thirty-five pounds and looked very attractive with his jet black horns five or six inches long.

During the stalk on the oribi I found the remains of a baboon which had been killed by either a lion or a leopard. I also found the skeleton of a giraffe, which had evidently been the prey of a big jungle cat.

It was raining hard next morning as I climbed into my new platform which had been built by the boys the evening before. A short while after it stopped raining, and for the first time since our arrival in Africa I was glad to see the sun come out. Presently a doe and fawn kob came in to get their salt.

I had brought my lunch with me and had planned to stay all day in this retreat. At noon I made several small stillhunting trips back into the bush and occasionally got a long or a running shot at various animals. Early in the afternoon, a hartebeest of 300 or 400 pounds walked by within twenty yards of me. I loosed an arrow at him, but he was so alert that he flinched ahead and low at the sound of the bow string and the arrow went over his back.

I have found that the guinea hens, of which there are many, and the baboons are the only inhabitants of Africa that are alert to life in the tree tops. Other animals keep their eyes on the trail and never seem to look above them. Accordingly, if the hunter rests quietly overhead he is not seen.

One of the most interesting birds in this country seen mostly at night, is the parachute bird, sometimes called a goatsucker. When in flight, it has what appear to be extra wings that give the appearance of three birds flying.

We were up early the next morning and I headed back for the same blind. In the middle of the morning a wart hog came along

close by me and for the first time in my life I led an animal too
much. The arrow passed right in front of its nose, and the beast
ran into it as the missile stuck in the ground. Another hartebeest
came by and, hearing the vibration of the bow-string at a distance
of thirty-five yards, flashed off like lightning. I was beginning to
change my mind about stalking game in the bush with a bow.

After this stillhunt I stole silently back to my platform in the
trees, surprising four kob does at the salt lick. More cautious
and jittery animals I have never encountered. They took three-
quarters of an hour to advance the last hundred yards to the lick,
getting at a distance of twenty yards the scent of the arrow
that I had shot earlier at a hartebeest. It pleased me to see does
coming to the waterholes because they were bait for the bucks.
The rutting season was on and I knew that bucks come to the
waterhole when does are present. In this case a kob buck did
arrive while the does were still there, giving me a twenty-five
yard shot at him but, alas, he jumped the string of my bow. There
was considerable snorting, then the buck and the does took their
leave. After the excitement was over I returned to the waterhole.
A score of water bucks in the near distance and five times that
number of kobs and reedbucks were within sight at one time. The
nearest part of the waterhole, however, was at least twenty-five
yards from the edge of the bush, out of distance of course for a
bow shot.

Many water bucks are very large and handsome, the heaviest
weighing close to 500 pounds. They are correctly named, for most
of their time is spent wading in the shallow water of the lakes
grazing on the lush vegetation.

That evening after dinner in camp three of us had a discussion
about bowhunting in Africa. One was of the opinion that platform
hunting at the salt licks was not the best method to adopt, that
inasmuch as we had the best tracker in all Africa—meaning
N'Gokoutou—I should follow him to within shooting range of
the game. When we reached the place which he selected he would
hand me the bow for me to do the shooting. I put little credence
in the idea, but being on the spot I could hardly do other than
accept the suggestion.

With this in mind the three of us went out the next morning.
Before long we spotted a small herd of kob 200 yards away.
They had seen us and were looking in our direction.

N'Gokoutou got off the track and motioned for me to follow.

He maneuvered us behind a tree, which was between us and the distant animals, and we were able to walk up to within thirty yards of them. The trunk of this tree was not large enough in girth, however, to cover our entire bodies, so the herd could see us making the approach. But, incredible as it sounds, they stood there while we walked to within twenty-five yards of them.

N'Gokoutou handed me the bow as we got close to the tree and it was only necessary for me to expose myself for an instant in making the shot. But this final moment of visibility in which I raised the bow and drew for the shot had the effect of a thunder-bolt, for the animals went off in tumultuous flight.

After several attempts with this strategy the others agreed with me that it wouldn't work.

On the way out that morning we beheld the forms of six lions slithering in line through the tall grass, returning across the plain apparently from the night's hunt and moving toward the river which was half a mile away. We spent an hour trying to shake them out, but never saw them again. We had sighted them at the exact spot where a white hunter was killed two years ago. He had wounded one of the beasts and had incautiously gone into the bush after it. The lion took refuge in a small thicket out of sight of the hunter. He proceeded to fire a shot into the thicket with his double elephant gun in the hope of hitting him or drawing him out. The lion immediately bounded out spurred on by this second shot which hit him but was not instantly fatal.

The hunter made a dash for a nearby tree and jumped on the lower branches, but he was not quick enough, for the lion leaped up and fastened his great teeth into the lower part of his body. The hunter died within two hours, the lion almost immediately after he had bitten the hunter.

The next morning we decided to go out in the open plains that lay off to the south of us. These are generally thickly populated with both damalisque and hartebeest. We saw a great number of both animals, some mixed in single herds and others with separate species in smaller herds.

We spotted one herd of damalisque and hartebeest that were on the edge of the plain into which the bush jutted out. This made an approach within bow range easy. It was an extremely hot day and the water fairly ran off me as the exertion of the undertaking and its excitement pressed hard on my energy. The herd of damalisque on which I was working was noticeably less alert because of the heat, for I was able to approach, partly on my knees, to within sixty yards of the fringe members of the herd. I was still too far away for a proper shot. Another damalisque buck that had not been in my vision, suddenly appeared from nowhere, came to a halt and faced directly away from me, while looking at the rest of the herd. Up went my bow and with a perfect aim my arrow went through the lower inside of the right hind quarter, ranging forward into the abdominal area.

The wounded animal, startled by the blow, dashed into the herd, stampeding it helter skelter out of danger. My prey came to a halt and lay down in the grass for his last few minutes of life.

He was a beautiful animal, weighing close to 500 pounds and, according to an expert, his horns were within two inches of the record. I was overjoyed at the success which made our motion picture perfect and gave me further confidence in the ability of an archer to stalk and kill game in Africa. Much time was then consumed in completing the sequence of pictures of the damalisque.

The next day was the final one of the hunt. I decided to go to the big upper blind with my long-range movie camera to get pictures of waterbucks and various animals which visit the water hole adjacent to the platform. I got there early in the morning to catch the activities of the morning hours.

About 8:30, I discovered a tribe of baboons crossing upwind from me, leisurely returning to the water hole. When they see an unfamiliar object they halt and indulge in vociferous barking which, incidentally, frightens other game and spoils the shooting.

Silently waiting for a half hour for events to develop, suddenly, down through the clearing came a big baboon. Loping along with his head turned sideways, he looked straight in my direction. Obviously, the entire troop had spotted me and had sent a big fellow to investigate and determine whether I was a friend or foe.

Sixty yards in front of me the baboon, like a streak of lightning, crawled clear up to the top of a tree and sat up there watching me.

I studied him through the glasses and could see his little black beady eyes glued to my movements, the other baboons flitting about in the trees and on the ground immediately in back of him. I had read in articles on African hunting that baboons can be really tough when they are together in a group. If one is wounded, the entire tribe may attack; when that happens, and you should be the victim, you would be fortunate to come out of the attack alive. It is said that they are strong enough to tear a leopard apart. With this in mind, I thought it would be best not to start a fracas.

The baboon investigator, still looking me over, sat up in the tree for fully five minutes, then reaching a decision, he made a quick descent and came loping across the open space straight toward me. At this point I began to wonder if he was a decoy for a rear attack. Taking a quick look behind me into the bush I could see nothing suspicious. The scout meantime advanced to within thirty-five or forty yards of me, pretending to examine something on the ground but he kept furtively squinting at me out of the corner of his eye.

After another few minutes he scampered back toward the tree from which he had come. A little beyond it he climbed up another tree taller than the first, which was about seventy-five yards from my nest. Again he scampered up to the top like all possessed, wrapped his tail around a branch for support and sat there looking over at me again, and began to bark briskly. This excessive barking aggravated me because it spoiled my antelope hunt. Without giving the puzzling situation further thought I drew an arrow and took a careful shot at the miscreant.

He watched that arrow from the time it left my bow. The arrow was at the right elevation, but two or three feet off to the right. He watched it coming all the way as it cut the leaves beside him and then turned his head to follow it, stretching his neck to look around a bush until it hit the ground far beyond.

Then, without a moment's hesitation, he slid in haste down the tree, ran on all fours over to the arrow, smelled it and immediately knew that I was of the human race. Then the whole gang, chattering excitedly, made off through the bush in the opposite direction.

The way being clear I crawled down the tree and, with my big telephoto motion-picture camera, made my way back through the bush to the water hole, where I spent a few hours running at least 500 feet of film on all breeds of animals and birds. A great many waterbucks, oribi, reedbucks, kob, wart hogs and several other species of game paid me calls from time to time.

Then I heard in the distance another storm brewing and as I was a quarter of a mile from my platform blind, where I had tarpaulin to cover my camera equipment, I lit out for the blind just in time to get everything covered when the shower hit me.

Gerin picked me up at my blind fifteen minutes after the shower started. We had a very wet ride, and as we were driving through a low area a few miles from camp the truck went off the solid track and bogged down in the swamp, all four wheels sinking up to the hub. Gerin put the half dozen natives we had with us at work getting the truck out of the mire. I took one good look at it and I came to the conclusion that only a larger force could do the trick. So, with Gerin and N'Gokoutou, I walked into camp.

Upon our arrival we went to the village and enlisted twenty of the huskiest black boys there. They hit the trail immediately and an hour or two later the truck came in victoriously with a great cargo of blacks aboard.

The next morning we left early for our return trip to Fort Archambault. The recent rains had brought this sun-parched, hard-baked land into bloom and it was blossoming like a rose. There was green grass everywhere and flowers that any tropics would be proud of.

Before I left I found a native who possessed a headdress made from the body and head of one of the large black birds so common to Africa. The natives in the game countries use it for hunting. The hunter straps this camouflage over his head and silently navigates, on his hands and knees, through the grass and brush toward his prey. The animal, hearing the faint rustle and seeing the motion, looks at the bobbing of what seems to be a bird. After a quick glance he decides that it is just another one of those pesky birds, and lets it go at that.

In spite of all the arts of men African game is hard to kill. The animals have the deeply inherited instinct to live, which is enlivened all the more by human hunters, that makes them less vulnerable to both the bow and gun.

CHAPTER ELEVEN

THE PERILOUS NILE

"THERE are three men alive today who are convinced that the most fabulous topographical feature on the face of the earth is the Nile river. I am one of them," said John M. Goddard, who headed the world's first successful exploration of the mighty Nile River. The expedition traveled the entire length of the world's longest river, enduring unimaginable hardships and the constant threat of death from charging hippos, man-eating crocodiles and treacherous cataracts. "The others who steadfastly share this conviction are two Parisians—Jean Laporte and Andre Davy. Only after nine months of the most arduous travel did we come to this irrevocable conclusion, for it took us that length of time to explore from Alpha to Omega this most fascinating of all earth features; a watery highway of adventure which stretches sinuously across 4,200 miles of Africa, its basin containing an abridged edition of the world from the standpoint of the rich diversity of climates, altitudes, bodies of water, animal life, and races of man."

No other subject in the field of geographical exploration has so intrigued or so fired the imaginations of men for a period of so many thousands of years as has the river Nile. For over 6,000 years it has functioned as the most supremely important and influential water-course, and intermittently during all these millenia men have set out to trace its interminable channel through Africa and discover its sources. Yet, remarkably enough, not one expedition had succeeded in traveling its entire length from one end to the other at the time we embarked on our attempt. It wasn't until 1862 that Lake Victoria, the head reservoir, was discovered by the British explorer Speke who became the first white man to behold its vast expanse.

From the beginning Government officials and authorities on the river pronounced our undertaking a foolhardy attempt to do the impossible. They were at all times courteous and helpful but invariably pessimistic about the outcome. They seemed to feel duty bound to warn us that our project was not only completely impractical and dangerous beyond words but downright suicidal. They would recount the fearsome obstacles which turned back or brought disaster to the explorers of the past and which would face us during our expedition unchanged—the same impenetrable jungles, trackless fever-ridden swamps, the raging cataracts, the deadly diseases, suffocating sandstorms, hostile natives, and the ever-present heat, hunger, and hardships. Considering all these formidable stumbling blocks their attitude was easily understandable. However, we had taken all these negative factors into consideration during our months of research before

setting forth, and still we felt that the Nile could be conquered
with the proper equipment and the right breaks. The thrill of
experiencing such an adventure seemed well worth the risks to us.

We commenced the French-American Nile expedition at the
most distant headwaters of the great river which we located,
after considerable difficulty, on a mountain top 6,500 feet high
in Urundi, a pint-sized country bordering the Belgian Congo and
administrated by the Belgians under a mandate issued by the
League of Nations. Lake Victoria is generally thought to be the
source of the Nile, but from a technical view the head-springs of
the main feeder to the lake are the site of the actual birth of the
Nile. So it was here, at the beginning of the Kagera River,
supplier of water to Lake Victoria, that we dedicated ourselves
to the never-before-accomplished feat of traveling the full length
of the longest river in the world.

Half expecting that we would be among the first white men to
visit this inaccessible spot, we were amazed upon our arrival at
the summit of the wind-swept mountain, at the sight of a cement
pyramid ten feet high jutting against the sky. Later we learned
from the District Commissioner of the region that the triangular
monument had been erected in 1938 by a German explorer Dr.
Burkhart Waldecker to commemorate his discovery of the Nile's
exact fountainhead, after years of exploration and research.

So here we stood The Three Nileteers as I referred to us,
beholding the birth of the Nile river in the form of ten tiny
springs which ran down the steep slopes at our feet in dark, lush
stripes of vegetation. In just a few miles these freshets would
become a husky stream which in turn would swell and deepen
as the vigorous Kagera, named The Mother of the Nile by the
natives. It was our plan to push off down this river and follow
its course right to Lake Victoria, paddling in our kayaks, the
little Eskimo-type boats which we had chosen as the most ideal
craft to carry us on our river odyssey. Upon reaching Victoria
we would cross to the northern-most extremity and continue
down the Nile proper all the way to the Mediterranean.

With the assistance of the District Commissioner we traveled
downstream to our point of embarkation at the village of
Kakitumba where we spent the night with the jolly, beer-drinking
Belgian Customs Officer, the only white man for miles around.
Just before dawn we were startled into wakefulness by a clamor
of shouts and cries coming from a cluster of native huts a stone's

throw from our sleeping quarters. After scrambling into our clothes, we ran to see what the commotion was all about and found our host standing in the midst of a group of excited natives, clad in shorts and trying his best to calm them. When he saw us approaching he explained that a leopard had entered a hut, snatched up a sleeping baby and carried it off into the jungle surrounding the village. The frantic Africans were trying to get the Belgian to pick up his rifle and go with them after the savage kidnapper. As soon as it grew light enough to track, the official set out with several natives to hunt the culprit. It proved to be a fruitless search, for even though they were gone most of the day they never did find any sign of their quarry and finally returned, shrugging off the incident as just another jungle tragedy.

While the revengers were out hunting the leopard, Andre, Jean and I tramped along the banks of the Kagera a mile distant from our Belgian friend's headquarters. After selecting a suitable camp-site we transported all our equipment to the spot, set up our tent and prepared to spend the night before pushing off down river.

We lay awake for hours, after retiring to our sleeping bags, finding it difficult to drop off to sleep because of the symphony of night sounds resounding all around us—produced by an enormous variety of articulate nocturnal animal and insect life. I was reminded of the famous song "The Night Has a Thousand Eyes"; in Africa not only a thousand eyes but a thousand voices I thought. From the river surging a few yards away a hippo bellowed in deep thundering snorts against a background of barking and scolding from the troop of baboons bedding down in a huge banyan tree at the river's edge. The wealth of insect life kept up a steady whirring and chirping, occasionally being obscured by the weird whooping of a grotesque hornbill or the maniacal wail of a prowling hyena which sounded like a lunatic child in hell.

The next day dawned hot and clear. We awakened to the profane chatter of a bevy of monkeys, feeling a sense of excitement and urgency for this was the day that we were to test our kayaks on an African river for the first time. It is perhaps a queer paradox that we should choose, as our mode of transportation down a tropical river, through jungle, swamp and desert, a craft designed and developed by the Eskimos of the frigid arctic regions. As it turned out, however, the kayaks were the most practical and effective boats we could possibly have used. They were small and light, only 15 feet long and 60 pounds in weight, consisting of a canvas and rubber envelope over a wooden framework of oak. Each one was capable of accommodating 200 pounds of equipment besides the paddler.

With mounting enthusiasm we threw ourselves into the job of assembling the three mummy-like packages of our collapsed boats, spreading out the thin sheaths then fitting the wooden skeletons inside them. Having finished with the kayaks, we carried them through the swampy border of papyrus to the river's edge and carefully loaded the waterproof rubber bags. There were twelve bags in all, four for each boat, containing just the barest essentials for our long voyage. The heaviest sack of all contained our precious store of photographic film—12,000 feet of Kodachrome for our Ciné Special and Pathe movie cameras and 100 rolls of colored and black and white film for our three still cameras. In the other sacks were a three man nylon tent with three light sleeping bags, a cooking outfit with a small store of food staples, a compact and well-stocked medical kit, and our own personal outfits which included clothes, trade goods for the natives, knives, ammunition for our three guns, maps, books, repair kits, etc.

With everything carefully packed away and securely lashed inside our kayaks, Andre and Jean set their boats into the water, jumped in and pushed off into the current while I stood on the bank and filmed their departure. The Kagera is one of the swiftest rivers in Africa and by the time I had taken the pictures, climbed into my kayak and packed the camera away, my companions had been swept far downstream out of sight. I had no sooner gotten underway, hurrying to catch up, than I was startled half out of my wits by the sudden violent appearance of a huge bull hippo. The monster bobbed to the surface with a great splash, blowing and snorting like a fairy-tale dragon, forcing me to swerve close to the papyrus to dodge him. Deep down I had always believed a hippo to be a good-natured though lazy critter with no malice towards humans. I had heard vivid accounts of enraged hippos attacking boats and even killing people, but I always took them with a grain of salt crediting them to an overworked imagination. My private opinion that hippos were not dangerous to man was completely and everlastingly refuted when the hulking behemoth came plunging after me in a vicious charge that left no doubt as to his intentions. With my arms working like a windmill in a high wind, I churned the water to froth and managed to pull away from the enraged beast, leaving him to gloat over driving the strange creature from his domain.

I was just heaving a sigh of relief over my narrow escape when I looked downstream and saw, to my horror, a whole family of hippos dotting the rich silt brown water. They were strung out across the narrow river in a formidable blockade. At the speed I was being swept along by the rushing water there was no way to stop in time to avoid passing through. My only alternative was to head for the widest gap separating them and pray for the best. I streaked through the picket line in a cloud of spray and left them far behind before any of them were aware of what had happened. But the worst was ahead.

For the next ten or twelve miles I was kept sweating in a constant state of hypertension from the threat of disaster from these unpredictable animals. They swarmed everywhere on the narrow river and in the bordering papyri-swamps. My arms soon became stiff and sore from my frantic efforts to evade and outstrip the several rogues who took it into their heads that it was their duty to run me off their premises posthaste. One old bull saw me coming and seemed to take an immediate dislike to my kayak. He submerged with an indignant roar only to lurch to the surface just a few feet away from me, deluging me with water as I passed by. Not content with scaring the daylights out of me, he came lunging along in my wake seemingly intent on clobbering me on the spot. I could see he meant business and again whipped my little boat through the water at top speed. Watching a hippo from a bank or even from a launch is one thing but paddling in the midst of them in a fragile bite-size cockleshell and having them play ring around the rosie with you as rosie is quite another and proved to be one of the most unnerving experiences of my life. At times it seemed as if I was right in the water with them positioned as I was, with the seat of my kayak actually below the waterline and the top of the cockpit a scant eighteen inches above. I managed to elude the cantankerous brute after a nip and tuck chase in which I saw an animal weighing at least two and one half tons go charging through the water at a speed I never would have dreamed possible.

I finally caught up with the boys just as we reached a stretch of rapids. I found them, too, in a state of nervous exhaustion from encounters with hippos, and Andre informed me that he counted 112 along the way in the water alone. The stretch of rapids which we negotiated was short but tricky and gave our kayaking ability a real test. This white water was a new experience to Andre and me, for even though we had gone on a shakedown trip on the Marne and Seine rivers in France, we had never before attempted rough water. Jean was a skilled paddler with many years of kayaking experience on all the big rivers of France, so we did our best to follow in his wake and imitate his technique. Even so it was all we could do to avoid the masses of rock looming in our path with our boats sluggish and difficult to maneuver with their heavy cargo. We managed to debouch free safely with only a few minor tears on our rubber hulls from the submerged rocks we couldn't avoid.

Passing through the rapids safely, I took my place in the lead as it had been agreed that I was the logical one to act as leader of the expedition because of my experience in the jungles of Central and South America; also because I was the cinematographer and hunter, it was my duty to photograph every scene or subject of interest and provide food for us with my rifle. By scouting ahead I was in a better position to film and to bag game. The boiling current was whisking us along at an uncomfortably fast speed and I realized that we were in a very dangerous predicament with no way of stopping without capsizing our skittish boats. It was like being on a ski-slide; a start is made and from then on there is no turning back, the course must be followed to the end. I was just considering the most practical thing for us to do if we were forced to call a halt when I became aware that the river just seemed to disappear behind a low green screen of foliage a hundred yards or so downstream.

As we glided closer I could see that this phenomenon was caused by two small islands parallel to each other in the middle of the river, both so rank with luxuriant tropical vegetation that their vines and branches intertwined forming an almost impenetrable net of growth. I found myself almost on the islands before I had a chance to properly survey the situation. There were only two courses of action open to me; either attempt to plough through the ivy-choked channel separating the islands or dodge to the right and take a chance on getting through the span of water between the right bank and the first island. I made a split second decision and headed for the channel just ahead of me, leaving the right passage open for the boys following close behind as insurance against a pile-up.

I waited until the last possible second then laid back as far as I could to avoid the vines and limbs that clogged the gap separating the islands.

The most hellish and unforgettably horrible minutes of my life followed immediately after entering the leafy tunnel. I had just flattened myself in the kayak when I struck the interlaced web of vegetation. Submerged roots snagged the prow of my boat, causing it to heel over sharply. Instantly the torrent rushed over the tilted craft, filling and then engulfing it. I found myself being dragged along upside down under the kayak with my legs ensnared in the lashings which secured the bags. I was in no condition for any strenuous activity as I had been suffering for several days from an attack of dysentery, which had left me weak and devoid of energy. To make matters worse the rifle, which I had stuck down between the bags of equipment in the prow of the boat, came hurtling out and struck me full in the face, momentarily stunning me. My senses had no sooner cleared than I gave one mighty heave, desperately summoning all my strength, and wrenched free of my death trap.

As I kicked away from my capsized kayak I was nearly strangled by the raging water sucking at my broad felt hat, secured around my neck by a leather strap. I tore it from me with a fleeting moment of regret and a picture ironically flashing across my mind of me in bareheaded misery under a blazing African sun. My heavy tennis shoes were like lead weights dragging me down, I clawed at them frantically to tear them from my feet, but without success. I was drowning and I knew it. Completely powerless in the grip of the madly swirling water which buffeted and bowled me along with such overpowering turbulence that I couldn't even determine where the surface was. So this is the way I go was my thought as I felt my life ebbing away.

Every detail and emotion of the experience stands out as vividly in my memory now as when it happened, especially my fervent petition when all seemed lost: "Dear God please help me."

Just as my lungs seemed about to explode and but a second or two before I reached the point where I *had* to inhale, I broke the surface of the water. Only for a brief, glorious moment, but enough to gulp in great draughts of delicious, resuscitating oxygen before being sucked under again. This brief breather enkindled my will to live. This and the realization that I was dying so needlessly, before our expedition had even had a good start, aroused my fighting spirit and enabled me to exert every last ounce of strength I possessed in a desperate struggle to survive.

I fought to the surface and managed to keep from going under again. As I was being swept along downstream half expecting to be gobbled up at any moment by crocodiles, I caught a glimpse of the river behind me and realized that I had been whirled through a dangerous stretch of rock-studded rapids. The water calmed down somewhat in the next few hundred yards though still fast and forcible. I managed to work my way close to the right bank where I made several attempts to grab and hold on to stalks of papyrus before I succeeded in getting a good hold on one and pulled myself painfully out of the racing water. I lay panting and nauseated, half dead with fatigue on a floating mass of rotting vegetation, when I heard a voice behind me asking if I was all right. It was Jean. I told him I was all right and asked, Where is Andre? He responded by gravely holding up a sodden hat and one water-soaked bag which he had retrieved from the river as the only evidence of our other companion.

For a moment or two I couldn't quite grasp the fact that Jean was the only one who had safely passed through the islands and over the rapids and that Andre had disappeared and was possibly dead. Then as my grogginess wore off the full enormity of the disaster really hit me. The French-American Nile Expedition had been finished before it had barely gotten underway—and after only one month in Africa! I could hear the officials saying, "We told you so!" Especially the District Commissioner who had driven to Kakitumba just before we left, for the express purpose of warning us that the country through which we would pass in paddling down the Kagera was not only uninhabited by any native tribes but virtually unexplored. He had strongly urged us to give up the venture saying that he had been in office for twelve years but had to confess ignorance of this region and he could not be responsible for any one attempting to pass through it, particularly in flimsy boats on the treacherous Kagera. When he saw that we were uninfluenced by his arguments and still firm in our resolution to carry out our plans he graciously wished us luck and requested that we send him a complete report on what we saw and experienced along the way. Now the only report we could send him would only confirm his warning and predictions.

As soon as I had energy enough I floundered my way through a jungle of papyrus and reeds to the steep bank which I climbed to search for our lost comrade. Jean crossed the river to do the same on the opposite bank. My shoes were heavy with absorbed water and encumbered me so that I removed them along with my soaked shirt and continued on barefooted, clad only in my khaki shorts. I stumbled and fell several times as I followed a faint game trail along the bank upstream towards the roar of the rapids. My whole body was so numb I scarcely had control over it. I felt just like a post-operative patient coming out of the ether. My ears were clogged with water and throbbed and rang so I could barely hear. I had to stop several times to retch up the stomachful of silty water I had swallowed while underwater, aggravating the stricture in my throat which was making me gasp for air. I even had trouble focusing my eyes.

Staggering along in my wretched condition, I made my way back to the scene of our disaster without seeing any sign of Andre. I experienced a brief sense of elation when I spied my kayak at the foot of the cascade, floating bottom-up against a reedy islet. Over the sound of the water I could hear Jean shouting for Andre and soon after I found my voice and was able to join in.

We called out and searched for over an hour to no avail; Andre just seemed to have vanished. Never before have I known such abject anguish with every evidence that Andre was drowned; no response to our shouts, just the sound of the clamorous rapids to be heard; nothing to meet our anxious gaze but the rushing, boiling torrent sweeping along below us, framed by the towering papyrus.

Finally we postponed the search temporarily to salvage my kayak. As the boat had lodged near the left bank I was forced to enter the river again to cross to the other side. A feat that filled me with naked terror at the mere thought.

I didn't think for a while that I would have either the nerve or the stamina to cover even this short distance, but I steeled myself and slipped cautiously into the river and worked my way to the other shore utilizing the vigorous current, again feeling intense concern over the crocodiles that abounded everywhere. Jean and I hurried to the islet, righted my boat and drained the water out. My spirits sank even lower when I saw that our priceless movie camera—a Ciné Special, and its five lens were sopping wet along with 500 feet of exposed film containing scenes never before photographed. I realized the closest place where I could have the camera and lenses opened and properly cleaned and dried was Nairobi in Kenya nearly 1,000 miles away.

Having finished draining the boat I forced myself to climb in and push off downstream to the hippo wallow where Jean had beached his kayak. With pounding heart I guided the delicately balanced little shell to the landing, using my original aluminium paddle which Jean had snatched out of the water before it could float away. I had a bad scare or two in attempting to stop in time, but finally succeeded with the help of the papyrus which I grabbed from time to time to slow me down.

While I waited for Jean to join me I did my best to clean up the camera and other doused equipment, wiping them off with the big red bandana which I had tied around my head as a sun-shade and setting them in the sun to dry. As I sat on the bank slapping at tsetse flies and sorrowfully trying to think how I could face Andre's family or ever explain to them what had happened, I heard Jean crashing through the thick brush obviously excited. With a whoop of joy he bounded over to me and dispelled my gloom with the wonderful news that he had found Andre! He didn't stop to explain how or where but just pushed me into his kayak, untied it and began ferrying us across the river. The next thing I knew Jean had led me with rapid strides over the same game trail I had followed previously to hunt for Andre. After reaching the rapids we plowed our way through the morass to the water where we could look out over the thundering cascades and see our companion waving to us from a mass of granite where he had crashed in his kayak and was completely marooned. I felt a profound relief and feeling of thanksgiving to find Andre alive and unharmed. I had been blaming myself for the whole catastrophe because it had been my idea to start the expedition from the headwaters of the Kagera and paddle down it to Lake Victoria.

We had not been able to see Andre during our search because he had smacked into the rocks right at a blind spot where the right bank formed a horseshoe curve around the rapids. He was unable to hear our shouts over the tumult of the water and, he told us later, when we didn't show up he feared *we* had perished.

Had he attempted to reach either bank by himself he would have been mangled on the rocks, as he had piled up in the midst of the ugliest part of the rock-studded cascade and could never have swum to safety on his own.

Yelling our directions, we had Andre tie a rock to his kayak mooring line and throw it to us. We held our breath as he got in his badly damaged boat and gingerly pushed away from the rocks. Jean and I commenced pulling him towards us as fast as we could, using all our strength in a tug of war with the madly racing torrent which washed over and tore at the frail craft. Just as we had Andre almost to shore, his kayak, its back broken by the collision with the rocks, folded at the center allowing the rushing water to enter and engulf it. Andre was spilled out but made a lucky grab for the rope just in time to keep from being carried away. I held fast to the line with my arms almost being pulled out of their sockets by the swamped boat, while Jean plunged through the dense papyrus to help Andre out of the water.

Just as it seemed as though I couldn't hold on a moment longer, Andre heaved himself out of the water and began assisting Jean with the kayak, which released me from my intolerable burden. After flopping down for a few minutes' rest the three of us beat a trail through the papyrus which formed a miniature, dark-green forest towering to a height of fifteen feet over our heads, then proceeded to wrestle the baggage and the battered boat through to dry land. This strenuous exertion completely exhausted us; but the real misery came from the kamikaze attacks of the Bug Air Corps, which tormented us to the point of hysteria as we wallowed and staggered in muck up to our knees. It seemed every creeping, crawling, flying vampire for miles around had come to us for a feed; stilettoing us from head to toe until we were a mass of stinging, itching welts.

After a rugged battle with the stifling swamp and the voracious insects, we finally staggered into a grassy glade surrounded by formidable thorn bushes where we found a suitable spot to cache Andre's wrecked kayak. We then gathered up the bags which it had contained and trudged wearily downstream to make a camp near our boat landing. By the time we had made a fire and set up our tent it was nearing evening. A spectacular African sunset brought a fiery conclusion to the longest and most unforgettable day of our lives. As the light faded into night we laid out all the damp equipment on the coarse grass, built up the fire with heavy branches, then collapsed into our sleeping bags, groggy with fatigue. We were covered with chigger, tsetse fly and mosquito bites, and smarting from the scratches and cuts by the thorns and saw grass, but tremendously grateful just to be alive; alive and in one piece!

We slept like dead men until late the next morning, then arose to finish our drying and salvage operations. After taking careful stock of our equipment, we found to our dismay that the two items of all our possessions which we considered almost indispensable had been lost the day before to the river—our heavy rifles. The only remaining weapon which we would have to rely on to bag fowl and fresh meat and the only thing left to us for protection during our journey through the heart of the big game country of Africa was one puny .22 caliber rifle with a bent sight!

For six days we recuperated, repaired our gear, and explored first in Tanganyika then in Uganda, crossing back and forth on the Kagera which forms the boundary between the two East African countries. Game abounded in our great wilderness surroundings. We were constantly scaring up herds of zebra, wildebeest, antelope, and impala. But I didn't even attempt to hunt any of this tempting game with our peashooter .22.

There was a day when we came to feel that our disastrous accident on the river was a lucky break and happened at just the right spot; although we never would have believed that such a conviction could ever enter our heads at the time of the mishap. This came about one afternoon when Andre and I hiked through the bush along the river several miles downstream, and came upon a real booby trap of nature in the form of a stretch of impassable rapids, with huge jagged rocks everywhere and the river churning through in a veritable avalanche of water. But so perfectly screened and camouflaged by overhanging foliage and trees that a man approaching in a kayak would never have seen it until too late. If we hadn't been stopped before reaching this deathtrap, it isn't likely that any of us would have gotten through alive.

It being the short rainy season of the year, every day around 3:00 p.m. we would have a torrential downpour of rain. No pennies from Heaven but mammoth silver-dollar drops would pour down accompanied by booming thunderclaps which fluttered over the angry sky in resounding rips and crashes which caused the ground to quake under us. The noise of the thunder reminded me of a ship being ground to pieces on the rocks during a gale. We found we could actually watch the progress of the storm as it swept over the undulating veldt towards us from the direction of Lake Victoria. A violent wind always preceded it by several minutes; sort of a meteorological John the Baptist, sometimes reaching such an intensity that we had to hold the tent down to keep it from being blown away.

It was while we were sitting out one of these short-lived but severe tempests that we heard voices hailing us from across the river, and scrambled out of our tent to find five natives huddled under a tree and waving at us with wide grins. They had been sent out to search for us by our District Commissioner friend when we failed to arrive at a village downstream about 100 miles, which, at the rate the swift current would have carried us, we should have reached easily two days before.

After I had crossed the rain-swollen Kagera to reassure them that we were safe and well, I gave them a message to the District Commissioner to the same effect and as tangible evidence of their successful quest. They slogged off through the bush just as the downpour ceased.

We spent the remainder of this the sixth day in transporting our outfit from Tanganyika to Uganda where we spent our last night beside the Kagera. The next dawn found us struggling to portage all our baggage and our three kayaks on two little boat cars back to Kakitumba, a feat that was a failure from the start. We had lost the third carriage in the river and with the other two bearing the added weight it wasn't long before they broke down. We abandoned the idea of getting our gear back by ourselves but instead hid everything under some brush then trekked back to Kakitumba to be greeted by our very worried Belgian friend, who was sure we had perished in the river when we didn't appear at the village downstream.

After a refreshing night's sleep in a real bed at the official's home we were ready to hike back to the spot where we had left our outfit, leading a party of five Africans who shared the task of transporting it back; hot, fatiguing drudgery enlivened only by the vicious attack of a big wild boar on Jean as he made his separate way over a scraggly hill apart from our line of march. With nothing to protect himself he was forced to the undignified expediency of shinnying up the closest tree until the irascible bully left him for other parts.

As soon as we were ready to resume our journey, we by-passed the unnavigable rapids just north of Lake Victoria and traveled fifty miles by train to Mamasagali. While there we ordered a new framework from Paris to replace Andre's crushed kayak, which was to be delivered to us at Juba, a month's travel beyond.

Also, while at Mamasagali, we recruited two local Jaluo native boys to accompany us in their large dugout on our further venture toward the mouth of the Nile.

We passed through the shallow, vine-cluttered waters of Lake Kyoga, after being snagged and bound securely at a standstill for many hours at a time. Then, on to Masindi Port, completely exhausted from struggling against the terrific wind and under-water foliage which constantly entangled our paddles.

From Lake Victoria we ploughed through the isolated regions to Lake Albert. We encountered numerous species of wild animals en route, even had a few narrow skirmishes with some of them.

Passing through the beautiful grove-like sections along the Albert Nile and on across the Sudanese frontier, where we were greeted by picturesque turbaned Moslems, we found ourselves bargaining in the marketplaces with all sorts of tribesmen similar to the variety with whom one might have to deal in the public trading plazas of Timbuctoo.

Local authorities forbade us to travel the Albert Nile by kayak through the dangerous sudd area, a swampy wilderness of floating vegetation extending thousands of miles in all directions between Bor and Lake No, in the region known as the Upper Nile. So, we took a paddle-wheel steamer as far as Tonga, which is only a comparatively few miles from Lake No, at which point the river becomes the White Nile.

Stopping at Malakal, the capital of the Upper Nile Province, we replenished our food supplies. It took us a month of torturous paddling to make the 500-mile distance down the Nile from here to Khartoum, soon taking us out of the Black Sudan and into the Moslem Sudan, the land of sand dunes and camels, to El Jebelein in the midst of Arab country.

At Khartoum, we had covered over half the distance down the Nile, 2,275 miles, after four and a half months. From here on the river really became beautiful in places. We traveled through endless miles of sun-scorched desert, stopping long enough to visit the historic Pyramids and other sights along the way through the Sudan and Egypt, dining with Bedouin tribesmen and sweltering through the insufferable heat.

Finally, after having made our way, at the risk of our lives, through the five great Cataracts, numbered as they are from the Sixth Cataract down to the Second as we got farther away from the source of the Nile, we portaged the First Cataract, and continued on, suffering hunger, fevers, death-defying heat, and beating off wild beasts and savage Arab bandits, as we paddled our kayaks down the 4,200 miles of the world's longest river to its mouth, where it left us and made its way into the waters of the Mediterranean.

CHAPTER TWELVE

INTOXICATED APES

"SLOWLY, a brassy taste filled my mouth. I looked around. The bull was standing, quiet as doom right above me, his trunk uplifted for the hammer blow that would flatten me," said Brian O'Brien, who after World War I signed up as an ivory trader with a firm in French Equatorial Africa, but found himself selling sardines, fish hooks and calico across a counter instead of running a canoe up a dark river. Then he joined a French charter society to open trade routes along the Cameroun-Baboun-Spanish Guinea borders and liked it—with plenty of time to shoot elephants, gorillas, leopards and buffaloes and was almost arrested for ivory poaching.

"For two days," he continued, "I had trailed this tusker by the blood-spray high up on the forest undergrowth from the wounds which, I was quite certain, had been inflicted by Pygmy poison arrows. It would not be long; puddles of coagulated blood showed he had stopped frequently to rest this morning. But he kept moving on.

I descended a slope, scouted a clump of bamboo. Beyond was a mangrove swamp choked with rushes and big-leaved plants and dominated by the bone-white, naked branches of a strangled tree.

And there my ivory bull awaited me.

He stood knee deep in muck. His trunk hung limply and his near shoulder glistened with blood. But when he saw me his ears fanned, his trunk went up and he screamed a final, brassy blast of defiance. Then, with shocking suddenness he charged.

I dropped him with a frontal shot and he crashed into the splintered bamboos ten feet away, his fine ivories driven deep into the ground.

Sala, my Bakoko shootman, came running to pat the tusks and shout his happiness at so much meat. Then:

Eke! he muttered, staring at the swamp.

Half covered with greenery were the skeletons of several elephants. I stared at the massive, stained bones and my heart began to slam. Had I found the fabulous graveyard of elephants?

Every first-timer, as soon as he lands in Africa, hears of the mysterious places to which the great beasts go when their instincts warn them of impending death. I had bought ancient tusks that had obviously lain long underground. I had examined massive ivories gnawed by hyenas and ivory rats. The Bulus, Fang and Yaoundes never told where they found those old teeth that had obviously come from beasts that had died naturally; for, had the creatures been killed the ivories would not have been left to be spoiled by scavengers. Furthermore, no one of my knowledge had ever seen an elephant dead except by gun, spear or trap.

Some old timers said there were elephant graveyards; some claimed to have seen mighty stores of ivory dug from them. I, myself, had come upon fences of enormous tusks placed about the huts of forest chiefs. These tusks they would never sell, nor would they tell from whence they had come.

But scientists said the tale of the elephant dying place was a myth. Of course no one ever saw a dead elephant. Carnivores ate the meat and ants cleaned the bones. Then the forest covered all traces.

What about the elephant roads? said the old-timers.

It was when I first saw the east-west elephant road in South Cameroun, French Equatorial Africa, that I made up my mind to see what was at the end of it.

The road paralleled the N'tem River. The bush people said that the beasts marched west in the dry season to escape the heat and feed and rest in the moist gloom of the coastal rain forest.

Then, at the coming of the first floods, returned to the high ground far to the east.

I was a trader, running a small factory where I bartered trade goods for jungle produce; boule rubber, ebony, palm nuts and a fair amount of ivory. Every month I sent the produce by head-load to Ebolowa, five days trek away. And I was expected to tour the country to open trade for my employers, a French exploitation company.

So, if I decided to tour the elephant road instead of the Fang and Bulu villages there was no one to forbid me. And I started out one fine morning, leaving Andrew, my Gold Coast captain, in charge of the factory, to find the ivory treasure of the world!

I had a .450 Westley-Richards, drop block express rifle I had bought second hand in Douala. It fired a 320 grain solid bullet and would stop anything I knew. My hunter, Sala, toted my 44-40 Winchester; best weapon in the world for the close quarter, quick shooting required in the dense forest country of West Africa—soft skin game, that is. Francois, my Yaounde boy, bore my camp kit, Ojo the cook head-loaded his pots and pans and three Bulus brought up the rear with food, drink and dishes for any chiefs I might meet.

Now don't get the idea that this was a properly organized safari, as they have in Kenya. In our country we seldom knew where game was until it jumped us. I was just a kid with a fine, big gun, out on my own. A big game hunter, so help me!

It was easy to follow the road. The undergrowth was trodden down enough to make fairly easy walking, low branches had been stripped by the reaching trunks. Here and there some under-privileged bachelor had taken out his frustration by tusking long strips from the smooth, gray tree bark. There were polished patches where the old ones had rubbed their crusty shoulders and uprooted saplings where strong bulls had tried their power.

We followed the road, day after day, past Ekin, Elanka's town, Akuafim. There, after passing the mouth of the tributary stream, we entered the concession country. Years ago this area had been leased for some mysterious purpose. But the lease had never been taken up. Still the surrounding bush people feared it like the devil. Only the nomad pygmies entered it on their endless hunts for meat. And here we began to see evidence of their traps.

Once Sala halted a thick-necked, muscular man, his blunt

features badly scarred by the explosion of his flintlock gun. We had an arrangement, Sala and I. When we hunted, he went ahead for he could see better than I. When he sighted something, he stood like a pointer waiting for me to come up to him. Then he lifted his chin to indicate his point, leaving me to search the cover until I too saw what he did. Sala saved me from a lot of grief, that way.

This time he looked upwards and I saw the trap, a shovel-headed spear shafted to a huge, vertical beam right over my head. It was made fast by a looping bushrope to a heavy, transverse branch and connected with a triplatch to a vine that stretched across the road at a height of eleven feet.

"So he catch elephant," Sala muttered. "But man and small beef pass—go under he."

I could visualize that ponderous weight driving the broad-bladed spear deep into an elephant's shoulders; the beast plunging away while the weighted spear worked deeper into his body until, weakened by loss of blood he stopped to wait for the spears of his hunters.

We moved on, sleeping between the buttressed roots of cotton trees, watching the trail for more traces of the pygmy ingenuity. Once Sala showed me a compost of leaves and brushwood. It filled a pit staked with hardwood points, he told me.

Some of the traps we saw looked fairly freshly made. Sala said that the small people had set them for the eastward march of the elephants at the end of the dry season. And once he indicated some charred sticks and a few worn patches that marked one of their tiny, lean-to camps.

Then, one afternoon, late, while looking for a harness antelope for food, Sala showed me the deep, oval pugs that meant an old bull.

"This one rascal," he informed me soberly. "Too cutta-cutta."

A solitaire usually meant an ancient bull chased out of the herd by the younger bachelors. Sometimes he was just an old gentle-man, weighted with years and ivory, who just couldn't keep up with the younger ones. Anyway, I checked my safety and we started to follow the trail.

It took us over the shoulder of a hill. We saw where he had pulled down young bamboo shoots and there were chewed balls of pith to mark his passing. By the number of droppings he had been in this bit of cover for some time. But the undergrowth was dense, thorn and evergreen ten feet tall and the trees close together.

Often the tracks stopped at what looked like solid walls of thorn. Sala crawled through small game tunnels and showed where the big brute had gently shoved his way through without breaking a stalk.

Next morning Sala got me out before dawn. He had been for a look-see, he said. I followed him and in the false dawn we found still-smoking droppings. We sat right down, waited for the darkness to close in and heard him moving. It was half an hour before the real dawn lightened the gloom and then we saw him, a dim, gigantic bulk near the base of an iroko tree. I followed Sala to circle him for a heart shot. But he disappeared. We found his tracks where he had run in that deceptively rapid single-foot gait of the elephant. He had gone through bamboo, dried grass and dense thorn without making a sound.

"Better we eat," Sala said.

We went back to camp and I had some tea and biscuit. Then we took off again. The trail was easy to follow and Sala made me go slow.

"Elephant old man," he said. "He no go far. He wait. He vex."

We moved into deep gloom. A stream, low and silent, was on our right. Giant ferns bulked ahead of us and a dense wall of small-leaved growth hemmed us in. We waited, listening for the belly rumbling that marks the nearby elephant. Nothing. Sala peered around the fern and moved on. I followed. The tracks veered suddenly to the left. I heard Sala catch his breath. He was staring over my shoulder, upwards.

Slowly, a brassy taste filling my mouth, I looked around. The bull was standing, quiet as doom right over me, his trunk uplifted for the hammer blow that would flatten us. I threw up my rifle and fired into the dark mass. There was a wrenching gasp and a terrifying crash. The heavy bullet knocked the bull off balance and the rifle, fired from the hip, knocked me sideways, my right thumb badly wrenched. I rolled for cover scrabbling for the rifle. Sala shouted. I got up, jumped behind a tree. The bull was gone.

For a long minute I stood getting my breath and composure somewhere near control. Sala, calm as a stoic, moved into the shadow where the bull had waited and motioned me to follow.

We saw where he had slammed against a tree, staggered, wheeled and bolted. Sala put up his hand, touched a leaf and showed me the blood on his fingers.

"Make we follow," he said. "He sick, too muckh. Pletty soon we catch he."

But we didn't. The blood spoor was easy to follow; flies buzzed noisily about it as we moved after the deep tracks. The beast was going fast, twisting and turning past big trees, skirting the infrequent clearings and moving towards the Great Dan swamp to the southeast. We halted late that afternoon and Sala went back to bring up the camp. We slept on the trail and moved out next morning. The tracks still maintained their direction. We found a deep, mushy puddle of blood where the bull had stood behind a tree to rest and watch his back-trail. Sala showed me the ant-busy smear of blood down the bark.

"He hit here." Sala pointed to his upper chest. "He sick; lean on tree."

The trail went on, down hill, up hill. The blood increased or I'd have thought he was healing and gaining strength. Three times that day we found where he had rested, the bloody ground muddled by his feet, the smears on the wide tree trunk. Then we descended the long slope that took us through palmettos, ferns and the tall cotton trees towards the swamp.

"Today we catch he," Sala said at the fourth puddle.

And then, as we rounded the bamboo clump, we saw him.

He was big and there were wounds of spear and bullet on his thick, wrinkled hide. His tusks were heavy, too. But he was gaunt, deep hollows above his eyes from the tremendous loss of blood. But he summoned strength for that last, desperate charge that ended when my bullet smashed through his forehead. I think he would have died anyway—rushed until he hit a tree and dropped —if I hadn't fired.

But I forgot him in the excitement of those mossy bones. I sent Sala back to bring up the others and waded carefully into the mud to examine the skeletons.

There were twenty-seven, some slimy with rot, others bleached, a few fairly fresh. I shoved aside the massive rib cages, many already broken, to examine the rock-like skulls. Sure there must be thousands of skeletons in the tangle of lush swamp growth; hundreds of thousands of pounds of ivory!

I scraped the moss from one skull lying on its side with water lapping into its trunk socket. There was no tusk visible. I looked more carefully. Axe marks! The tusks had been chopped out.

Maybe someone had taken out what he could get at. There was still another tusk in the water. I looked at another skull. The tusks were both chopped out of that one. Then, careful examination showed that the ribs had been scraped by knives.

What had happened? Had the pygmies come upon a band of elephants poisoned by the swamp? Impossible, for a snake swam away as I floundered out of it. What then? What had slaughtered twenty-seven elephants in the same spot?

I was pondering it when Sala came back followed by Francois and Ojo. They raised Cain, exclaiming loudly at the elephant. But the three Bulus didn't like it one damned bit. They kept rolling their eyes about them, pointing to the elephant bones and asking to go home.

"They say devils live here," Sala explained. "Better we chop teeth."

Sala was digging busily around the dead elephant when the pygmies showed up.

I'd never seen them, though everyone knew they lived and hunted all about the Fang and Bulu country. When they were near villages they advised of their presence by tapping little drums. Then they put out, at the edge of the village clearing, packets of meat which the villagers took, leaving ground nut paste, manioc and such in return. The pygmies were seldom seen or spoken to and never cheated; the Bulus had a deep respect for their stropanthus-tipped arrows.

And here they were right in the open, standing all about us, little pot-bellied men with old faces, their middles covered with bark-cloth dyed with camwood. Each bore little bows and had hide boxes of arrows slung over their shoulders. Some carried pouches made of whole monkey hides, hair out, slung over their shoulders by the tails slit at one end and slipped over the sad-looking heads.

The Bulus trembled, Ojo gripped a cooking knife, Francois whimpered. Sala made sounds at them. One, wearing a pot-shaped hat of straw, chattered, making gestures at the elephant.

"He say he want meat," Sala explained. "He say all elephant b'long he people."

"Tell him this elephant belongs to me," I said. "But his people can have all the meat they can carry away if he'll tell me how those other elephants all died in the swamp."

There was more chatter, broad grins and from out of the cover came little, dangle-breasted, shock-headed women with knives, choppers and baskets, to swarm over the enormous carcass and hack through hide and fat to the steaming meat.

Sala, shouting grandly, superintended the removal of the tusks and claimed the small brain for himself. The rest of my men put aside hunks of meat for their own use and inside a couple of hours there were piles of meat along the swamp edge and more and more pygmies, chattering happily, bobbing out of the bush. By late afternoon they had disappeared carrying their baskets of meat, leaving only the blood and grease-smeared chief and a few of his elders.

"Look," I said, "what about those other skeletons? How did they get there? Who killed them?"

"Chief say, he people kill them," Sala mumbled through a chunk of gristle.

"But how?" I snapped. "How did they get them there? Carry them, for God's sake?"

More chatter. Then the chief beckoned mysteriously and waded into the swamp. I followed gingerly. He called his men and they grupped in the muck until one yipped like a beagle and the others splashed over to scrape mud and growth from a long plank of timber into one end of which a small hole had been chopped.

"He say this catch 'em," Sala said. "Me, I no savvy."

I didn't savvy, either.

The chief made pacifying movements and beckoned us again. We trotted after him down the trail to the elephant road. At one side of it, close to a branch dangling with tempting foliage, was a heap of leaves. Carefully he scraped them to one side. There was a hole about two feet deep and about a yard in diameter. Covering it was a sort of wheel of woven bark, the spokes of which were sharpened bamboos, points almost meeting where the hub should have been. On the wheel was a slipnoose of green bushrope twisted to a cable of tremendous strength. The chief beckoned us along the rope from the noose. It was attached to a baulk of timber, ebony, by the look of it, a hole chopped in one end to take the bushrope. The log was about twelve feet long and more than six of us could lift. The chief made gestures of the elephant stepping into the trap, the spiked wheel holding until the noose tightened, then the dragging of the timber until the beast was exhausted.

"He say, elephant, when he tire, look for water place. Small people follow he, stick spear. Kill he.

I could see the enormous brute, fast to the immense drag rushing, checked by its weight, pulling it clear, toiling on again day after day until it reached the swamp. And there, anchored by the log, waiting for the small people to flit like evil things from the shadows, the bite of their tiny spears, the slow blaze of their poison and, finally, merciful death.

I asked about ivory. The little chief shook his head.

"He no sell," Sala told me. "Small people buy women with teeth."

I gave the pygmy chief presents of beads, cotton print and a few cutlasses. And his tribe put on a dance for us that illustrated their ways of hunting elephants. Some of them, including climbing the elephant's hind leg, hamstringing him and riding him until he dropped, were a bit on the grisly side.

When it was over they carried my ivory to the nearest Bulu village and I returned to my factory.

Many times after that I heard tales of the elephant graves. One man swore he had seen a valley dotted with skulls over in Uganda. But others swore just as plausibly that it was impossible. The elephant grave tale, one said, was most probably originated by the discovery, by some hunter, of the skeletons of a number of elephants in the waters of an alkali pool that had poisoned them.

Maybe so. But some years later, quite by accident, I learned of a man who had actually discovered the elephant sepulcher. He was Captain Singleton. And Captain Singleton was an invention of no less than that master of traveler's tales: Daniel Defoe.

When I was young, I went to the west coast of Africa. Being young, I just didn't seem to have the good sense to know when to be scared. I'd hunted the evil little red bush cow with a high velocity .220 that would have got me smeared over a quarter acre if I'd had the bad luck to get my sights on one. One day, riding a bicycle over a bush path outside Kribi, I was chased for nearly half a mile by a rogue elephant. Something distracted the brute and he sheered off just a couple of minutes before I hit a root and went arsyversy over the handlebars.

I thought it uproariously funny afterwards. Of course, I hadn't yet seen what an elephant could do to a person who annoyed him. And I was too dumb to imagine what would have happened if that crotchety old bull had caught up with me.

But I learned from the gorilla. Brother, how I learned!

I wandered into the Batanga district of South Cameroun, trying to drum up trade in bush produce. Some Americans who lived in a lovely little bungalow overlooking a quiet bay took pity on my ignorance of the bush and its people and put me up.

The Rices were grand, kindly people, sympathetic of a hare-brained youngster's lack of experience; they never let me see them smiling at my blunders.

And I was grateful. I'd been with them over a month, eating their good food, enjoying comforts I hadn't known for a long time. One evening I decided to go out and shoot them some meat, by way of showing my appreciation. It had to be a surprise so I didn't ask Rice for advice. Stupidity number one. I mooched off down the beach to a little village and asked the chief to give me a good hunter as guide. He called over an ancient with filed teeth and tattooed chest who, he said, knew the bush as well as his pocket—if he'd had a pocket. He could find me a bush buck, a harness antelope, anything.

We headed in from the beach about four o'clock. It got dark around there, with great suddenness between seven and seven-thirty. My guide figured, the chief said, we'd get a "beef" and be back before dark.

Stupidity number two was that I couldn't understand Bulu and my guide couldn't understand my talk.

He padded ahead of me, winding under lianas, through clumps of evergreen, along tiny game paths that were invisible to me, with a silent agility that was astonishing in one so old.

Once, deep within the forest gloom, he halted and stood like a statue until I came up behind him. He was chin pointing ahead. I stared long, saw nothing until something saw me, whistled and crashed away. The guide looked at me, spat and walked on.

I was carrying a 44-40 Winchester, lever action repeater, the best weapon I know for soft skin game at the close range necessary in dense rain forest country. It carried fourteen flat-nosed 200 grain chillers in the tubular magazine under the barrel. One of those big, soft slugs would bring down an antelope like a ton of brick.

But we didn't see any! Twice that guide stopped and chin

pointed. I saw nothing. I wasn't yet up to the trick of conditioning my eyes to movement in the cover rather than the shape of things to see. And we moved on. The old man was getting fed up, I could see. He bagged, made signs he was tired and sat down. Then we heard something scream not too far away. That brought my guide to his feet with a rush.

"N'gi!" he said beckoning me to follow him.

If I had known that n'gi means gorilla——!

But I didn't. We moved on, searching the cover. Once a chattering above showed me a troupe of diana monkeys, swinging from branch to branch like graceful acrobats. The old man wanted me to shoot one; they love monkey meat. I indicated I'd get one for him after he'd put me on a fat bush buck.

Following a stream we came upon wart hog tracks and heard them grunting beyond a smother of undergrowth. The guide went one way and I took stance beside a tree to wait for him to flush them down to me. Well they came, four of them, squealing like maniacs. I got one shot and missed; dared not fire again for the old man was right in the line capering and yelling his fool head off.

So they got away and we moved on. It was beginning to get darkish by now and I was feeling sorry I'd ever started out. We had come to a blow-down where great trees had torn a hole in the forest. It had grown up again but there was a fair visibility. The guide stood at the edge and carefully looked about him.

He froze. I could see his leathery shoulders trembling with eagerness. I stole close to him, following his chinpoint. He was staring at an ancient tree at a lateral branch some twenty feet above the ground. He whispered n'gi!

I looked, saw some leaves move, saw a mighty arm pull leaves to it. There was an immense head, half screened by leaves and a bulky shoulder.

What the hell, I thought, a big monkey, or a chimp, maybe. I'd shoot it for the guide and maybe have enough for the Rice boys to have a good meat feast. So I sighted carefully on what I thought was the shoulder blade and touched her off.

The bullet hit like a spitball hitting a blackboard. That brute let out a screech that made my blood run cold. I saw a branch that must have been seven-eight inches thick ripped off the tree like a twig. And a great, green-gray shape hit the ground with a thump. I jumped for another shot, lost my footing, lurched all

over hell and fetched up in the middle of a thorn bush that held
me with murderous, three-way points that were tearing the hide
off me. I wrenched my arms free at a cost of shirt and skin and
looked for the animal I could hear yowling somewhere close. The
guide was gone, his terrified wails fading in the distance.

I was for it, fast there in that thorn bush, unable to run if I had
wanted to—and I did. And somehow amid all the fear my heart
slowed and a tremendous calm took me. I stared at a window-like
opening in the undergrowth and I knew, somehow, that that
monkey or what would shove his head through there.

He did, and I wasn't ready for the horrible mask that glared
so ferociously at me. The crest was erect and under jutting brows
little eyes glowed with rage. The black, bony mask was
wrinkled like a cat's and the great mouth opened showing long
canines.

I fired straight at it. The head disappeared, then came again. I
levered out the shell and flipped home another. He was nearer;
I knew he was a gorilla now. I gave him another. He came on as
though I had missed him. At ten yards he was in the clear. On
his hind legs one massive arm stretched for me. I fired again, saw
hair jump. He checked, one hand touching the mouth. I had
time to give him another. Flicking that smooth running lever like
mad I put seven bullets into that gorilla until he lay shaking, and
grunting, his thick, short fingers digging into the ground not three
yards from my cringing feet.

I waited. He made no more movements. I began to shake now.
Sniffling, half choking with nerve, I managed to get myself out of
that damned thorn bush. Something rustled and I pumped
another two shots into that shaggy heap of meat out of sheer
panic. Then I had to sit down and get myself together.

After a while I pulled myself together, had a cigarette and took
a look at my kill. Man! He was an ugly devil. His arms, stretched
as far as I could pull them, were just under nine feet span. His
head was balding and his cape was gray. Some of the teeth were
badly worn but not those long, white eye-teeth. His fingers were
almost as thick as my wrist and the flaccid muscles of his arms
were tremendous. He had a mighty paunch, covered with thin
hair and alive with great gray ticks. He had four bullet holes in
his chest and belly and two in the head; one right through his
left eye. That monster must have struggled his last few yards with
a smashed brain!

And now I had the shakes all over again thinking what would have happened if I'd missed him. I'd heard plenty of yarns about gorillas and thanked my lucky stars my aim had been accurate. And that brought me to the clam spell right when it seemed death had its grip on my neck. I thought it miraculous then. But I've experienced it since. It's a sort of reserve of help, I guess, when we are really up against it.

But my troubles weren't over. While I was fiddling around that gorilla it became dark. Just like that. Just like a curtain going down. It was night. And I didn't know where the hell I was!

At first I was all for racing madly in the direction of the Rices' bungalow. But I didn't know where it was. I had enough savvy by now to sit down and try to figure things out. That old hunter had bolted. Maybe, now he had heard the firing, he'd come back and guide me home. I waited an hour and watched little green spots moving about me. Nothing happened. I yelled and there was a silence amid the whirring, chirping stridulations of night insects. No one answered my call. Nothing to do but wait—and think.

What would that guide do? He'd get back to the village and tell them what had happened; the chief would send someone to bring me in. If he didn't, the Rices would be looking for me.

Nothing. It grew cold, as it does in the big bush. There was no wind, only a dank chill. I began to think about the mate of my dead pal there, if he had a mate. Maybe I'd better move off in case she came looking for trouble. I knew the wild things can see in the dark. But I couldn't!

Little things moving in the undergrowth kept me jumping straining my eyes to see. I heard in the distance a harsh, sawing call. That, I knew only too damned well, was a leopard. Man! That killer, following the scent of blood, would be tough to meet. I fumbled around until I found a tree and backed against it, my heart thumping. Once monkeys burst into a pandemonium of screeching that scared the daylight out of me. I heard a crashing somewhere not too far off and wondering what was chasing them. Then there was a bloodcurdling scream. That leopard! I forced myself to be calm and watched the greenish sparks all about me. I saw two close to the ground. They moved. But they remained the same distance from each other. They came closer. I gripped my rifle in sweaty hands and tried to aim at those lambent green patches. I held my breath until my heart banged in my ears. I was about to fire when those green lights separated and disappeared.

Something rustled sharply beside me. I jumped a mile and struck at it with my rifle. It went away. At a great distance a long, infinitely desolate scream echoed. I felt my hair crisp on my nape. I wanted a cigarette but, so help me, I was afraid to strike a match. I stood there, stiff as a ramrod, waiting for someone to come and get me. It seemed that there were things all around, closing in with furtive little movements. They were all watching me, waiting for me to go crazy and stampede until I knocked myself to pieces against the tree trunks. I caught my breath that was rising to scream in my throat and forced myself to stay calm.

Then that dead gorilla moved. I heard it rustle and it groaned.

That did it. I fired twice at it and ducked behind my tree. Things crashed away in the forest and when my panic subsided I was clinging to a tree, my face against the cold bark, almost fainting with fear.

And I heard the leopard, a low, snarling, snoring purr. It was close. I craned my ears to listen. Something was disturbing the dense ground cover all around me. I swear it was creeping in. What would soon happen? The thing would get its bearings, crouch and with that paralyzing scream charge me. I yelled and something smashed away through the bush.

Now I felt that weak things watched me, things waited to catch me. My belly griped and I wanted badly to weep. I wanted to drop my rifle and just lie down there and let whatever it was get me. I had no strength.

I listened for sounds from the gorilla. Nothing. Something buzzed, wings touched my face. I swiped madly at them.

Then I heard the brain-fever bird. It began with a high, bell note and descended a weird chromatic scale. Again and again it tinkled in the blackness until I felt like screaming. Until suddenly it stopped. Gradually, the whirrings and chirpings came back. I felt my heart slow as my nerves relaxed. Then I must have slept.

I opened my eyes to a grayness. My legs ached with chill. But above the branches there was faint light. Something scrabbled, squeaking away, as my cramped feet moved and red hot pincers bit into my ankle. I stamped wildly away from driver ants that must have been attracted by the dead gorilla. Then dark closed in again.

I waited, trembling, until true dawn brought light. The brighter loom was over there. That was east. The coast, running north and south, was due west. I headed away from the light, running into trees, stumbling over lianas, fighting panic at the endless trunks that impeded me. Half an hour later I heard the booming surf.

Babbling with relief I burst out on to the beach. Fishing canoes were already out. Shouting Bulus came running down the beach, shouting, laughing and crowding to pat my shoulders.

The Rices were in the village sending out search parties to look for me.

"Didn't find out you were lost until just now," Rice told me. "Thought you'd gone up to Kribi for the night."

The guide, scared to death when the gorilla charged, had hidden, afraid to admit he had left me so he wouldn't be blamed for getting me into a jam.

I got back, ate a large breakfast and told my story while the Bulus went for the gorilla.

"What scared me most," I said, "was when he moved and grunted some couple hours after I had killed him."

Rice laughed.

"Must have been the air coming out of him when the big muscles relaxed," he said. "You were lucky at that, going into the bush with such a light weapon."

When the Bulus came back they verified it. There were leopard tracks all around the gorilla, they said, less than a couple of yards from where I was standing against the tree.

Thank the Lord I was asleep!

It is quite an acceptable fact in Africa that gorillas are harmless —at least, when not goaded into action. But I wouldn't know, because the only experiences I've ever had with them have erupted into the most devastating, blood-curdling encounters that were nothing short of weird nightmares.

I've seen sheep made drunk on wine and I've watched nice, well brought up Connecticut cows break into an orchard and get drunk as fiddlers' bitches on rotted apples.

I had heard tales of elephants, apes, lions and even gorillas getting plastered on fermented fruits. But I never saw one until I spent a mango harvest in the big bush country of French Equatorial Africa.

This American Mission friend of mine held that wild animals

like getting drunk just as much as civilized people do. He pointed out that the primitive natives learned to ferment palm sap, corn mash and other things to make high-proof drinks long before the whites came to teach them more bad habits. So, he reasoned, why shouldn't the animals have their ways of getting a little comfort.

"Sometimes," he told me, "I've heard gorillas in the night, barking and drumming on their mighty chests. I've heard them coughing and screaming and I'm almost certain I've heard them laughing. I've seen the places where they meet. They clear the ground by stamping it flat. They chew the bark from the trees, and all over the ground are scraps of rotten fruit rinds and seeds. The area smells like a brewery. And it's my belief that they gather the fruits together and go on a sort of spree with them."

That, misters, was a missionary; one I knew for years, a grand, unassuming man who walked alone in the bush with the confidence you have walking in your own backyard. He could have done a book on Africa that would have made the world sit up if Africa had given him the time. He knew almost all her secrets and that's more than most can say.

I knew he was a truthful man but I couldn't quite believe what he told me of gorillas until I saw for myself. And what I saw!

The bush, along the Campo River, between Cameroun and Gabon, is full of game; hippo, a dozen kinds of antelope, elephants, chimps, and a strange sort of gorilla. Not the black, pointy-headed brute like Gargantua was, but a smaller, round-headed creature with reddish hair; looked more human than the mountain gorilla.

I'd seen them often. They nested in the deep cover; usually a family; father, mother and baby. The family slept in the forks of trees while the old man kept guard in a foul nest of grass and twigs at the base. Sometimes, especially at the full of the moon, they were lively as hell, raced about the trees, screeching and slamming their chests until they boomed like drums. The Bulus told me that this was a good time to keep inside the village huts, for the screaming and carrying on meant they were making love.

I knew that many of the animals rutted at the same time and that they were dangerous during those periods. But I didn't connect it with the ripening of fruits like paw-paws, guavas, wild pineapples and certain bright-colored berries.

One night, I'd been far up the river making trade calls on some chiefs and was camped in a deserted sugar cane patch. I heard the thudding and hoarse barking of gorillas. My paddlers were scared and crouched about the crumbling bark hut in which I'd had Sala, my servant, put up my camp cot and other gear.

I ate my dinner and had a smoke, listening to the racket, which wasn't too far away and watching the moonlight dance down through the overhanging branches.

"Be n'gi," Sala told me. "Make palaver, too much."

That Sala was like a wild creature himself, short, stocky and tufted all over with hair. He could move silently as a snake and his senses were alert to the slightest change.

"Make we go look 'em," I suggested.

The paddlers promptly started whining and moved towards their canoes on the river bank fifty yards away. Sala told them what would happen if they ran away and we started off.

I took a Winchester .44 along. It's light but the slug is heavy and there are fourteen shots in the magazine. It was good enough for gorilla in that thick bush, as I had proved some months before. We moved cautiously down a grown-over path to the far edge of the clearing in which the cane had been planted many years before. As we moved the drumming and barking was louder.

"Softly-softly," Sala whispered and gently pressed me against a tree.

Then he went on flitting like a shadow from trunk to trunk. I waited, listening, smelling the gamey smell of animals and wondering just how close we were. Then Sala came back and motioned me to follow him. I crept after him, holding my breath, to where there was a depression. There the moonlight lit up a cleared patch. It seemed about twenty feet across and in it great figures bounded up and down with effortless and silent speed.

I felt the hair crisp on my neck at those great, shaggy brutes dancing like people. I could hear a chirruping and every now and then there would be hoarse hoo-hoo-hoo sounds. There was movement in the deep shadow around the edges of the cleared place and I moved closer to see.

Was it a sort of mating dance? Was it! I didn't know, I heard belching and I smelled the stink of fermentation.

Then Sala grabbed me and started dragging me back. An enormous shape had leaped at another. There was a roar, a hoarse scream and I saw mighty arms flailing at each other. There was screaming all about the clearing; now I saw other shapes and heard the enraged screeches of fighting gorillas.

That was enough. I backed away from there; Sala dragging at me. As soon as we were clear I ran for it.

We got back to the hut and the paddlers were gone. Damning them I ran down the path to the river. There was no sign of them. Sala and I made our way down the river bank searching the moon-lit reaches for a sign of the canoe. There was none. I returned to the path. Sala had not come back. I went up the path to the hut, dropped my rifle outside and turned in.

I was tired, I realized. I got the sheet under my neck and dropped off.

Then I awoke. Someone was calling. I lay there listening. It was Sala, calling softly, fearfully. Then I smelled it—that stink. I came awake as though I'd been shot at. I heard snoring! I listened in horror to muffled, grunting, bubbling, moaning snores!

It was like a nightmare, only it was no nightmare, for I could hear Sala whispering urgently outside. Then I stiffened with fear as I realized what was in that tiny hut with me.

It was a gorilla! It had to be. Probably hurt in that screeching battle, it had crawled into what it thought was a deserted hut for shelter. And the damned thing was drunk or it would have smelled humans and gone elsewhere.

My heart was thumping like a piston; cold sweat rolled off my body and I had a horrible pain in my belly.

I was afraid to call to Sala. Hell! I was too scared to move. I wondered where my rifle was, and remembered I had left it out-side for Sala to clean. I had a pistol under my pillow. But what good was that? I couldn't even tell where the stinking brute was!

Then the snoring stopped. He was awake, listening. I heard a mutter, a movement of lips and a sniff. In a moment he'd catch my scent. I lay stiff as a board in a silence, waiting for the pande-monium of screams that would bring him at me, ripping me to shreds.

My breath began to rattle in my throat. I held it, pulling gently to free my mosquito net. Maybe I could roll out and make it to the doorway, a faint gray oblong in the blackness.

Something moved near my head. The beast grunted sus-piciously. Something was being shoved through the bark wall. The gorilla grunted and I heard him scratching himself. Some-thing cold nuzzled my shoulder. I damned nearly screamed before I realized it was my rifle; Sala pushing it through to me. Then something big and shaggy blotted out the light from the doorway.

I pulled carefully at the gun muzzle; maybe I could get a shot while this thing was standing up. Then I smelled fetid breath.

That did it. My nerve broke. Wildly I yanked at the rifle barrel. It caught in the bark. The gorilla roared, a strident blast of sound that terrified me. His arms swung and something crashed across the hut. I felt my net go and rolled wildly away from the thing, still yanking at the rifle. The cot collapsed and was snatched away from me. In the screeching, bellowing fury I felt a tremendous blow as the shattered cot slammed across my back. I heard him crash about, fighting and ripping the canvas cot that had somehow got itself tangled in him. Outside Sala was shouting. With a terrific heave I got the rifle and fired it. In the flash I caught the black muzzle of the brute and the red fury in his eyes. I fired again. He screeched and mighty hands slapped at the ground beside me. I rolled, screeching myself and fired again.

I saw him reared against the doorway and tried to take careful aim. But my hands trembled. I could only hold the weapon and jerk at the trigger. Then there was a wild howl and he burst through the doorway.

Sala hollered outside and I managed to scramble to one knee and take a shot at the lumbering brute in the moonlight.

He was knuckling across the little clearing and I saw him run slap into a tree trunk. He staggered backwards and raced off in another direction. By this time, I could stand up and I fired after him.

I had no chance of hitting him; I was scarcely aware that I was shooting. But he was gone, thrashing through the cane and still bellowing.

I looked around to where Sala, spear in hand, was watching me. I saw a camp chair, set it up and tried to sit on it. I missed completely and fell on the ground. I scrambled to my feet and shook so that I could scarcely stand.

Sala lit a hurricane lamp and we looked inside the hut. It was a mess; the camp cot was in bits, the mosquito net ripped to a shred, the sheets wadded into a corner and stank of the beast's fouling. My wash basin was smashed in and my uniform case was flattened.

I told Sala to break out a bottle and I took a long pull and sat down, rifle across my knees, to wait for morning.

I heard them squalling and scrapping in the bush. But none

came near and when daylight showed I went down to the river.

My canoe was in midstream, the paddlers staring sheepishly at me from safety. Sala bellowed at them and they pulled in and after a lot of shoving went for my trade goods and camp gear.

We got back to my headquarters that night and soon afterwards I went north to Ebolowa and got to hell out of that bush.

Ordinary gorillas are bad enough to run across. But plastered ones—uh-uh!"

BIRTH OF THUNDER

Robin Cranford

"Birth of Thunder" is published by
Jarrolds Publishers (London) Ltd.

The Author

Robin Cranford was born in South Africa in 1923. After his education in Johannesburg he left the country to serve in Cyprus, Italy and Yugoslavia with the South African Air Force and the R.A.F. Returning home after the war, he attended the Witwatersrand University where he took a B.A. degree in English and Economics.

His post-graduate years led him into a variety of occupations: salesman, production manager, and company director. Recently, with his wife and two sons, he emigrated from Africa to seek a new home, and chose England as the country which, in his opinion, offered him the greatest intellectual freedom and his children the most enlightened education. Now a writer by profession, he lives in a sixteenth-century cottage in East Kent and finds time to engage in his favourite pursuits: sailing and shooting.

His first novel—*My City Fears Tomorrow* —was a stark exposé of high and low life in Johannesburg. It was banned by the South African Government after being acclaimed by one of the leading dailies as "the best novel with a South African setting to appear for a long while".

CHAPTER ONE

THE flak was bad that day.

They had flown from Termoli eastwards over the Adriatic: not the blue Adriatic of the pre-war summer tourist, but the winter Adriatic, clawed and scratched by the "Bora"—the hated north wind.

The wind was gusty, jostling the wings of the fighters as they bored through the misty air between the scudding grey clouds and the wrinkled sea.

The normally sleek and beautiful lines of the Spitfires were distorted by fat auxiliary fuel tanks strapped to their bellies; by 250-lb. bombs slung under their wings.

Like pregnant women with a bundle of washing under each arm, Jake Mancier reflected irritably.

He was flying in the Number Two position, fifty yards astern of the Flight Commander. One of his duties was to weave from side to side and make sure that no enemy aircraft approached unobserved from astern. Jake Mancier weaved without deigning to glance behind him. There *were* no German planes in this piece of sky—hadn't been for months. But he knew that if he ceased his criss-crossing for a minute his earphones would crackle with the Flight Commander's accusing tones: "Pull your finger out, Number Two!"

So Jake weaved, purposelessly, and brooded over the clumsiness of his plane with its extra weight of fuel and bombs. The Spitfire hadn't been designed for this sort of nonsense. It was an interceptor fighter, built for aerial combat, not long-range ground support. When they—whoever the powers that be were—formed the Balkan Air Group they should have traded in the dainty Spitfire for something more rugged and utilitarian: for Mustangs or Thunderbolts, planes with the toughness and weight to stand up to dive-bombing and flak.

Maybe they'd wake up one day. But by that time he—and a lot of his buddies—would probably be pushing up daisies, or whatever it was that grew in the mountains of Bosnia and Croatia.

A hundred yards away on Jake's right another pair of burdened Spitfires were playing follow-my-leader. They—all four planes of the section—were flying in the loose, untidy-looking but wonderfully effective pairs formation which the R.A.F., after much trial and error, had copied from the Luftwaffe.

At the beginning of the war, Jake remembered, R.A.F. fighters had flown in Vee patterns. Why? Because that was the way geese did it. What was good enough for the birds was good enough for the Royal Air Force in 1939 and 1940. The pundits had failed to realize that a goose was solely concerned with following his leader and staying clear of his turbulent slipstream. He did not have to worry about someone creeping up the blind spot under his tail with a 20mm. cannon.

It took the R.A.F. quite a while to appreciate the difference between a fighter plane and a migrating goose; and in the meantime a lot of nice British boys who could fly impeccable Vic formations got shot up the backside by wily Germans who had perfected their own tactics years before in Spain.

Jake Mancier mused about these things and pulled a wry grimace under his oxygen mask. He was a Canadian with somewhat irreverent ideas about the Service whose uniform he wore and the "limeys" with whom he flew.

"Limeys"—Englishmen—were not his favourite people. Sure, there were lots of nice guys amongst them. But as a nation, in Jake's opinion, they numbered an unwarrantably high proportion of stuffed shirts.

And riding a scant fifty yards in front of Jake's nose was the stuffiest of them all . . . Godfrey Brathwate, the Flight Commander.

Brathwate was such a stuffed shirt that even his fellow Englishmen thought him stuffy—and that was saying something. He was tall and thin, with an inbred air of elegance. He had a prominent bony nose and a tight mouth. His features were permanently set in an expression of supercilious disdain; like a camel, or one of those woolly llamas from the Andes. An expression of wanting to expectorate at life, but being too genteel to do so.

Before the war he had run an exclusive private school in Surrey. His pontifical manner was suited to such a position.

He employed this manner on his subordinates; and some of them were suckers enough to fall for it.

Carraday for one. Poor "Twitty" Carraday, who had "fagged" for Brathwate at boarding school and never recovered from the inferiority feelings induced by such concentrated patronage and contempt.

Jake felt sorry for Carraday, in an impatient sort of way. It must have been a rotten break for the kid to walk into his new squadron, all tail-wagging eagerness to please, and hear that drawling, superior voice exclaiming: "Good Lord, if it isn't Twitty Carraday! Do you still cry for your mother, Twitty? Or did I succeed in beating that out of you at school?"

There was no hope for the poor guy then. Everyone had called him "Twitty" from that day onwards. And what associations the name must have carried! Every time it was applied to him he cringed back into his shell.

Jake had once seen a small dog, with its tail between its legs, running down the street; and all the other dogs—the bold and especially the not-so-bold—rushing out of their front gardens to take a bite at the inoffensive stranger. That was Richard Carraday. His sheer defencelessness, his aching vulnerability, elicited a streak of latent cruelty in even quite kindly people.

Poor "Twitty". Non-smoker, teetotaler, virgin at the age of twenty-three; carrying around with him always, like a stern rebuke, his mother's red-leather pocket Bible.

When you tried to find words to describe a guy like that, Jake thought, the only expression that came readily to mind was the familiar four-letter term for the feminine reproductive apparatus. Yeah, the Anglo-Saxons had a word for Richard Carraday.

Not that Twitty himself had any sort of acquaintance with the female anatomy, except the necessary preliminary relationship attendant on the act of being born. And even that was open to doubt. When one looked at Carraday one was tempted to place credence in the stork or the gooseberry bush theory. The guy was hardly flesh and blood.

Jake grinned, remembering the time he and Cobber and Maria had conspired to deprive Carraday of his virginity.

Maria was Jake's particular piece of tail; one of the teenage Italian trollops who brightened the life of the squadron at Termoli. Maria was probably not her real name: a lot of Italian whores seemed to adopt the title of the Madonna in part atonement for their nightly activities.

This Maria was one of the better ones; about sixteen at a guess, with lustrous hair and dark merry eyes and that early flowering of Italian beauty which so often carried within it the seeds of premature decay.

No unwilling convert to a life of sin, Maria. In her philosophy sex was one great bundle of fun. She adored young men; she adored the things young men traditionally did with attractive girls; and above all she adored the cornucopia of tinned foods, cigarettes and crisp occupation lire with which her complaisance was rewarded. For these young airmen *were* generous. It wasn't much use saving your pay when you flew out over Yugoslavia each day.

And being so much in love with love, it distressed Maria immeasurably to hear that the young, sensitive-looking pilot-officer sitting alone in a corner of the mess tent was a total stranger to its delights.

"Davvero!" she exclaimed disbelievingly, rolling her big brown eyes in Carraday's direction. "Non è vero."

"It *is* true," Jake insisted. He appealed to one of his friends, a thickset Australian whose plethoric complexion bespoke the warming qualities of Italian vermouth. "Isn't Carraday a virgin?"

Cobber Catrick's eyes were bloodshot and his hand a trifle unsteady, but he rallied to Jake's support. "Isht quite true . . . as pure-sh the driven shnow." He waggled a tobacco-stained forefinger under Maria's pert nose. "D'ya know what? Shome noble woman should take it upon hershelf to relieve him of the burden —the abshoolutely intolerable burden—of hish virginity."

"Hear hear," Jake added, looking pointedly at Maria.

Her eyes widened as the import of their remarks dawned upon her. "You want me sleep him?" she queried breathlessly.

Cobber nodded ponderously. "We want you to shleep him the besht way you know," he slurred. "Isht your shacred duty. In fact" —he banged his empty glass on the counter—"I am pershonally prepared to defray the entire cost of thish charitable enterprish."

He delved in his hip pocket and produced a crumpled roll of notes. "How much, Jake old boy? What prish Richard Carraday's vir-shinity?"

"Don't spoil her," Jake said pragmatically. "Give her the usual two quid."

"Two quid," repeated Cobber, fumbling with the notes. "How many lire-sh that? I can never work thish bloody currenshy."

"Here—give it to me." Jake deducted Maria's fee and handed the rest back.

"I go now?" Maria asked, eyeing the unsuspecting Carraday with avid interest.

Jake restrained her. "Not yet. Wait until he goes to bed."

"Thash right," Cobber agreed, "wait until he's all tucked up in hish liddle cot."

So they bided their time, gathering around them a small coterie of expectant companions who had been let into the secret. They waited while Richard Carraday sipped his grapefruit juice and played a modest game of shove ha'penny with the squadron Intelligence Officer.

At a discreet distance they followed him into the darkness and watched his shadow on the tent while he undressed, washed his face in the portable canvas basin, brushed his teeth, whispered his prayers and climbed into his creaking camp stretcher.

"Tally-ho!" someone hissed. "Slip the leash."

Jake patted Maria encouragingly on her well-rounded little derrière. *"Pianissimo!"* he advised. "Gently does it."

"Yep, take it easy," Cobber chortled. *"Solamente tre volte."*

They all crept closer, suppressing their mirth, eager to be aural witnesses to the seduction.

They heard Richard Carraday's startled: "Who's that?" Then Maria's voice, soft and low and cajoling as only Maria's voice could be: "You verr nice man. You strong . . . *Multo bello!* You love Maria—*si?*"

"No!" Carraday replied.

"Maria verr good girl,"—the stretcher creaked beneath her weight—"we sleep now, *si?* Maria love you: you love Maria . . . verr nice . . ."

"Go away," Caraday pleaded in tones of desperation. "Please go away at once."

"Che cosa intende dire?" Maria sounded hurt. "You no like me —no?"

"No!" Carraday shouted. He came running from the tent, supporting his pyjama trousers with both hands, to be greeted by guffaws of mirth from Jake and his companions.

The girl followed, trailing her feet despondently. "He no like Maria. Me give money back—*si?*"

"You keep it," Jake chuckled. "It was worth it, just for the show."

He and Cobber put their arms around Maria and they all went singing back to the mess tent, leaving Carraday standing alone in the darkness with tears of anger and shame on his cheeks.

Well, maybe it was an unkind thing to do, Jake thought, turning his helmeted head to watch Carraday weaving in the Number Four position. But not altogether unkind. Behind the ribald mockery lurked a genuine desire to see the poor little guy sharing in the joy of the bountiful earth. Hell's bells! One of these days Carraday might stop a piece of flak without ever having savoured the red-blooded fun of human existence.

I mean, just look at him: he even manages to weave his Spitfire in a servile sort of way—like a puppy crawling back for a beating.

The island of Vis slid below Jake's starboard wingtip. On the way back—if fuel was running short—they would drop in there and fill up. The island was held by the partisans and boasted an air strip which the British had built.

There were more islands down below, then the bare, inhospitable coastline climbing to the Dinaric Alps. The mountains were like bared teeth . . . fangs of ice, snowy cusps and the black dental fillings of naked rock.

"Jeezes, what a place!" Jake commented to himself as the wild uplands of Bosnia unrolled beneath them. Dark forests of spruce, slashed by the whitened scars of freezing rivers. Windswept plateaux of lichen-crusted stone. Bottomless gorges unblessed by the sun. "What a stinking bloody place!"

He spread his map on his knees and tried to orientate himself. He saw a railway clinging to a cliff; then a road and a river twisting away to the north. They were somewhere south of Banja Luka then. And the river would be the Sana . . . no, the Pliva. Oh, blast this effing country—everything looked the same!

Anyway, if he became separated from the rest of the formation he had only to head south-westwards until he hit the coast. It was easy to pick up a bearing from there. He folded the map and shoved it away in the thigh pocket of his flying suit.

A voice, dehumanized by the crackle of atmospherics, vibrated in his earphones: "Red three to Red leader. Road transport at ten o'clock."

Jake looked; then shouted involuntarily: "Christ yes! Hundreds of the bastards!"

As he leant forward to switch on his reflector sight he felt a chill of premonition. A big road convoy meant a lot of flak. He'd have preferred a few undefended vehicles. The end of the war was in sight and he wasn't nearly as brave as he used to be.

But these were the days of big convoys. Belgrade had fallen to the Russians and the Germans were engaged upon a bloody retreat from the Balkans. The roads from Sarajevo northwards to Zagreb were choked with their vehicles: ammunition trucks, ambulances, troop transports, tanks, armoured cars . . . and flak! Flak of all kinds, from the tremendous 88mm. guns down to the little four-barrelled horrors on their mobile mountings. Jake hated the latter most of all. The sight of one hosing 20mm. shells at him in a fiery stream was enough to put a strain on the sphincter. His plane had been hit three times in the past few months and somehow struggled home. Now he had the worrying feeling that his luck was running out.

"Red section . . . Echelon starboard—Go!"

Brathwate was positioning his four aircraft to swoop down out of the sun. As Jake closed with his leader the first dirty black puffs began to pock the sky.

"The bombing target is the small bridge and the concentration of transport around it," Brathwate was drawling calmly. "At nine o'clock."

He caught sight of Carraday lagging behind the formation and shouted angrily: "Wake up, Number Four! Get your bloody great finger out!"

Then he rolled his Spitfire over and down, giving Jake a glimpse of pale blue belly, elliptical wings, jutting cannon, gaping radiators and two sleek bombs with cylindrical fins.

Jake watched him go, then pressed his own weight against stick and rudder. The earth rose and twisted under his toppling wing.

Settled in his dive, peering through the lighted screen of the reflector sight, he watched the ground coming up at him. The German vehicles were black beads on the tawny string of the mountain road. Then some of the beads began to wink and flash and his mouth went dry as he watched the tracer shells climbing with deceptive slowness towards his racing Spitfire. They flicked past him on all sides like streams of wind-blown sparks.

Brathwate's bombs had burst fifty yards beyond the target. Jake fixed the orange bead of his sights on the small stone bridge and struggled to hold the Spitfire steady as the airspeed built up and the rudder became heavier and heavier to control. The air around his perspex canopy was full of smoky trails and distracting streaks of light. He hunched himself into a ball and began his pull out. The target disappeared under the nose and the G-force pressed him into his seat. "One—two—three!" he counted deliberately, and pressed the bomb release with his thumb.

In a steep climbing turn he watched intently for the bomb bursts. They mushroomed just short of the bridge, amongst a group of trucks. The bright flashes of their detonations were succeeded by a ball of fire and a soaring column of black smoke.

"Watch that ammunition go up!" Jake yelled into his mask. Still spiralling under his leader he saw the other two pass unscathed through the flak and lob their bombs into the conflagration below.

Brathwate came on the air again.

"Red section . . . Line abreast—Go! We'll make one straffing run from north to south. Buck up, Number Four!"

Richard Carraday was lagging again.

If anyone gets the chop it'll be him, Jake thought. The last plane over always got the hottest retaliatory fire.

They screamed down to treetop level several miles from the crowded road and sneaked up under cover of a high hill. At three hundred miles an hour the spruce forests blurred into green velvet under their wings. Then they were skimming the hillside like driven grouse and the road burst into view.

The vehicle in front of Jake had a red cross painted on its side. Ambulance? Medical stores truck? Or merely an example of German duplicity? No time to wonder. No chance of turning left or right in search of a different target without colliding with another aircraft.

Jake pressed both thumbs on the firing button and blew the red cross to flaming fragments with a blast of machine gun and cannon fire.

Then he was over the road with streams of flak converging above his head. He pressed the racing Spitfire lower until its radiators sucked at the swaying treetops. Still the flak followed him. Uttering a prayer he hauled back on the stick and skidded the climbing plane from side to side with savage thrusts on the rudder bar.

He was away. He was safe. The attack was over. After the squadron's severe losses of the past month they had orders not to make more than one run over heavily defended targets. Jake relaxed and felt the sweat trickle, cold and clammy, under his armpits.

"Setting course for base," Brathwate ordered. His voice rose. "For Christ's sake, Number Four, are you lagging again?"

There was a pregnant silence; then Richard Carraday's voice, high-pitched and a trifle unsteady:

"I think I've been hit . . . my temperatures are going up fast."

"Serve you bloody right," Brathwate said unsympathetically. "Number Two, take a look at him. See if there's any visible damage."

Jake, obeying orders, throttled back and swung down beside Carraday's aircraft. The engine cowling seemed unmarked. There wasn't a scratch on wings or fuselage.

Flapping over nothing, Jake thought sourly.

Carraday was peering appealing in his direction, like a nervous patient awaiting a doctor's diagnosis. His goggles were pushed up on his forehead and—between helmet and oxygen mask—his face was white.

Jake eased his Spitfire lower until he was hanging a scant ten feet below Carraday's tailplane. Then he perceived the cause of the trouble. Through a tiny, ragged aperture in one of Carraday's radiators the coolant was issuing in a silver flicker of vaporizing liquid.

"Yeah," he commented laconically, pressing the transmitting button, "he's been hit all right. The glycol's pissing out of him."

Poor bastard, he thought, rising beside Carraday's plane and staring into his dilated eyes from a distance of less than thirty feet. Poor Twitty!

He had just pronounced sentence of death on Carraday's plane; like a doctor telling a patient: "You have an inoperable cancer."

That little rent in the metal was the wound through which the Spitfire's life was running out. Nothing could save it.

The Rolls-Royce engine still thundered out its thousand horse-power. The plane was as sleek and proud as ever in every panel and rivet. But doomed!

In Carraday's cockpit the temperature gauges, climbing steadily towards their fatal peak, foretold the end of the Spitfire as surely as a thermometer in a dying patient's mouth.

They would climb and climb until the lubricating oil broke down under the destructive heat, until it seared and carbonized, until metal met metal in a savage mating. Then mechanical agony and—Fire.

Poor Twitty, Jake thought, and searched the terrain below in a vain attempt to find a place where Carraday might get the Spit-fire down in a belly landing.

Fangs of rock. Gleaming facets of scree. Towering forests. Snow and ice. Dear God, what a place, Jake reflected. There's only one thing for you, Twitty my boy, and that's to hit the silk.

Brathwate was of the same opinion.

"How are your temperatures now, Red Four?"

"Right off the clock," Carraday admitted. "The engine's beginning to roughen up."

"You'd better bail out then. Do you understand?"

"Roger."

"Remember the drill?"

"I—I think so."

"Throttle back and reduce your speed," Brathwate lectured. "Jettison your canopy. Roll on your back and wind the elevator trim forward. Pull your harness pin . . . and for God's sake get rid of your wireless and oxygen leads." The weary patience in his voice implied: I don't know why I'm bothering to tell you all this. You're sure to make a balls-up.

"Roger." Carraday's voice was almost a whisper.

Oh, you poor sod, Jake thought. Going down into the wilds of Bosnia without even a pat on the head from your mother.

He grinned at Carraday and raised a gauntleted hand. "Cheerio, Twitty. Don't shag too many of the partisan girls."

Then, laughing at his own wit, he veered off sideways to watch the fun.

CHAPTER TWO

WHEN Carraday removed his helmet the onslaught of noise on his unprotected eardrums was absolutely terrifying: the roar of the windmilling prop, the grinding of the stricken engine, the shrill whistle of the airstream past the open cockpit.

For what seemed an interminable time he sat motionless, numb with fear. By severing his wireless leads he had cut off his last tenuous contact with the world he knew: with friendly voices; with advice and encouragement. He was utterly alone.

The engine vibrated violently, reminding him that he would surely die unless he bailed out. He passed his clammy hand across his face, trying to remember Brathwate's instructions.

It was a young, thin, sensitive face. Not bad looking—almost handsome—if one considered it feature by feature. But a curiously unformed face; needing the acid of some powerful emotion—anger or passion or sorrow—to burn and mould it into a characterful visage.

The eyes were very blue; defenceless, like the eyes of a young child. The mouth was full, with a hint of latent sensuality. The eyebrows prominent and dark, habitually curved upwards in an expression of timid query. The forehead high, intelligent, puckered now in a frown of bewilderment and fear.

"Roll on your back," Brathwate had said. "Elevator trim forward. Pull out the harness pin."

Carraday obeyed like a man in a hypnotic trance. The horizon revolved slowly and his full weight sagged sickeningly on the straps. Something loose in the bottom of the cockpit—his helmet? a map?—fell past his face and was sucked away by the slipstream. He jerked the harness pin and gasped as the furious force of the hundred-mile-an-hour wind struck him full in the face.

He was falling free, turning over and over, with the earth appearing at regular intervals between his feet and swinging over him into the confusion of grey sky.

From long habit—an action performed at the end of every flight—Carraday's hand went to the release box of his parachute. He twisted the safety lock and was about to hammer it with the heel of his hand when a terrible chill of premonition arrested the action. The impact of his hand would have released all four straps and sent him plunging down without a parachute.

For a while he was too demoralized to do anything further, while the earth—more detailed now—swung up at him in regular, remorseless circles.

Then his trembling hand found the rip-cord handle. He summoned the last of his strength and pulled it. There was a whip-crack of sound, a violent jerk, and he found himself swaying beneath the opened chute.

To Richard Carraday at that moment it seemed that there had never been anything so beautiful as the translucent dome of silk above his head, riffling gently like the sails of a yacht in a zephyr of wind. His right hand still grasped the rip-cord handle with its short attachment of wire cable. He dropped it and watched it go twinkling away, down, down, down, into the void between his feet.

There was a rushing snarl of sound and a Spitfire fell from the upper air and banked steeply around him, the contrails wisping from its wingtips. The cockpit canopy was pushed back and the pilot had released one catch of his mask so that it hung awry, exposing his face. It was Jake. He was grinning and making crude signs with his left hand.

Carraday felt a helpless pang of envy. Within an hour Jake would be back in the comfort and warmth of the officers' mess, with his vermouth and chianti and his little Italian mistress; with the rough, ribald male companionship which Carraday had always scorned but secretly longed to share.

Overwhelmed by bitterness, he watched the Spitfire pull up and go winging away with the other two towards the south-west.

The parachute, thrown off balance by the mountain gusts, began to oscillate wildly, swinging Carraday from side to side. He reached up and grasped the shroud lines in an attempt to check the vertiginous movement. His efforts only seemed to worsen matters.

He was drifting with the wind towards a snow-covered mountain slope. The ground began to rush up at him with frightening speed. He bunched his knees and covered his face with his arms.

Instead of the bruising shock he expected, the landing was as soft as a descent into cotton wool. A deep drift of snow engulfed him and it was only the pull of his chute, billowing in the wind, which saved him from sinking in over his head.

He struggled free and managed to collapse the tugging chute. It was a cold and silent world he found himself in: innocent of all sound except his own laboured breathing and the plaintive dirge of the wind. Above him was a waste of rock and snow; below him the uninviting gloom of the forest. He sat down on the bundled silk of the parachute and lost himself in despond.

But the cold wind, penetrating his clothing like a knife thrust, aroused his instincts of self-survival. He remembered the lectures they had been given by Pawlings, the Squadron Intelligence Officer, on how to escape from enemy-held territory. On the I.O.'s advice the pilots had discarded their fleece-lined flying boots for stout leather footwear, suitable for the long walk home.

Carraday was weighted down with equipment gathered on Pawlings's instructions. He took it all out now and laid it beside him.

From the pockets of his Mae West came a pack of emergency rations and a first-aid kit . . . bandages, burn jelly, a hypodermic needle and several shots of morphia. They were joined by a .38 revolver and twelve rounds of ammunition, his pocket Bible and a bulky "Escape Kit".

He and his companions had never taken the escape kits very seriously. Carraday broke his open now and examined the contents. There was a packet of American dollars, for rewarding the helpful. There was a large silk map of Yugoslavia which made an excellent scarf. And there were several miniature magnetic compasses: small enough—Pawlings had pointed out—to be secreted in the rectum.

The Squadron I.O. had been extremely keen on the rectal hiding place in the event of capture and search. So keen in fact that the pilots had protested they would suffer permanent and painful injury if they followed his suggestion to the letter.

"Arsehole" Pawlings they had christened him as a consequence, or A.H. for short—much to his chagrin.

As well as the compasses there was a small steel file, suitable for sawing through prison bars but of a shape which would have defied even the most stoic fugitive wishing to follow Pawlings's instructions for concealment. And there were a couple of magnetized fly buttons which, balanced one atop the other, unerringly sought out the north.

To this array of useful objects Carraday added a clasp knife, a wristwatch, a Serbo-Croat phrase book and some matches in a waterproof box. These completed his worldly goods.

His watch warned him that nightfall was less than three hours away. The temperature was falling perceptibly. Carraday's teeth began to chatter as he packed his things back into his pockets.

The bright yellow Mae West life-jacket was bulky and conspicuous. Carraday decided to discard it. The dinghy pack was no use either. But it seemed a pity to leave the parachute behind. The silk would cover him warmly at night and the strong, thin lines might meet a multitude of needs. He cut off the harness and made the rest into a portable bundle. Slinging it across his shoulder he began to trudge down the slope towards the shelter of the forest.

He was still a hundred yards from cover when some sixth sense prompted him to glance behind. A flurry of movement on the skyline instantly caught his eye. A score or more of dark figures came plunging over the crest of the hill and swooping down towards him.

Their swift, silent descent puzzled Carraday until he distinguished the unfolding trails of their skis. As they drew nearer he perceived their shoulder-slung weapons against the brilliant backdrop of snow. The slope between him and them was too steep and studded with rock to take at a rush. They came at him diagonally, like tacking ships, in great scythe-like sweeps.

There was something sinister about their appearance; something efficient, remorseless, terrifying. On a panicky impulse Carraday turned and plunged for the shelter of the forest.

The snow was knee deep. He floundered and fell and picked himself up again in a nightmarish sequence. And now, to add to his terrors, there was a new sound: the sharp, echoing "spang" of Mausers and the kissing noises of bullets striking the snow around him.

He was at the edge of the trees. Something cracked like a whip over his head and he was deluged in snow dislodged from the branches of a laden spruce. Gasping with effort he threw himself down behind the bole of a tree.

The German ski patrol had paused, as though fearful of the forest. Then, covered by the guns of their companions, two men detached themselves and came sliding down to the spot where Carraday had landed. They retrieved his abandoned gear and trudged back up the slope. After a few minutes consultation the whole patrol set off along the mountainside and vanished over a saddle.

Carraday rose to his feet and brushed down his blue serge battledress. Except for the occasional cascade of snow from an overladen branch the forest was as silent as a tomb. But for all its gloomy solitude it seemed a friendlier place than the bare slopes above the tree line. He turned and went down the declivity under the close-pressed spires of the towering firs.

It was almost dark in the depths of the forest. After a while he heard the plash and purr of running water and turned towards it. He emerged from the trees on the banks of a mountain stream, gurgling between ice-encrusted boulders.

There was a track running beside the stream. It had not been used since the last fall of snow and the deep footprints of horses and men were half-filled by newly drifted flakes. Carraday followed the track downstream, hoping it would lead him to some habitation.

He came around a bend and found the body of a man lying in the middle of the path. It was an old man and he had been there for some while. The snow had drifted up against one side of his body and turned his beard into a mask of ice crystals. Carraday had read about throats being cut from ear to ear but had taken the expression to be some sort of thriller-writer's licence. It wasn't. This old man's throat had been cut with such efficiency that only his spinal column still joined his head to his body.

Carraday was almost totally unaccustomed to the manifestations of death. In his whole life he had seen only one dead person at close quarters. That was his father, lying in his coffin, with his pale features composed by the undertaker in an expression of simpering benignity utterly at variance with his previous character.

No one had composed this old man's features. They were frozen in the snarl of hatred and fear with which he had bidden farewell to his enemies. Through a light dusting of snow he glared up at Carraday now. There was such malevolence in his glance that Carraday took an involuntary step backwards.

Sickened, hardly knowing what he was doing, he went on down the path. As he stumbled along he tried to imagine what sort of human being would deliberately cut the throat of another, as casually as a butcher slaughtering a pig. To shoot a man was one thing; even to bayonet him in the heat of battle. But to take the life of an old man—in cold blood! Carraday shuddered.

He was so preoccupied with his morbid thoughts that he almost blundered into the village. It was set in a clearing beside the stream; a small village of one main street, with a wooden mill beside a weir. A quiet village. No lights, no smoking chimneys, no human voices . . . no sounds at all except the hiss of the black water gliding through the mill race and the creaking of the turning wheel.

It was a deserted village of blackened, roofless cottages and gaping doors. The mill was the only building left intact. Over the scene of desolation hung the cloying stench of death.

The stench emanated from human corpses lying in the street. There were many of them: men, women and children. The whole population of the village seemed to have met its end in the narrow corridor between the gutted houses. The bodies of the men were mostly clothed, but many of the women were naked or partly clad in torn vestiges of garments. It was the young women and girls whose clothing seemed to have been interfered with most.

How long they had been there was difficult to tell, for the cold had done much to preserve them. All had met violent ends. Some had their throats cut, others their skulls smashed in as though by rifle butts. One small girl had been transfixed on a pitchfork and thrown, with the instrument of murder, on top of a corn crib. She hung there, perfectly preserved, with her dark tresses frozen like a veil.

Some of the corpses—especially the unclothed ones—had been attacked by carnivorous animals which had eviscerated them and dragged their entrails over the bloodstained snow. The surrounding ground was patterned with dog-like tracks.

Carraday wandered through the village like a lost child. His eyes recorded each detail of the scene. But between vision and comprehension there was a mercifully numbing barrier. The full import would only dawn upon him later, returning for many months to haunt his dreams.

At the edge of the settlement he sat down on a log and buried his head in his hands. There were tears on his cheeks. The odour of death crept into his nostrils and he retched uncontrollably.

A stealthy movement behind him brought him stumbling to his feet. In the tenebrous gloom of the forest he could discern nothing. But the sound went on . . . the furtive padding of feet on the hardened snow, backwards and forwards between the trees, restlessly.

The hair began to prickle on the nape of Carraday's neck. He drew the pistol and cocked the hammer with his thumb. The click of the sear was followed by silence.

Then there was a sound which Carraday had never heard before, but which plucked some atavistic chord of terror deep within his being. It was the deep-throated baying of a wild beast. It echoed through the forest and was taken up by other throats around the perimeter of the stricken village.

Coming down the main street were several large animals; like Alsatian dogs, but lower in the quarters, with bushy tails which swept the ground. Their coarse fur was greyish-brown and their yellow eyes shifted warily under alert, pointed ears. They fell upon the corpses in the snow, ripping savagely at the frozen, unyielding flesh.

Wolves!

What childish terrors the word evoked. What stories—read by the firelight on a winter's night—of flight and pursuit; of the laden sleigh and the faltering horses and the exultant cries from the dark.

Behind Carraday was the forest, sombre with shadow. Before him was the village of the dead . . . and the fierce living. He fled for the only refuge in sight: the mill beside the stream.

The stout wooden door gave to the pressure of his hand. He slammed it behind him and fumbled for the bolts. Then he stood for a few moments, recovering his breath.

The sound of the turning water wheel was a recurrent low groaning in the empty building. A dark object, larger than a sack of grain, hung motionless from a rope thrown over the sturdy beams supporting the idle machinery.

Carraday felt in his pocket and struck a match. Then he gave an involuntary cry of terror. The object hanging from the rafters was the body of a man: the naked, castrated body of what had probably once been the jovial miller.

The plump face, pulled awry by the rope, still had a creased and genial expression. The whole figure possessed an air of ribald humour, like some grotesque puppet jerked into view for the delectation of a childish audience.

The match extinguished itself between Carraday's nerveless fingers. Then he had only a hazy memory of beating against the bolted door, of flinging it open and running like a demented being into the forest.

He ran until he was exhausted, until each shuddering breath was a searing agony in his lungs. His stumbling feet sought the rising ground. The frozen slopes above the timber line, death from a German bullet—anything was preferable to another hour in the forest. His revolver was still gripped in his right hand. The bundle of parachute silk bumped like some persistent incubus on his back.

The sounds of his hurried footsteps seemed to trigger off cascades of snow from the overweighted trees. Every now and then some laden spruce would dip its branches and release a ghostly avalanche which blew its powdery breath into Carraday's face.

As he fled he speculated on the atrocities in the village. Who had committed them? The Germans? It was known that they were resorting to terror tactics in their efforts to crush the partisan rising.

Or the *Ustase*? The Catholic Croats whose religiously-inspired massacres of thousands of Orthodox Serbs had been one of the grimmest chapters of the war.

Pawlings, the squadron Intelligence Officer, had been very dramatic about the *Ustase*; especially about their leader—the

Poglavnik. Ante Pavelic was his name. He was installed in the splendour of the old governor's palace in Zagreb and it was related that his followers brought him tributes of human eyes as token of the zeal with which they were prosecuting the ideal of a Catholic Croatia, independent under German protection.

Emasculation and blinding, Pawlings, averred, were the least one could expect if taken prisoner by the *Poglavnik's* men.

After his little lecture on the *Ustase* and their methods the I.O. had made a gesture which had imprinted itself on Carraday's mind. With macabre humour he had handed each pilot a single .38 bullet: "For yourself if you look like falling into the hands of the *Ustase.*"

As Pawlings never flew over Yugoslavia himself, but merely awaited the pilots' return in his comfortably furnished trailer with the pin-up girls on the walls, he was able to make jokes of this kind.

The fliers themselves found less humour in the situation. There were even some who admitted to bad dreams about the *Ustase*; with their U-shaped cap badges, their banner of red and white squares—like some bloodstained chessboard—and their raised arm salute: *"Za Dom—Spreman!"*

Thinking of the *Ustase,* Carraday slowed his pace and gripped his revolver more firmly, resolved to sell his life dearly rather than risk capture and torture.

When the challenge did come, he whirled towards it, raising his weapon defensively.

"Staj!"

The shouted command was repeated. But search as Carraday might he could see nothing of his challenger. His hand holding the revolver slowly dropped under the strain.

"I'm English," he called. *"Engleski."*

Now he could expect either a bullet or a friendly gesture, depending on the identity of his unseen adversary.

For what seemed a long while nothing happened. Then the failing light gleamed on metal and from behind the bole of a tree stepped the figure of a man, holding a sub-machine gun at the ready.

Carraday found himself looking into a fierce young countenance, grimy and stubbled, with dark eyes which evinced no anger, no sympathy, no emotion of any kind except a steel-cold speculation.

Carraday's life hung in the balance. He knew instinctively that this silent stranger would kill him with as little compunction as a man stepping on a beetle. Then the light gleamed momentarily on the small red star affixed to the stranger's cap and Carraday felt an upsurge of hope.

"*Engleski,*" he repeated. With the fingers of his left hand he turned back his lapel to expose a similar emblem, cut from scarlet cloth, which he had sewn there on the I.O.'s instructions. As final proof of his identity he swung forward the parachute for inspection. When these overtures had no effect he reversed the revolver in his hand and offered it to his captor butt first.

If he had expected any relaxation of hostility he was to be disappointed. With his index finger still curled around the trigger of his sub-machine gun the partisan reached out his left hand, seized the revolver and thrust it into his belt. Then he gestured up the slope with the muzzle of his own weapon and barked: "*Pravo!*"

Carraday shrugged resignedly and obeyed. When they had been going for some while they came to a well-trodden path lying athwart their track. "*Desno!*" ordered the man with the gun, gesturing to the right.

The path climbed until Carraday guessed they were not far below the timber line. He smelled wood smoke and glimpsed the flicker of a fire between the trees.

"*Stoj!*" The now-familiar challenge rang out ahead. Carraday stopped while his captor and the unseen sentry engaged in conversation. Then the prodding of the gun in his back urged him forward again.

They advanced into a small clearing, made at some time by woodcutters working the forest. There were logs and bundles of cordwood lying about. Half a dozen people were reposing around the fire which crackled invitingly in the centre of the clearing. The slightly damp, resinous wood burned brightly, with billowing clouds of aromatic smoke.

Carraday saw heads lift at his approach, but otherwise the people around the fire evinced little interest. They reclined on logs or pine branches in attitudes of exhaustion; like languorous children resting between violent party games. Thus, unmoving, they turned upon him their silent appraisal.

Halted by the fire, awaiting the outcome of their examination, Carraday had an opportunity of studying them in return.

There was a swarthy man, as thickset as a bear, who squatted on his hams, warming his hairy paws over the flames. Beside him, looking tiny and frail by comparison, was a boy of no more than fifteen or sixteen with his mouth set permanently in a puckish smile. There was another young man, probably in his early twenties, whose cheek was disfigured by a recent wound. And there were two girls. One was a blonde, with a bony resolute face. The other was brunette and much more feminine. Her hair curled softly from beneath an Italian military cap.

They were clad in a strange mixture of captured and cast-off uniforms; German and Italian mixed with the buff and grey of the old Yugoslav army. Both the girls had, under their tunics, bright-coloured blouses made from the rayon of supply parachutes. The young man with the scar wore a pair of British battledress trousers. All the clothes were worn and patched.

They were armed to the teeth. Even the girls had grenades and knives on their belts. Their weapons—all British Sten guns, Carraday noticed—lay close at hand.

In silence they stared at Carraday and then turned expectantly towards a lean, white-haired old man whom Carraday had not noticed at first because of his withdrawn position from the fire.

One glance confirmed that this was the leader of the band. The others' air of deference towards him was unmistakable even had he not emanated such a palpable aura of dominance.

Carraday's captor subsided cross-legged beside the fire. Without removing his eyes or the menacing muzzle of his Sten gun from his prisoner he conversed with the old man in rapid, guttural Serbo-Croat. The old man nodded approvingly and subjected Carraday once again to a piercing scrutiny from a pair of eyes which looked blue even in the firelight.

The suspicious atmosphere was beginning to get on Carraday's nerves. He pulled the small green phrase book from his pocket, tilted the pages to the light and read what seemed to be an appropriate phrase:

"Ima li neko koji govori engleski?——Is there anyone who speaks English?

His pronunciation seemed to amuse them. To his relief they smiled. Then, in surprisingly good English, the old man announced: "Yes, I speak it."

"Thank God for that," Carraday exclaimed. He indicated the wings on his blue battledress. "I am an officer of the Royal Air

Force. I was shot down several hours ago. Here is my parachute."
He was glad to see that the muzzle of the Sten gun no longer
described menacing circles in his direction.

"We are pleased to see you," the old man said warmly. He
advanced towards Carraday and held out his hand. "I am Gregorich. The others call me 'Stari' because"—his blue eyes twinkled
—"of my extreme age. What is your name?"

Carraday told him.

"Ree-shard," the blonde girl repeated, and the others attempted
Carraday's christian name with varying degrees of success. All
except the bear-like man. He tested the word experimentally
several times in his mouth, then shook his shaggy head stubbornly
and said with emphasis: "Rikardo."

"*Da* . . . Rikardo!" The others showed their approval of this—
to them—more euphonious version.

One by one they came forward to shake Carraday's hand.
"*Zdravo*," the men said heartily and the boy with the puckish
smile added: "*Zivio, Engleska!*" and gave the raised arm partisan
salute.

The blonde was next. She eyed Carraday with thinly-veiled
hostility and her reserved greeting was in marked contrast to the
welcome accorded by her companions.

The dark girl, however, made up in warmth for her friend's
chilliness. "Hello," she said, giving Carraday the benefit of good
teeth in a generous mouth.

He held her small hand in his, reluctant to let it go. "You speak
English?"

"A little." She turned her eyes down modestly.

"Jelena is our scholar," the old man said proudly. "She speaks
Italian, German—and English."

"Stari praises me too much," the girl replied with a deprecatory
lift of the shoulders. "I do have a few words of Italian and German, it is true. But English is—how you say?—my best. It should
be. My father worked for many years for a British company."

"Here? In Yugoslavia?" Carraday asked, surprised.

"Yes, many of the mines here were owned by British firms." She
looked at Carraday reproachfully. "They paid very low wages."

"Capitalists!" the old man exclaimed and spat expressively.

The epithet "Capitalist" seemed to touch the blonde on a
tender spot. She nodded and gave Carraday a sour glance of
disapproval.

"Zdanka does not like Englishmen," the old man remarked teasingly. "Nor Americans. You offend her Marxist-Leninist convictions." He laughed. "Look how she regards you: wondering if you are hiding cloven feet and a tail."

"Yet she carries a British Sten gun," Carraday retorted. "And those look very much like British grenades on her belt." He found it impossible not to return the blonde's dislike.

"Ah, that's where you are wrong," the old man said, jogging Jelena's elbow in what was obviously a private joke. "Those are Russian Sten guns. Ask Zdanka: she is our political commissar and knows all about these things. Her Sten gun has only been British once—when it went off accidentally and killed one of our own mules. Then I heard her disparaging the badness of British workmanship."

"I don't understand," Carraday replied. "How can a thing be Russian at one moment and British the next?"

"It is very simple," the old man said, glancing at the surly blonde out of the corner of his eye and smiling cynically. "All good things come from Mother Russia; all bad things from the capitalist West. Do you understand?"

"I'm beginning to," Carraday said. "At least she has nothing against me personally."

"Of course not. She is a good girl and a very brave fighter. But you have caused her disappointment. She believes that all the planes we see overhead are Russian planes of the glorious Red Army. It is very confusing for her when one crashes and an English pilot steps out. Are you sure you are not a Russian in disguise?"

"I'm afraid not," Carraday said drily.

"Then perhaps you are paid by the Russians," the old man insisted gently. "It would make Zdanka much happier if she could believe you were paid by the Russians."

"Then tell her so," Carraday said. He hoped he would never be the butt of this old man's sardonic humour.

Stari spoke to the blonde in her own language. But even the information that Carraday was paid by the glorious Red Army failed to mollify her cold anger. She shrugged haughtily and turned away.

Stari's mouth twitched. "Perhaps you have some of this Russian money with you, Rikardo. Zdanka suspects that we may be—how do you English say it?—pulling the leg."

Carraday shook his head. "The only money I have is some American dollars."

"That will not do at all," the old man said hastily. "No, you had better keep that piece of information to yourself, eh, Jelena? Maria Madonna! An English pilot in the pay of the vile American capitalists. What a viper do we harbour here." He threw back his head and laughed aloud.

This is a joke that could be carried too far, Carraday thought, noticing how the blonde commissar was fingering the Mills bomb on her belt. "How do you speak English so well?" he asked the old man.

Stari drew himself to his full six feet, clicked his heels and bowed stiffly from the waist. "I was in a profession which presented me with unequalled opportunities for learning European languages."

"The diplomatic service?" Carraday hazarded.

Stari smiled. "It is flattering of you to say so. No, to put it bluntly I was—a waiter. But only in the best hotels, you understand," he added hastily.

"Naturally." Carraday smiled. "A head waiter."

The old man shook his distinguished head. "No. I was never quite obsequious enough to be a maître d'hôtel. The 'nouveaux riches' always brought out the worst in me. It is not easy to be a waiter, Rikardo, when one is proud."

With a flourish of his hand he indicated a log beside the fire. "The best table in the place, M'sieur. Will you be seated while I consult the chef?"

From Jelena he enquired: "What is the *specialite de maison* tonight? Tournedos Héloïse? Or something of the country—say *pohovana tikvica* with a little *sagan dolma* sauce?"

"I wish you would not talk of food so much," the girl said, a trifle irritably. "There is a crust of maize bread left, and a cupful of *palenta*. That is all—as well you know."

Carraday suddenly realized how thin she was; how thin they all were. Even Bradko, the bear-like man, looked as though his skin was stretched tightly over his tremendous armature of bones.

"I am not hungry," he said hastily.

"That's a pity," the old man said, "because if you are not hungry I doubt whether you will be able to stomach the *palenta*. But I can say this of it: it is hot. Let our guest try some, Jelena."

Despite Carraday's protests the cup of hot gruel was pressed upon him. He sipped it obediently. It was not unpalatable. When he had finished he remembered the malted milk tablets and barley-sugar sweets from his dinghy pack. The effect they produced upon his companions confirmed Carraday's worst fears. These people were starving.

He watched the face of the boy, awaiting his turn to take a sweet. His throat worked convulsively and he followed the tin from hand to hand with the beseeching eyes of a hungry spaniel. But when his opportunity came he would take one and no more, despite their persuasions. I am a man, his firm refusal hinted, not a child craving indulgence.

Carraday's revolver was returned to him. "A poor weapon," Stari commented, testing the balance in his hand. "Not to be compared with the Luger. You English have a lot to learn about making guns."

"We have some good weapons," Carraday retorted. He paused, trying to remember what they were. All the ones he could think of—the Bren, the Browning machine gun, the Hispano cannon— had been designed by foreigners. Even the British Army rifle was a crib of the bolt-action Mauser.

"We have yet to see them," Stari said. "The German stuff, on the other hand, is first class; well designed, well made. Not like this." He held up his Sten gun disparagingly.

Jelena disagreed. "It may look cheap, but it does its work. You yourself admit that it's more reliable than the Schmeisser. Drop it in the mud, in the snow, in the dust—it still keeps firing."

"And often it fires of its own accord," Stari added sarcastically. He smiled at Carraday. "But don't think me ungrateful. We couldn't do without these guns. I will try and get one for you. If you are to be a partisan you must have a proper weapon."

"I don't wish to be a partisan," Carraday said. "I want to get back to my squadron. Perhaps you'll show me the way in the morning."

"I will show you the way now," the old man replied, smiling grimly. "There—towards the south-west. When you have walked a hundred kilometres, and crossed fifty mountain peaks, and evaded a score of ambushes—not to mention several well-guarded main roads—you will be safely on the Dalmatian coast. Your chances I would say, being an optimistic man, are about one in a thousand."

"What other alternative is there?" Carraday wanted to know.

"You had better stay with us," Stari said. "At least we know the country. At some future date, I hope, we might get you to the coast, or to a British landing strip. There is one thirty or forty kilometres north of here, they say. We shall be travelling north-wards tomorrow."

Carraday looked puzzled. "Why northwards? Surely the front line is south of here." He untwisted the silk map from his throat and spread it on his knee.

"We go northwards because we must," the old man stated. He knelt beside Carraday, stabbing at the map with a gnarled finger. "You know how the front line runs now, eh? If there is such a thing as a front line in this mountainous country. From here—a hundred kilometres west of Belgrade . . . southwards, so—to Sarajevo. Then westwards to the coast. Now the Germans can no longer retreat up the Vardar valley. They must come this way: through Bosnia."

His finger came to rest on the map. "We are here . . . thirty kilometres behind the lines, exactly on the main route the Ger-mans have chosen for their retreat. That is why they harry us night and day: they are very sensitive about their lines of com-munication."

Carraday studied the map in the light of the old man's infor-mation. "I can see you're in a bad position here," he said. "At the very place where the Germans are consolidating their front. Wouldn't it be easier to break out southwards than to go north: deeper into enemy territory?"

Stari's jaw muscles hardened. "We must go where we are most needed. We must cling like leeches to their supply arteries. In a month or two our Army of Liberation will be commencing its Spring offensive from the south and the east. We—and those like us—can be of great use to them here." He laughed and slapped Carraday on the back. "Never mind, Rikardo; you will find fight-ing on the ground just as exciting as in the air."

There's likely to be some truth in that, Carraday thought, retying the silk scarf around his neck. He rose to his feet and stood beside the fire, staring reflectively into the coals. He could, of course, strike out on his own and try to reach the coast. But what chance would he have? One in a thousand, Stari had said. It was probably a fair estimate.

Where did his duty lie? In running and hiding for several months in an attempt to regain his unit? Or in staying and fighting with these patriots? The R.A.F. had spent several years and many thousands of pounds in training him and was entitled to some return on its investment. He certainly would not render that return by playing bandits in the forest.

But—despite its promise of hardship and hunger—the idea of joining the partisans held out a certain appeal. No one knew him here. No one doubted his manliness. The destructive image fastened upon him by his late companions had gone up in smoke with his Spitfire. These new friends would judge him on his present actions, and on those alone. No slur from the past would sully their vision.

Staring into the red cavern of flaming logs he experienced a curious surge of elation. Within him—waiting to break out of the "Twitty" chrysalis—was a new self; resolute, capable and courageous. He had felt it there for some time, but each effort at emergence had recoiled from the mirror of his companions' contempt.

Now that inhibiting scorn had been removed. Now, emerging from his old integument, he could flaunt what colours he wished and have them accepted at face value.

He found that he was smiling.

The others were watching him curiously. They saw a gentle, sensitive young man; with a trick of appearing smaller than he really was by reason of his customarily diffident stance. In fact, when he straightened up and squared his shoulders—as he was doing now—he revealed himself as of average height, or even a shade more, with a straight back and graceful carriage.

Without rationalizing the idea, they were vaguely conscious of some subtle change taking place in him. A trick of the firelight, perhaps, but he seemed to be growing in stature and confidence under their eyes.

Stari was the only one who mentally coined words to fit the situation. In his simple, uncomplicated way he thought: The parachute jump must have dazed him. Now he feels the ground firm under his feet again.

"You have made up your mind to stay with us?" It was a statement rather than a query.

"Yes," Carraday answered. "I hope I shall not be a burden to you."

The old man's gesture of assurance was abruptly terminated by a shrill whistle from one of the sentries in the forest. It was followed almost immediately by the chatter of a Sten at full automatic.

Within three seconds Carraday was the sole person left beside the fire. The others had grabbed their weapons and were slipping like wolves into the shelter of the trees. Only Stari paused long enough to beckon frantically with his left hand.

Carraday recovered from his stupefaction and pelted after the old man's crouching figure. A grenade exploded beside the abandoned fire, hurling up a column of sparks. Rifle shots punctuated the hysterical yammering of Stens and Schmeissers.

His eyes still red-glazed with the light of the fire, Carraday could see nothing but the dark shapes of the tree trunks and the old man's dancing shadow. A pin-point of flame trembled momentarily on his right and he heard the crisp smacking sounds of bullets striking frozen wood.

The old man was shooting back; firing in short, controlled bursts; never pausing in one place for more than a moment. The acridity of cordite fumes pricked Carraday's nostrils.

He was hopelessly confused. Who was friend and who was enemy in this dark and savage skirmish? The old man seemed to know. Carraday heard the snick of metal as he fumbled with a fresh magazine, and then his urgent whisper: "On your left, Rikardo! Look out on your left!"

Carraday's scalp seemed to drag tight on his skull. His vision became preternaturally sharpened. He perceived the figure of a man slipping from tree to tree in the twilit gloom. Without knowing how it happened he found his .38 revolver in his hand. His finger was on the trigger and the hammer was falling even as the clamour of the Schmeisser burst upon his ears.

He was hardly conscious of the enemy bullets cracking like whips about his head. Within him, cold and sure, was the knowledge that he had to kill or be killed. He walked steadily forward with the .38 exploding and bucking in his hand.

Then the hammer fell dully on an empty shell and the old man was tugging at his arm and shouting excitedly: "Yes, Rikardo! Yes!"

Pushing him in the back and yelling: "Get his gun. Get his gun!" And Carraday found himself advancing towards the silent shape crumpled in the snow.

The sounds of the battle were receding. There was less firing and it was more remote. Carraday knelt beside the body and heard a sound he had never heard before, but would hear often in the coming few months. The soft, choky gasping of a human being breathing out his last few seconds of life. The sound ended in a gurgle and a spasmodic tremor of the limbs.

Carraday picked up the sub-machine gun and rose dazedly to his feet. Then the old man brushed past him and fell like a ravenous predator on the corpse.

"Take these!" A pair of heavy, round objects were thrust into Carraday's hands. He felt their corrugated surfaces. Hand grenades. "And these!" Spare clips of ammunition in a small web haversack.

"Now the boots," the old man hissed, tugging with stiff fingers at the frozen leather.

Carraday disposed the things he had been given about his person. The old man was stripping the still-warm body, rolling it unceremoniously over and over in the snow as he tore off jacket and trousers, woollen jersey, shirt and even underclothing.

The other members of the band were filtering back through the forest. They gathered around and chorused their approval.

"Not me . . . Rikardo," the old man said, rising to his feet.

"Rikardo?"

"*Da*." Stari broke into an excited spate of words. Carraday could understand none of them, but the accompanying mimicry was as graphic as a familiar language . . . the menacing advance of the enemy soldier through the trees; the empty magazine in the old man's Sten; and Carraday standing his ground, defying a spitting sub-machine gun with no weapon but a revolver.

There was a respectful hush, then Carraday felt the weight of their congratulatory hands on his back. He could not take his eyes from the pale corpse in its cradle of blood-stained snow.

"You are a brave man, Rikardo," Jelena said. The pressure of her hand lingered on his arm.

No one had ever called Carraday brave before. It hit him in the guts like a draught of fiery liquor. He felt a foot taller. But at the same time he was aware of the irony of the situation. For he had not been brave at all. His action with the revolver had been a reflex of fear—nothing more. And the hit he had scored was the veriest of flukes: the other five bullets had probably missed the mark by twenty feet. But that, after all, was the fortune of war. Who received the medals and the accolades?—the lucky ones who survived. Why should he, Carraday, complain because the red gods had suddenly smiled?

"Come!" Stari said, and led the way into the forest.

They did not pause for several miles. Although he was weary to the marrow of his bones, Carraday welcomed the hard exercise of plunging in single file along the slope of the valley. It warmed his blood and sent it racing down into his numbed feet.

Breaks were appearing in the scudding cloud. A thin blade of moon scythed the waving tips of the firs and scattered a silvery chaff on the snowy forest floor. When they halted it was in the lee of a high bank, fanged with bare rock. The old man gave an order and they all put down their various burdens and began to scoop and trample a hollow in the snow drift under the overhanging bank.

Carraday was puzzled by their actions until they commenced lining the hollow with cut branches from which they had shaken the snow. They were making a crude nest into which they could crawl for warmth during the night, it being too dangerous now to build another fire. Carraday was delighted to see Bradko step forward with the bundle of parachute silk which he had believed abandoned at their last bivouac. He pulled the draw cord and spilled the silk into the hollow.

The blonde *partizanka* lay down first. Then the dark-haired girl, Jelena. Carraday noticed how they placed their weapons within easy reach above their heads.

He was motioned in next. He placed his captured Schmeisser beside Jelena's Sten and lay down at a discreet distance from the girl. But Bradko, the bearish man, shoved him over impatiently until he was pressed tightly against Jelena. The old man covered their prone bodies with fir branches before taking his place in the nest. Soon they were all lying down except Venco, the cruel-looking young man whom Carraday had first encountered in the forest. He strode to and fro on sentry duty, puffing his silvery breath at the moon.

The parachute silk grew warm under Carraday's cheek. And there were other warmths . . . the gross animal heat of the big man like a furnace at his back, and the gentler warmth of the girl where the curve of her hip fitted his belly and thigh.

Unaccustomed as he was to close human contacts, Carraday was profoundly unsettled by the proximity of his sleeping com-

panions. Especially the girl: after a while he could think only of
the girl.

As their warmths mingled, his imagination stripped away the
layers of clothing between them. He could feel the heat and softness of her flesh in contact with his own, and the sweet tumult of
emotion this aroused in him was so disturbing that—had he been
free to move—he might have sprung to his feet.

But Bradko's great bulk pinned him from behind. And the
girl, in drowsy complaisance, had twisted towards him so that the
weight of one relaxed thigh fell upon his own.

No fully conscious act of Carraday's could ever have been so
bold, but in the unguarded languor of the moment his left hand
seemed to move of its own volition and gather her closer for
comfort and protection. Reposing thus it lay upon her breast,
cupping the softness and the warmth with instinctive gentleness
and skill.

The girl stiffened and Carraday waited nervously for her anger.
Then she sighed and her hand came up to cover his. She turned
her face towards him and he felt her breath on his cheek and the
gossamer touch of her dark hair.

So she fell asleep.

Carraday lay awake, thinking: This is absurd. You can't love a
woman whom you have known for only a few hours; a woman
whose face is so recent in your gallery of images that it comes to
you mistily, like a face in a dream. Love—real love—has to be
based on long acquaintance; on mutual interests; on cumulative
affection.

But the message of his heart denied all reason. It was a joyful
message, clamorous beyond anything experienced in the past. And
it said—Jelena!

CHAPTER THREE

THEY rose at first light.

The snow was steel-blue and pitted with the sentries' night-
long pacings. How often they had changed in the night Carraday
did not know, but it was the old man who lay beside him when he
awoke. Bradko and the boy were in the forest, protecting them
against a dawn surprise.

The two girls struggled up from the hollow, rubbed their eyes, ran their fingers through their tousled hair and pulled their caps on their heads. They checked that their weapons were in working order before gathering wood and starting a small fire.

Seeing them all going about their appointed tasks, Carraday felt a little out of things. "I am under your orders," he informed the old man. "Tell me what I should do."

Stari smiled wanly. He looked weary and fine-drawn in the cold morning light. They all did.

"Bring me your Schmeisser, Rikardo. You had better learn to use it before the day is much older."

He and Carraday squatted near the fire, on which the girls were melting snow in a small pot, while Stari explained the workings of the German sub-machine gun. Briefly and simply he demonstrated how to unfold the stock, change magazines and engage the cocking handle in its safety recess.

"Remember—short bursts only," he warned, handing the weapon back to Carraday. "And keep the action clean. This is not a Sten: it will jam on the slightest dirt."

The girls had accumulated a pint or so of boiling water in the blackened pot. They added ingredients from the dwindling store in their haversacks: a handful of beans, a little ground maize. Carraday's minute share of the resulting *palenta* was totally insufficient to allay his hunger. If anything it accentuated it. Yet his stomach had been full only yesterday. God knew when his companions had last had a square meal.

"There are times when we live better than this," the old man said apologetically. "We used to get our supplies from the village in the valley, but that"—he shrugged—"is no more."

"I know," Carraday replied grimly. "I came through it."

"A pretty sight is it not?" Stari remarked without emotion. "That, my friend, is the fate of those who help us. Yet we continue to receive help. The Germans will have to kill every man, woman and child in this country before they can claim to have conquered it."

Leaning against a tree, familiarizing himself with his new weapon, Carraday was able to study Jelena. His eyes recorded, not dispassionately, that her hair was ragged and needed a wash; that she had a smear of wood ash on her right cheek; that her eyes were dark with fatigue and strain . . . and that she was beautiful.

Not pretty. There was too much honesty, too much strength of purpose in her face for mere prettiness. The hazel eyes disturbingly direct in their gaze; the forehead high and intelligent; the mouth unashamedly sensual.

It was a face free of contradictions; a face of elemental and unequivocal passions. This was a woman incapable of coquetry or dissimulation. If she returned Carraday's love she would apprise him of the fact, simply and without delay.

He watched her and waited, knowing that sooner or later she would feel the pull of his regard and turn towards him.

She was kneeling beside the fire, scouring out the pot with a handful of pine needles prior to packing it away in her haversack. Then she looked up at Carraday and smiled. She had big flawless teeth in a wide mouth, and eyes that crinkled at the corners, spilling warmth. Carraday felt like flinging his Schmeisser over the treetops and shouting with joy.

Then he noticed Bradko and the boy hurrying towards them, anxiety on their faces. Stari was standing stock-still, his head cocked, listening.

At first Carraday could hear nothing. No sound broke the snow-muffled silence but the snapping of small twigs in the fire.

"Tap—tap tap!" The sound continued, puzzlingly, even after Bradko had scattered the fire and kicked snow over the smoking embers. Wood on wood, it came first from one side of the valley, then the other. And faint human cries, picked up and passed on as though along a line.

The sounds plucked a chord in Carraday's memory. Frosty days in the woods of Kent. The beaters and their dogs coming steadily through the leafless oak and chestnut, tapping the boles of the trees.

All it needed was the harsh clatter of pheasants' wings up over the treetops, towards the waiting guns.

Except that we're the pheasants, Carraday thought grimly, comprehension dawning. We're the pheasants who can't fly. The foxes who have no earth. The hares without any speed.

His fingers brushed the cold metal of the Schmeisser and he thought: No, by God, but we have teeth. If I were in command here I'd go straight at their line of beaters: at the noisiest part of it—that's always where there are fewest guns.

He looked at the old man expectantly.

Stari grimaced. "Do you hear that, Rikardo? A *potjera*—a man hunt. We're unwelcome in this valley, it seems."

He and Bradko held an urgent conversation, the others adding their suggestions from time to time. Finally they reached a decision. "This way," the old man said, beckoning.

They set off at a brisk pace, up the slope towards the timber line. "Our only hope is to cross the ridge," Stari told Carraday as they hurried along. "The forest on the other side stretches unbroken for twenty kilometres. We'll be safer there."

Carraday looked dubious. He had participated in enough shoots to know how the guns would be disposed. "They'll be waiting on the ridge for you," he said.

The old man shrugged. "Probably . . . but if we hurry we might beat them to it—take them by surprise. The bold move is usually the best, Rikardo."

Koyasin, the tall Montenegrin who was leading the way, stopped suddenly with an exclamation of surprise and pointed at the ground. Their own tracks converged on a trampled trail made by scores of feet. It disappeared into the forest ahead of them.

"Germans?" Carraday demanded, unslinging his gun.

The old man shook his head. "No, look"—he indicated some small impressions in the snow—"there are children with them. Refugees who escaped from the village, probably."

They found the party—about forty women, children and old men—huddled at the edge of the trees, fearfully eyeing the bare, forbidding ridge. They were exhausted and ill-clad. Some of them had no shoes and had bound strips of bloodstained cloth around their frostbitten feet. Even if they made up their minds to brave the ridge, Carraday doubted whether they could summon the energy to get moving again.

Mixing with this flotsam of humanity, Carraday's own companions seemed infected with the general apathy. Even Stari's shoulders slumped as though the additional burden of the refugees had sapped the last of his resolution. For two pins, Carraday surmised, they'd all collapse in the snow and wait for the Germans to overrun them. Death could be no worse than the hunger and pain they had already endured.

He walked to the edge of the forest and examined the saddle ahead of them. It was absolutely bare: devoid of the slightest cover. Not a single footprint flawed the gleaming mantle of snow. And the snow was almost knee deep. Once they ventured from the cover of the trees they would be like flies on a vast sheet of sticky white fly-paper, at the mercy of any guns concealed on the ridge.

Stari stood beside him. "It looks all clear," Carraday said hopefully. "Any movement on the skyline would be visible from here."

He was praying that the old man would not elect to slump down and die where they were.

"Yes," Stari said dully. "I'd better reconnoitre ahead and give you the signal if it's safe."

But he made no move from the trees. He just stood there, grey and hollow-cheeked, waiting—it seemed to Carraday—for some miracle of fresh energy to impel him up the slope.

That the miracle would not materialize was fairly obvious. One couldn't expect that sort of energy from a few mouthfuls of saltless *palenta* twice a day.

"I'll go," Carraday said.

Stari merely nodded, too exhausted to demur. "Wait," he called as Carraday, sub-machine gun in hand, stepped into the open. "Let me cut you a camouflage cloak from the parachute."

He hacked a ragged panel of material with his sheath knife and draped it over Carraday's head, securing it at the waist with a length of shroud line. Against the dazzling purity of the snow the silk was pale yellow rather than white, but still far less conspicuous than Carraday's dark blue battledress.

He trudged doggedly up the slope, the snow creaking and crunching as it compressed beneath his boots. Not for a moment did he take his eyes from the skyline. The pale backdrop of dawn sky would silhouette any movement and warn him of impending danger. Then he had only to drop face-down in the snow beneath his parachute cloak to become an almost indistinguishable mark.

For the first hundred yards he felt a kind of braggart courage; striding out brave and self-important under the admiring eyes of his new companions. Then the cold loneliness of the high ridge began to oppress him and each step forward became an act of fearful resolution. Of course the enemy would be waiting on the saddle: lying back a few yards from the crest, exulting at his approach.

Carraday continued climbing because there was nothing else to do. He had passed the point of no return. He eased the cocking handle of the Schmeisser out of its safety recess and curled his finger around the trigger. At least he would get in one good burst before they shot him down.

It was almost with a sense of anti-climax that he realized the saddle was unguarded. For a few moments he stood there, breathing hoarsely, unable to believe his eyes. Then, crouching low, he scuttled forward and peered down the reverse slope into the next valley.

There he saw them . . . a platoon of German ski troops, herringboning their way up the steep incline from the road. They were a quarter of a mile below him, moving slowly, leaving behind them on the crisp snow their strange fish-bone trails. Twenty minutes later and they would have been in a coign of vantage on the ridge, able to sweep all the bare slopes below them with their fire.

Carraday slithered back from the edge, rose to his full height and beckoned urgently. Figures began to emerge from the forest and soon the whole crowd of refugees was in sight, toiling painfully up the incline. Carraday was horrified by the slowness of their progress. At this rate they and the Germans would arrive on the ridge together.

He beckoned again, hoping that his partisan friends would forge ahead on their own. But they were too busy helping the women and children to pay any attention. Even Stari was dragging a small figure by the hand.

For a few seconds Carraday stood there irresolutely, wondering if he had condemned them all to massacre in the open. Then it came to him that everything depended on his own ability to delay the German ski patrol. He turned and crept to the edge of the saddle, clutching the sub-machine gun in his half frozen hands.

A spur of rock, glittering with ice crystals, gave him the cover he needed. Crouching in its shadow he could look down on the heads and shoulders of the enemy soldiers, jogging steadily with the laboured plodding of their skis. They too were clad in white and carried their weapons slung across their backs as they balanced on their ski sticks.

Carraday longed for a rifle at that moment. Close as they were —he almost felt he could spit on them—the Germans were beyond the effective range of the small 9mm. sub-machine gun bullets. Carraday turned up the 200 metre leaf of the backsight and waited patiently. His mouth was dry and he moistened it with a little snow.

The Germans came on steadily. He could read the expressions on their faces as they threw back their hoods and searched the skyline. He threw an anxious glance over his shoulder but there was no sign of his friends. Setting his mouth grimly he lifted the Schmeisser, took careful aim at the leading soldier and pressed the trigger.

The sheer vehemence of the weapon surprised him. It bucked in his grasp, spraying most of the burst over the heads of the enemy. He hauled it down and this time merely tapped the trigger, controlling each discharge to three or four well-aimed rounds.

Whether he had hit anyone or not was difficult to tell. Every man had unslung his weapon and flung himself down in the snow. The air above Carraday's head began to hiss and crackle. A close ricochet went whimpering away over the ridge.

The Schmeisser bolt fell on an empty chamber. Carraday wrenched out the empty magazine and inserted a full one from the web haversack. As he drew back the bolt he heard a confused shouting behind him.

The partisans were pouring over the saddle in extended order, firing their weapons as they ran. They made a formidable sight; the snow kicked up by their plunging feet obscuring the shapes of those behind so that old men and women and staggering wounded took on the forms of armed men.

Carraday could see the Germans wavering. For a little while they resisted the lure of the downward slopes and the swift skis on their feet. Then they sprang upright, slinging their weapons, thrusting with their sticks, and soared away down the mountainside, leaving one inert figure stretched in the snow.

Carraday fired a long burst after them to keep them moving. Then he ran to help his friends. At that moment guns began to boom along the road and the first shells pitched on the ridge.

Later, when artillery fire became a commonplace, Carraday would be able to distinguish between the slow, droning approach of howitzer and mortar projectiles and the whip-crack of flat-trajectory 88's. Now all he was conscious of was *noise*.

Nothing in all his combat experience had prepared him for this terrifying onslaught of sound. War in the air was a war waged in silence. The thunder of a fighter's engine, muffled by cockpit canopy and helmet and earphones, became a kind of toneless quietude: a quietude in which bombs blossomed soundlessly, anti-aircraft shells opened into black silk fans, and planes disintegrated like flickering images on a silent screen. Even one's own machine guns produced no more impressive a cacophony than the rattle of breakfast food in a cardboard box.

But this was noise which slammed with physical violence against one's protesting eardrums. Bewildering, overpowering NOISE! It drove them like panic-stricken sheep into the shelter of the trees, and then made a mockery of that shelter by bringing the tall firs crashing down about their heads.

Carraday was dragging a child in either hand. The mother lay on the ridge, the top of her skull shaved off by a splinter of steel. Her husband staggered along beside them, holding his viscera in his two clasped hands. He kept up for half a mile before dying on his feet.

Deep in the thickets, safe from the shellfire at last, they flung themselves down in the snow. Then Bradko's Sten gun rattled and was followed by the big man's bellow of triumph. A roe deer, disturbed by the barrage, had floundered past and fallen to his weapon.

They ate the flesh raw, stuffing it warm and palpitating into their encrimsoned mouths. The effect on them was immediate and miraculous as though the creature's blood, hot with feral energy, had passed direct into their veins.

Stari rose to his full six feet, wiped the back of his hand across his lips, and said confidently: "There is a village on the mountain eight kilometres from here. It is strongly held by a force of partisans under *Majore* Ninkovic. If we reach it we shall be safe."

"Come," he said gently, helping a young mother to her feet. "Get up!" he ordered roughly, kicking a man whose only pre-occupation was to lie in the snow and die.

So alternately cajoling and threatening he got them on the trail once more, moving slowly but steadily towards the north. There were other scattered bands of refugees travelling in the same direction. By a process of accretion their numbers grew with each succeeding mile until the *pokret*—the forced march—comprised over a hundred souls.

At one fork in the trail they were joined by twenty wounded partisans evacuated from one of the secret hospitals in the forest. Each man in the party was blindfolded and could maintain contact only by clutching the belt or clothing of the person ahead. The doctor who was leading them was taking no chances that one of his patients might fall into the hands of the Germans and reveal, under torture, the hospital's location.

The *pokret* taught Carraday many things about life and death and the human spirit. It taught him that the will to survive is often strongest in the frailest bodies. There were the old women, bowed by years of peasant toil, who marched doggedly forward when young men were succumbing to despair and falling by the wayside.

There was the wounded partisan who stopped and turned aside from the trail when the snow began to fall. His face, which had been taut and grey with strain, softened into a beatific smile. He caught the drifting flakes in his cupped hands and Carraday, who was trudging at the rear of the column, could hear his laughter— his carefree, childish laughter—long after they had passed.

There was a woman who found that she could carry one of her small children but not both, when all those around her were too weary or burdened or sick to offer their help. She unwound the black *ruta* from her head and strangled the weaker child, before picking up the other and going on her way.

The snow fell all that afternoon and most of the night. It hampered them terribly but covered their tracks from the Germans. It also killed one-sixth of their number during the hours of darkness, when perforce they had to halt three kilometres from their goal.

One of the children in Carraday's charge succumbed that night, and the other had the blue-black line of frostbite half way up her legs when dawn broke. He carried her for the next three kilometres with her feet tucked in the front of his battledress jacket, but he knew that she would never walk again.

The *pokret* lasted only two days, but it was ten years in the development of Carraday's character. He went into it a sentimental boy, and came out a hard-eyed man, with a hatred of the enemy which no amount of killing would assuage.

CHAPTER FOUR

They lived in a shingle-roofed cottage at the top of the main street. There were Stari and the two girls, Bradko, Ivor the boy courier, Carraday, Venco and Koyasin. Carraday liked them all except the blonde *partizanka* who was imbued with a sour, Marxist-Leninist zeal. Venco was a moody, taciturn young man who seemed to be happy only when he was killing Germans. Koyasin came from Montenegro and displayed all the fierce hauteur of his mountain warrior race.

The village was crowded with partisans under the *Majore's* command. At night forty or more would pack into the living-room of the cottage and sleep on the wooden floor around the glowing stove. How none of them asphyxiated Carraday never knew, for they blocked up every crack in windows and door and by morning the air was almost too foul to breathe.

By getting in early, he and Jelena usually managed to sleep together in one corner of the room. Then when the lights were out and the darkness noisy with the snores of the sleepers, they would touch and kiss and whisper endearments. All this done very quietly and furtively, for there was an edict against love-making, even of this innocent kind, and the penalty was death.

Stari—or Comrade Gregorich as he was called by those who were not his intimates—seemed to be an important figure in this new command, subordinate only to the *Majore* himself.

Major Ninkovic still wore the grey uniform of the Regular Yugoslav army. He was a thickset, dapper man with a grizzled moustache. Although he came from a bourgeois background the partisans held him in high esteem, for he knew all about mortars and artillery, machine guns and mines. Best of all, he had a wireless set with which he could call up airborne supplies from Italy. Among the more simple peasants this was considered a miracle.

His followers respected him for his knowledge and his military punctilio, but they reserved their affection for Stari. And when they were in trouble it was to the old man they would go, with a plea that he intercede on their behalf.

Stari's relationship with Carraday was less that of the father than of the slightly raffish uncle initiating an ingenuous nephew into the pleasures and pitfalls of the world. He never missed an opportunity for a gentle gibe at Carraday's English correctness and schoolboy religiosity. It was he who persuaded him to take his first drink.

"Come, Rikardo—a little *rakija*. Just the thing to banish the cold from your bones."

They were sitting around the scrubbed deal table in the living-room of the cottage, eating their supper of unleavened maize bread and *kajmak*, a kind of cheesy butter.

"No thank you," Carraday said politely. "I don't drink."

"You make me very sad," the old man remarked, pouring himself a small glass of the fiery liquor and savouring the bouquet with half closed eyes. "The good things of life are so few in number. Wine, women and food; in that order. But then I am an old man. When I was younger women came first." He glanced slyly at Carraday. "Is that how it is with you, Rikardo?—since you do not like wine."

"I know very little about women," Carraday admitted shyly. Jelena was sitting beside him on the wooden bench and he could feel the warmth of her thigh against his own.

"What purity!" the old man commented with feigned admiration. "You would make a fine communist, Rikardo."

"I—a communist?" Carraday exclaimed indignantly.

"But yes," Stari said. "All these young communists are as pure as the snow that falls from heaven. I will prove it to you."

He held out the flagon of *rakija* persuasively. "Koyasin, a little drink? No? But it is only made from plums. Venco then? Ach, look how he spurns it. Jelena, are you so abstemious? Zdanka? No, of course not: you are the guardian of our morals." He laughed and shrugged. "Do you see what good company you are in, Rikardo? All sworn to abstinence and celibacy . . . except me. But then I am an old man. The years imposed celibacy upon me before Tito did; but neither God nor Tito will take from me the little comfort of the bottle. No, not even Zdanka with her black book of sins."

He grinned wickedly at the blonde commissar. "What will you write in your book tonight, Zdanka? That Comrade Gregorich, in tempting the younger members of the group, proved himself unworthy of the lofty ideals of the National Army of Liberation? Be kind to me, Zdanka: even recording angels should have a little mercy."

"You talk too much, Stari," Jelena said. "Even the smell of *raki* makes you garrulous. Have your drink and leave us in peace."

"All right," the old man replied mournfully. "I will drink a toast—just a small one, you understand—to you, my pure comrades. Then Jelena can sing us that touching children's song:

'Comrade Tito, the little white violet,
    We will make him grow in our hearts . . .'

And Zdanka will follow it up with a lecture on Marxist principles. The evening will be—as one of my American patrons used to say —a bundle of fun."

He peered over the lip of his glass at Carraday. "But I am disappointed in you, Rikardo. When you fell like a little white violet from the sky I hoped you would provide some relief from all the purity by which I find myself surrounded. Will you not break your vows for once and share a drink with an old man?"

Out of the corner of his eye Carraday saw Zdanka watching him sourly. "Yes," he said recklessly, "give me some of your *raki*."

"Now you are talking, Rikardo," the old man cried delightedly, reaching for another glass.

It burnt Carraday pleasantly all the way down to his stomach and left a tingling warmth behind. Zdanka was looking more disapproving than ever. "That was good," Carraday said. "Give me another."

Stari complied. "Be careful, Rikardo," he said mockingly. "Zdanka is watching. It will all go down in her black book. 'Comrade Rikardo is addicted to strong drink and is therefore unworthy of a position of trust in the Forces of Liberation'."

"She can do nothing to me," Carraday said uncaringly.

"Unless she catches you sleeping with the girls," Stari warned. "Then she will have you court-martialled and shot. Ah yes, there are advantages to being an old man. If I were young, Rikardo, I would have been shot long ago. I would have been shot a dozen times just for the sake of little Jelena here. Your purity aside, Rikardo: is she not worth risking a firing squad for?"

"Be quiet, old man," Jelena retorted, colouring prettily. "It is lucky for you our guardian angel does not understand English."

"You are right," Stari chuckled. "How suspiciously she glowers at me. What she really needs is a man—though she does not know it. Marxism-Leninism is a poor substitute for love." He grinned at Carraday. "Some charitable young man should relieve her of her clamouring virginity, even at the risk of being shot. You Rikardo . . . a British pilot would get a special dispensation of mercy from the authorities."

Carraday felt himself blushing. "She doesn't attract me," he said shortly.

"I know," Stari said. "You have eyes only for this little one here. It is a wonderful thing, is it not—this birth of young love? Cherish it, my children. It comes only once or twice in a lifetime and the memories will be tender even when your hair is as white as mine. But watch out for the guardian angel with the Sten gun. You are both too young to die."

They finished their meal with some ersatz coffee.

"Oh, for a cup of real *turska kava*," the old man complained, stirring the substitute dubiously. "You must come back here after the war, Rikardo, and we will show you what Slav hospitality really means. Are you a shooting man?"

"I have done a little."

"We have good shooting here: some of the best in Europe. I remember before the war there was an English colonel and his lady wife who came year after year to the Evropa in Sarajevo. It was his ambition to shoot a bear and take the skin home for a hearthrug."

"Did he succeed?"

"No; he was a man of great bulk, and heavy boots, and a martial tread. Bears are by nature shy creatures and they fled through the forest at his approach. So he took his revenge on the red deer and the ducks of the Neretva swamps. He was a good shot, but rather too fond of the bottle."

"Like someone else we know," Jelena murmured.

Stari affected deafness. "His lady wife was a formidable woman. She had a photograph of herself in an English society paper: wearing a black hat and sitting astride a charger. I believe she was the scourge of the foxes in your country, Rikardo. You must have heard of her: she was the wife of this Colonel Poppleton."

Carraday shook his head. "No, I don't think so."

"You surprise me," the old man said. "I thought such a person would be famous in your country . . . on such a magnificent horse, in a black hat, with the blood of so many foxes on her hands. Maria Madonna! She had hands like a butcher, that woman. Square, scrubbed pink, with the nails pared down to the quick. And she would break a bread roll, Pktt!—like that. I used to shudder for the foxes every time I saw her do it."

When the supper things had been cleared away they covered the table with sheets from an old copy of *Borba,* the communist newspaper, and sat down to clean and oil their weapons.

"There is a fault in this gun, Rikardo," Stari remarked, using a wisp of steel wool to remove the flecks of rust from his Sten. "When you get back to England you must tell Comrade Churchill so that he can rectify it. Look at this—if you carry the gun with the magazine loaded and the bolt forward, it will go off at the slightest knock. I have seen two men and a mule killed in that fashion."

"You should never carry it thus," Jelena told him. "You yourself taught us to pull the bolt back and turn it into the locking slot."

"And it cost us two men and a mule to find out," Stari said crossly. "Will you tell that to Comrade Churchill, Rikardo?"

"Oh, certainly."

"Good." The old man's eyes sparkled teasingly. "Now the Russians would never dream of supplying us with such junk."

"The Russians would never dream of supplying you with any-thing—except a lot of free advice," Carraday riposted.

Jelena was crooning *sevdalinkas*, the wistful folk songs of her native Bosnia, as she worked on her Sten. She had a sweet voice, low and husky, with a hint of pathos. Carraday closed his eyes and listened to her, enraptured.

"She is good, is she not?" Stari's voice broke into his reverie.

"Very good," Carraday replied.

The girl smiled at him. "Sing us a song of your country, Rikardo."

"What sort of a song?"

"A patriotic song: like our *Partisani Nasa*."

The only patriotic song that Carraday could remember was "Land of Hope and Glory". The thought of a solo rendering froze him with shyness.

"We English are not singers," he admitted ruefully.

Stari nodded. "So the noble colonel used to say. Although on one occasion—when he and his lady wife made their first acquaintance with *slivovitza*—he did sing us a song about ten green bottles. That was the night his wife mounted the leather sofa in the lounge of the 'Evropa' and shouted 'Tally-ho!' in a voice which caused the manager to come down from his room on the first floor. Do you know the song about the ten bottles, Rikardo? The melody was rather elusive, from what I remember of the colonel's rendering."

"I've heard it," Carraday said, "but I couldn't sing it."

"That's not surprising," the old man remarked, "for it was a song of great length and, as I said, the melody was somewhat elusive. However"—he smiled at Carraday—"if you will not sing for us then we shall have to sing for you."

So they all sang, very melodiously, while Jelena translated the words for Carraday. He was warm and drowsy from the *raki* and only the odd couplet engraved itself on his memory:

"Oh, Slavs, you are still alive,
    The Slav spirit will survive centuries . . ."

The room was filling with people, and cigarette smoke, and the close warmth of human bodies. The voices—young ardent voices —swelled in volume, rose with passionate fervour to the inevitable climax of all their singing: the glorious *Na jurish!*—We will fight!

Carraday was surprised to find that there were tears on his cheeks. He blamed them on the smoke.

CHAPTER FIVE

THE weather cleared at last, and they sat in the sun behind the cottage, ridding their clothes of lice.

It was warm and sheltered in the curve of the stone sheep wall; pleasant to disrobe and feel the sunshine like a benison on one's naked skin.

Carraday had come to accept the lice. You cleansed your clothes very carefully, turning each seam and crease to the sun, and then you slept beside forty other lousy people and the next day you were back where you started. But at least there was no typhus in this village. If and when it came it would claim more victims than the Germans.

Some of the men—and the girls—shaved their bodies completely. But this was difficult to keep up under their usual nomadic living conditions. With soap and razor blades in such short supply it was an achievement even to keep one's face close-shaven. After a while Carraday gave up the unequal struggle and was soon as hairy as a *Cetnik*. The face that looked at him out of the mirror was the face of a Montenegrin bandit; lean, weather-beaten and not very clean. He hardly recognized it as his own.

Now, leaning back against the sun warmed stone of the sheep wall, he let his eyes play over Jelena in her cotton shift and reflected that life was not unendurable.

The partisan girls did not suffer from false modesty. Sex had been abrogated for the duration of the war. Women were soldiers with the same duties and responsibilities as the men. They fought beside them, slept beside them and used the same toilet facilities —when any existed.

But love—young love—imposed a modesty which military exigency neglected. Jelena, who had on occasion washed naked in a stream under the eyes of a score of men, now blushed when Carraday's glance rose to the hem of her plain white petticoat.

She longed for a brassière, such as girls in American magazines wore, to lift her breasts into greater prominence. She feared that her breasts were too small and her legs too thin. And she—who went unflinchingly into battle—trembled when Carraday's hand brushed her own.

She trembled now; for Carraday, emboldened by the privacy of their sun-warmed corner, had put his arm around her waist and was lifting her chin with a firm but gentle hand. She knew better than he the dangers of their conduct, but his face—with the glossy new beard and the white teeth and the blue, blue eyes— was very close to her own. And life was short and uncertain after all. And his mouth was as soft as hers, and warm, and ever-so-slightly salty with desire.

Then, when all her conscious thoughts were absorbed in the shape and texture and the taste of his mouth, there was a shriek of righteous indignation and Zdanka appeared like an avenging angel at the gates of paradise.

Carraday could not understand a single word of the torrent of abuse falling about his ears. Nor did he want to. He released Jelena and leaned back against the wall, looking up at their persecutor with amused contempt.

Jelena, after her initial surprise, went on with the examination of her clothing, while translating Zdanka's more apposite remarks for Carraday's enlightenment:

". . . Slut! . . . Street-woman! . . . have you no shame? In broad daylight . . . and with a foreigner—a petit bourgeois! . . . disgrace to the glorious Army of Liberation. If you are the kind of bitch who always needs a man then why not have the decency to pick one of our own partisan boys? . . . Yes, the *Majore* shall hear of it . . . fornicators to the firing squad!"

Then the venomous mouth, the threatening red star, the gesticulating hands, were gone. Carraday sighed, rested the back of his head on his arms and looked up at the sky, feathered by the American bomber stream on its way from Foggia to targets in Eastern Europe.

The bombers were very high, like sparkling darts at the head of each snowy quill. Their fighter escort was higher still, invisible except for the fine-drawn filaments of its protective web.

"It must be lonely up there," Jelena said, lifting a comb to her dark hair. "Do you pine for it, Rikardo?"

Carraday smiled sleepily. He was close to her; close enough to see the flecks of green in her hazel eyes. When she raised her arms, tugging this way and that at her recalcitrant tresses, he could see her small breasts lifting against the cotton slip with an unconscious arrogance of their own.

"I like it better here," he said.

There was a promise of real heat in the sun; a foretaste of spring. Every now and then one of the tall spruce trees at the edge of the forest would lower its green skirts with a sigh and let its burden of snow slip unresisting to the ground.

Thin grey cracks were opening in the sugar icing of the cottage roofs and the eaves were selvedged with shining droplets.

"It will be perfect weather for the air drop tonight," Jelena said.

"You believe they will come?" Caraday had never witnessed a dropping of supplies and viewed the coming event with a certain scepticism.

"Most certainly." Jelena put down her comb and began to don her faded uniform. "The *Majore* has never failed yet. Tonight's drop, he says, will be the biggest: with machine guns and mortars—even a mountain gun." Her eyes shone. "If what he promises is true, we shall be able to cut the road to Banja Luka."

Orders were being shouted in the village street and there was the sound of marching feet on the cobblestones.

"They are going up the mountain to build the fires," Jelena said. "Come, we must hurry."

She and Carraday finished dressing, gathered their weapons and joined the tail end of the loose column marching up the trail to the head of the valley. As they marched they sang. Carraday could not sing with them, but he joined in every now and then with a resounding *Na jurish!*

Jelena tramped beside him, her Italian cap pushed back on her head, the grenades jolting on her belt and her right hand steadying the butt of her slung Sten. Everyone was in high spirits. A supply drop meant not only weapons and ammunition, but food and medical supplies, warm clothes, soap—even cigarettes.

The trail hairpinned so that the head of the column came snaking back towards them, higher up the rocky slope. They could see Stari and the *Majore* out in front; the old man taking the gradient effortlessly with his ranging stride; the *Majore* strutting beside him, every inch the military figure in his buff grey uniform and calf-high German jackboots. Bradko rolled behind them on his thick bandy legs, carrying a barrel of old motor oil. Other partisans bore bundles of dry kindling and axes and saws with which to cut wood for the fires.

It seemed to Carraday that there were more men than ever. He was beginning to appreciate the astonishing ability of the partisan army to gather or disperse as the occasion demanded. When they were needed they seemed to materialize from the forest. As German pressure became too great they vanished like smoke before the wind. It must have been very baffling for the enemy forces of occupation.

The column wound into a large clearing not far below the timber line.

"Stoj!"

The command to halt was passed from mouth to mouth. The men broke ranks and divested themselves of their various loads. Then they took a breather while Stari and the Major strode about the clearing, marking with stakes the sites of the fires.

They were reclining in the sun when the American bombers began to cross over on the return journey to their Italian fields. They were flying lower now, below condensation level, and left no vapour trails in the clear sky.

It was obvious to Carraday's experienced eye that they had come in for a rough handling over the target. The once impeccable formations were ragged and there were lame ducks limping along at lower altitudes. Each cripple had its watchful escort, usually a pair of twin-tailed Lightnings. Carraday could distinguish the shrill whine of the supercharged Allison engines as the fighters criss-crossed back and forth over their struggling charges.

The partisans were silent, watching the great concourse of aircraft across the sky. Carraday could see that they were impressed against their will. He jogged the elbow of the nearest man and said *"Amerikanci!"* But the "drug" merely looked surly, averted his eyes from the evidence and muttered, *"Ne, ne— Redeci Armada!"*

"Red Army my foot!" Carraday retorted. But he knew it was no use.

Minutes after the last aircraft had disappeared over the western horizon, there was a laboured sobbing of engines and a solitary Fortress came staggering along. It was flying very low, not more than a thousand feet, and Carraday marvelled that it could still stay in the air.

Most of the rudder had been shot away and the inner starboard engine hung by a few bolts from the twisted spar. The three remaining engines groaned under the strain. All down the metal flanks of the silver giant were the wounds of 88mm. flak. Carraday could imagine the pilot up there, sweating to hold her straight against the drag of the dead engine; the fuselage behind him full of dead and dying men, and the cold grey waters of the Adriatic still ahead. "Red Army be damned!" he said, angry this time, and wondered who would get the credit for the air drop that night.

They worked all afternoon, gathering wood for the fires. Dead trees were cut down and sawed into manageable logs, then dragged to the clearing on improvised sleighs. The five huge piles were arranged in the shape of a cross, on cores of oil-soaked kindling.

When the work was done they sat and ate their evening meal around small cooking fires. Carraday and Jelena shared a bowl of *palenta* and a few pickled plums which the peasant woman of the cottage had given them. As darkness fell the tension began to mount. Would the weather hold and the sky stay clear? Would the planes find their way to the dropping area? Might not the Germans try to interfere?

Patrols were being sent into the forest and up the bleak ridges above. Men were checking their weapons.

Stari, free of duties for the moment, slumped down beside Carraday's fire. "Well, we can do nothing now but wait."

"What time are they due?"

"Nine o'clock."

"That's early."

"Yes, it is better that way. Then we have most of the night in which to gather the stuff and hide it away, in case the Germans decide to retaliate." Stari peered earnestly through the smoke. "Tell me, Rikardo—as a pilot: are the fires adequate?"

Carraday glanced over the huge piles of timber and nodded reassuringly. "On a night like this they'll be visible for fifty miles."

"Good," Stari said, then his eyes sparkled teasingly. "These Russian pilots are not good navigators. They always come from the west instead of the east. The *Vozhd*—our benefactor, Stalin— must send them on a roundabout route."

"I'm getting tired of that joke," Carraday snapped.

"It is no joke," Stari assured him. "Ask any of the commissars . . . ask Zdanka."

"To hell with Zdanka. I hope a crate of British grenades falls on her head."

"That can happen," Stari chuckled. "Have you ever watched an air drop? Sometimes the parachutes fail to open and the stores come down—swish! boom!—almost as bad as bombs." He became serious. "I hope the parachutes open on the gun."

"What sort of a gun are you expecting?" Carraday asked.

"A small howitzer . . . one that comes to pieces and can be carried on the backs of mules. A mountain gun. I know nothing about it, but the *Majore* has seen one before. Very useful, he says."

His glance strayed to Carraday's belt. "I see you still have your .38 revolver. Any ammunition?"

"A few rounds."

"What will you do when it is finished?"

Carraday shrugged. "Throw the gun away, I suppose."

"No, don't do that," Stari said. "I will show you a way of using Sten gun bullets."

"I've tried," Carraday replied. "It's no good. The bullets have no rims: they drop through the chambers."

Stari smiled. "Give it to me." He took the revolver and emptied it. Then, extracting a 9mm. bullet from his pouch, he carefully raised several rags of brass on the rimless case with the sharp blade of his clasp knife. "Try that," he told Carraday.

Carraday dropped the altered bullet into one of the chambers. The raised brass edges acted like a rim and held the round in position where the hammer could strike the percussion cap. "Guerilla war has certainly taught you the art of improvisation," he remarked admiringly.

"That's nothing," Stari boasted. "You should see our petrol grenades and the road mines we make from unexploded bombs. Remember, we have been fighting this war for three years—without much help from anyone."

"I wish our people at home knew more about your achievements," Carraday said.

Stari beamed. "We do not seek praise, Rikardo. But we are grateful for recognition and help. The fact that your people are sending us arms now proves that they appreciate our efforts. And

so they should. We are holding down as many German divisions
here as all the British and American armies in Italy . . . did you
know that?"

"No," Carraday admitted, "and I find it hard to believe."

"It is true," the old man insisted. "High-ranking prisoners have
told us so. At this moment there are no less than seven German
army corps in Yugoslavia; but our own Army of Liberation is
three-quarters of a million strong. Do you wonder that we are
on the offensive?"

He leaned forward, his face taut with emotion. "Within a few
days our 4th Army will advance from the south. Then, with the
arms we receive tonight, we shall be able to strike a blow in their
support. The *Majore* has it all planned."

"That's more like it," Carraday exclaimed, infected with the
same ardour. "I'm getting tired of running."

Jelena laughed. "Don't be misled, my friend. There will be
plenty of running yet . . . not so, Stari?"

"True," the old man conceded. "We shall be forced to disperse
again immediately after the attack."

"And then?" Carraday asked.

"I have spoken to the *Majore* about you," Stari said. "He has
agreed to my plan. When we split into small parties again I am
to escort you to the nearest Allied landing strip. There is a new
one within thirty kilometres of here. You will be back among
your own people very soon, Rikardo."

"Oh?"

"Are you not pleased?"

"I—I—yes, I suppose so." Carraday glanced at Jelena but she
had turned her face away.

"Perhaps you will come back again—after the war," Stari said
gently.

"Why should he come back?" the girl interrupted brusquely.
"He has his own country and his own people. There is nothing
for him here."

"There is a girl," the old man said. "A girl who loves him."

Jelena made an irritable gesture. "Old men see love everywhere. It is the way they compensate for their loveless
lives."

Stari chuckled. "You had better take her with you, Rikardo.
She will be impossible when you are gone."

"He will go—and not come back," the girl said.

Stari studied Carraday's face closely in the dancing light of the fire. "Is that so, Rikardo?"

Carraday hesitated.

"Of course it is so," Jelena snapped. "He has his friends, his family—perhaps even a wife waiting for him. To talk about his coming back is foolishness."

"I have no wife," Carraday said.

"A girl then."

"No girl," Carraday said.

"There, do you see?" the old man exclaimed triumphantly. "No wife; no girl."

"He is a liar," Jelena retorted. "The English are renowned liars."

"It is undoubtedly love," Stari remarked musingly. "Ever since I mentioned your leaving Rikardo, she has been like a hen with a nest full of broken eggs. You had better treat her kindly: she has it very badly."

He ducked the girl's backhanded slap and scrambled laughingly to his feet. "Now I will check the fires again. There must be no mistakes tonight."

He disappeared into the darkness and they heard his voice instructing that a tin of oil be placed ready beside each pile of wood.

The sky was cobalt blue and crowded with stars. Then the moon came up, the biggest moon Carraday had ever seen, struggling to break through the barbed black fronds of the forest pines. It shone on Jelena's face and on the glistening track of a tear across her cheek. She sensed Carraday's regard and turned away with an abrupt movement of her head.

"Is it true what the old man said?" he asked gently.

"What?"

"That you love me?"

"Of course not," she said harshly. "It's my habit to kiss and caress with men. When you are gone it will be Koyasin—or someone else."

"I will come back," he said.

She shrugged with feigned indifference. "Perhaps."

A jingling and creaking of harness and the clip-clop of hooves told of a mule train coming up the trail in readiness for the ammunition and stores. Men were getting to their feet and craning expectantly at the sky. *"Koliko je sati?"*—What time is it? they asked one another.

"What does your watch say, Rikardo?" Jelena asked.

He held it to the light. "A quarter to nine."

"*U cetvrt do devet,*" she told those around her.

Major Ninkovic shouted an order and blazing torches were applied to the oil-soaked kindling. The flames crackled upwards, dancing and hissing in the icy air. The snow absorbed their gamboge hues, so that the black shadows of the men seemed to be standing in rivulets of molten metal.

Hotter and redder the fires blazed, crucifying the clearing on a burning cross. And above the roar and the crackle Carraday heard another sound: the sonorous muttering of aero engines. Someone pressed the trigger of a Very pistol, sending a red star curling in a slow parabola over the treetops.

Carraday recognized the familiar, throbbing roar of the Rolls-Royce Merlins and knew it was a Halifax bomber long before the black silhouette drifted into the snow-reflected light from the fires. It was low, not more than five or six hundred feet, and as it passed over the clearing the parachutes puffed from it like wind-borne seeds from a shaken pod.

The parachutes were grey against the starlit sky. Then the firelight caught their true colours and they were blue and green and black and red, brighter than festival flowers. The partisans were running aimlessly about the clearing, holding their arms aloft and prattling happily like children under a shower of Christmas balloons.

A blue parachute dumped its heavy wicker basket at Carraday's feet. He and Jelena fell upon it, struggling light-heartedly with the entangling lines and voluminous folds of cloth. They hacked the lines free and were jostled aside by three excited men who bore the basket away in triumph to the assembly area between the fires, dominated by Stari's angular figure.

The Halifax swung out of the night a second time and laid another stick of parachutes. One streamed instead of opening and the attached canister came down, going whuu-whuu-whuu, and smashed its contents to fragments against the bole of a tree. Carraday ducked, and felt a fool, because no one else seemed to have noticed such a trifling incident.

The bomber turned again, flashing its navigation lights in farewell. Dot-dot-dot—dash, went the signal. V for Victory.

Carraday felt all choked up inside.

The diminuendo of the Halifax's engines blended into the

rising note of another aircraft's approach. Four times this was repeated in less than an hour. Even the partisans seemed impressed. "*Zivio* Churchill!" someone shouted.

The cry was taken up: "*Zivio* Churchill! *Zivio Engleska!*" Friendly hands thumped Carraday on the back.

That's fair enough, he thought sardonically. But tomorrow, when the commissars have had their little say, it'll be "*Zivio* Marshal Stalin" again, and to hell with the bloody capitalists. In the meantime he accepted their plaudits with a good grace, because he could see that it made Zdanka angry.

Stari and the Major were check-listing the supplies. Everything they had hoped for had come—and more besides. Light and heavy mortars, Bren guns, Sten guns, grenades and ammunition. And on one side, in reverential isolation, the complicated bits and pieces of the 75mm. pack howitzer.

Apart from the weapons there were other treasures. Cases of medical supplies; bandages, surgical instruments, drugs. Warm British battledress uniforms. Rice, flour, dehydrated vegetables and meat. Cigarettes and whisky.

Everyone around Carraday was smoking, even those who normally abstained. The sight of so many unaccustomed luxuries brought on a temporary profligacy. Jelena drew deeply on her cigarette—one of the ubiquitous V's—and handed it to Carraday. He copied her example. It tasted terrible to his clean palate: terrible—and wonderful, because the butt had touched her soft lips, the warm glow had been reflected in her eyes. The same feeling of communion possessed him when it came to his turn with the whisky bottle. He took it from her hand and drank deeply, grateful for its scalding warmth.

"Now I've sampled all the vices," he thought recklessly, wiping the back of his hand across his mouth, "except one."

He looked into Jelena's eyes and detected the same impetuous glint, a reflection of his own. She was watching him strangely, expectantly, as though some unspoken question hovered in the air between them.

The fires were burning low, twitching like dying beings under their shrouds of grey ash. Men were starting off down the trail with boxes and canisters humped on their shoulders. The mule train jingled away into the forest. Darkness and silence waited patiently to reoccupy the clearing.

Carraday loosely gathered the blue rayon parachute at his feet and tossed it over his shoulder. Then Jelena slipped her arm through his and drew him away into the gloom.

They paused at the edge of the trees, beside the fire which had been the northern arm of the cross. The quietness of the moonlit forest was accentuated by the faint voices of the men going down the trail. Over a radius of twenty yards the snow had been melted by the fierce heat of the fire and the ground beneath Carraday's feet was warm and dry. He let the parachute slip from his shoulder.

They stood for a while in silence, their fingers linked. Then suddenly, with a catch in her voice, Jelena said: "Oh, Rikardo," and turned against him, her eyes closed, her face lifted expectantly.

He kissed her. Her mouth went slack and she seemed to have to cling to him for support. Quite naturally, without knowing how it had happened, they found themselves curled on the parachute, whispering "Yes, yes" and "*Da, da*"; helping one another with their clothing, and feeling on their exposed flesh the gently radiated warmth of the glowing ash. Jelena made soft, unintelligible sounds in her throat and locked her hands on the nape of Carraday's neck.

He was fully aware of the danger in what they were doing. But he knew that he had to do it, even if death—this very night—was the inevitable consequence. All the accumulated love and passion had to be fulfilled, no matter what lay before them in the future. He pressed her down and smothered with his mouth her small, helpless cry of abandonment.

Afterwards they dressed and donned their weapons and gathered up the parachute. Carraday tore a scarf for each of them from the blue material. They stood in the darkness and knotted the scarves around one another's throats. The act of tying the knots seemed as symbolic to Carraday as the full ceremony of the church.

Jelena moved her cheek softly against the roughness of his beard and said: "I love you, Rikardo . . . I love you now, and forever."

They walked down the trail to the village. No one had gone to sleep. There were lights in all the windows of the cottages and the people were singing in the streets and dancing the *kola* to the music of a concertina.

Carraday and Jelena danced with them, and then they went

down the street to the *gostiona*—the village inn—which was crowded to the doors with celebrating *drugovi* and *drugarittsa*.

Stari and the Major had assembled the 75mm. howitzer and it stood in the small cobblestoned square beside the *gostiona*. The peasants of the village came to bless it and touch its cold metal with their toilworn hands.

Stari was inside the inn. He saw Carraday and Jelena at the doorway and beckoned them inside. They obeyed shyly.

"I was wondering where you were," Stari said. Then he studied Jelena's face, and Carraday's, and the identical blue scarves around their throats. He smiled gently and laid a finger on Jelena's cheek. "What do you think of the English now, eh, little one?"

Without waiting for an answer he turned to the innkeeper and requested two more glasses. There was a bottle standing beside him on the counter. Stari picked it up carefully and poured a little white wine into each glass. "*Zilavka*," he said. "The best wine of the country."

Then, lifting his own glass, he said softly, so that no one else could hear:

"Your happiness, my children."

CHAPTER SIX

THE German convoy was three miles long.

In the pre-dawn blackness, with dimmed lights, it wound along the Bosnian mountain road like a slow, glittering serpent. The noises it made—rumbling of motors, crunching of tyres on gravel, clatter and squeak of half-tracks and tanks—blended into a sullen roar, like surf on a shingle beach.

Carraday watched it from the mountaintop, lying face down among the loose boulders on the summit, and felt his heart bumping in his rib cage with excitement.

In the hollow behind him he could hear the ring of spades on stone as they dug in the gun-trail of the 75mm. pack howitzer. A mule brayed and someone smacked it on the flank with an open palm and hissed: *"Ti Shina!"*

Stari came wriggling up beside Carraday. "It's ready at last," he grunted. "Maria Madonna, but the ground is hard there. We

were lucky to find enough soil in which to bury the trail. I hope
we have placed the gun to the *Majore's* satisfaction."

"Has he not come yet?"

"No, he sent a courier to say that he will join us as soon as he
makes wireless contact with Italy. If he can call up the fighter
planes in time they will massacre this convoy today . . . they and
we together."

"If we can hold it here," Carraday reminded him. He was a
little overawed by the mass of trucks and armour rumbling
towards them.

"We will hold it," Stari said confidently. "Bradko has never
failed yet. He has enough gun cotton under the bridge to lift
every stone of it into the next valley. If the *Majore's* demolition
man does his job properly and brings down the high bank at the
tail end of the convoy we shall have them as securely as flies in
a bottle." He laughed softly, exultantly. "You will witness some
killing here today."

"I don't doubt it," Carraday replied. Not all on one side either,
he thought, listening to the creaking and clatter of tank tracks
on the rough road.

Stari's teeth gleamed in the faint grey light beginning to filter
down from the sky. "You can never guess what it means to us to
hit back for a change."

"I can guess," Carraday told him. "We have been fighting the
Germans longer than you have."

"Yes, but not on your own soil. Not in the smoking ruins of
your own towns and villages. You have not seen your wives and
children put up against the wall and shot. You have not seen
the tortured bodies of your patriots hanging on lamp-posts in
your public squares."

"We have been bombed," Carraday said.

"Bombing is not so bad," Stari replied. "Bombing is impersonal. There is more horror in one body hanging from a
lamp-post than in a dozen ruined houses. Did I ever tell you
why I joined the partisans, Rikardo?"

"No."

"It happened when I was working in Karlovac . . . just a waiter
in a black suit, you understand: minding my own business. I
had to cross the square on my way to the hotel and one day I
found a hanging in progress. Two men and a woman: all accused
of supplying food to the partisans. It was one of those slow

hangings where they do not drop the victim but hoist him slowly, kicking, on the end of the rope. The woman kicked most of all, and this delighted the *Ustas* quislings in the crowd, for the peasant women of Croatia wear nothing under their skirts.

"The two men were unable to stand unsupported as the ropes were put around their necks and the Fascists shouted: 'Look! What cowards they are!' But when the bodies were cut down and stripped for burial it was seen why the men could not stand. They had been beaten between the legs until their testicles were swollen to the size of oranges."

Stari paused, watching the convoy labouring slowly up the twisting mountain trail. "These hangings and shootings were meant to impress the civilians: keep them fearful and sub-servient. But they had the opposite effect on an old waiter in a black suit. Instead of going to the hotel that evening to serve the German and *Ustas* officers, he donned his warmest clothes and went out through the back streets into the hills. And there, when dawn broke, he found other men of the town—tradesmen and shopkeepers and clerks. All they said to one another was: 'We witnessed the hangings yesterday.' "

He smiled again, grimly. "This was happening everywhere: all over the country. They say it happened in Russia too. When the German armies rolled forward across the steppes they found an indifferent—sometimes even friendly—peasant population. But behind the army came the S.S. and the Gestapo, with their whips and their ropes and their Luger pistols. And before long the once-friendly peasants—what was left of them—were in the forests, waging guerrilla war. They are very stupid people, these Germans, Rikardo: for all their mechanical genius."

He was watching the leading vehicle in the convoy, gauging the distance between its probing headlights and the dark twist in the road where the stone bridge spanned the gorge.

"And now we will kill them," he said softly. "Kill them and keep on killing them, without mercy, without pity, until not one remains on our soil. We, the waiters and the shopkeepers and the peasants; Serb, Croat and Slovene. We will inscribe the name of our country in blood across the pages of their history books."

His sinewy fingers clamped themselves on Carraday's arm. "Watch, Rikardo! Watch how Bradko uses his little presents from the English."

It started as a flash. Then the flash expanded into a bright vermilion glow, and the glow kept billowing out and out, soundlessly, like the unfolding petals of a flower.

Carraday's mind recorded the passing seconds. It had counted up to four when the sound of the explosion smashed against his eardrums. It was followed by the distant patter of boulders striking the mountainside.

Then in the far distance, behind the tail of the serpent, there was another flash. This time, at a thousand feet a second, the crump of the explosion took fifteen seconds to reach Carraday's ears. The rumble of the rockslide blocking the road took a little longer.

"Trapped!" Stari shouted, thumping Carraday so violently between the shoulder-blades that he almost knocked the air from his lungs. The lights of the convoy had gone out as though at a single command.

The partisans opened fire.

Vickers machine-guns and Brens, set up on fixed lines the previous evening, hosed their streams of tracer and incendiary bullets down on to the road. Their positions, dug into the rocky heights, covered by partisans in slit trenches lower down the slopes, were impregnable to anything but a full-scale infantry attack. This was unlikely to materialize before daylight.

Meanwhile their bullets were setting fire to the crowded transport. Before long every twist in three miles of road was a necklace of glowing beads. A heavy three-inch mortar thumped regularly on Carraday's right and on the lower slopes, within four hundred yards of the road itself, he could distinguish the twinkling flashes of the little two-inch mortars as they lobbed their bombs into the inferno.

The light improved as the eastern sky faded from indigo to grey. Now they could see the German infantry digging themselves in beside the road, and watch the tanks angrily swinging their turrets from side to side as they sought their targets. Smoke billowed from the gun muzzle of a crouching Mark IV and the shell burst near the crest of the ridge on which Carraday was lying.

"It's time we used the howitzer," Stari muttered. "Do you know anything of gunnery, Rikardo?"

"Nothing," Carraday said.

"You may have to help me: if the *Majore* does not come soon."

"Then he had better come," Carraday replied, "for I shall be of no help. I'm a pilot, not an artilleryman."

"But you have some idea of range," the old man said persuasively. "You can judge an angle in degrees. That is more than most of these *drugovi*. I am relying on you, Rikardo, if the *Majore* does not come soon."

Carraday shrugged doubtfully. "I will do my best—if necessary."

They lay and waited, but the Major did not come. Instead Jelena arrived with a message that he was still trying to contact Italy on the wireless and that they must manage as best they could without him.

"How is it going?" she asked, crouching down beside Carraday.

"It goes well," the old man replied. "But it is a great pity we cannot use the gun. Look!—the German swine are busy repairing the bridge."

There was plenty of light now, and they could see the enemy engineers swarming about the gap in the stone arch. Several steel girders were already in place, and trees beside the road were being felled for use as additional supports.

"Go and tell the *Majore* to leave his wireless," Stari told Jelena urgently. "We shall have to forget about the planes from Italy and do the best we——"

"Wait," Carraday interrupted, "at least let us try the gun first. Do you know anything about it?"

"I can load and fire it," the old man replied. "The *Majore* has shown me that much. But where the shells will go only the Almighty knows." He narrowed his eyes to peer down on the scene of enemy activity at the bridge. "Can you guess the range?"

"Fourteen hundred yards," Carraday said promptly.

Stari gave him a dubious glance. "You sound sure of yourself. It looks less to me."

"No; I timed the sound of the explosion."

"I don't understand you."

"Four seconds," Carraday said, "at a little over a thousand feet a second. It's a rough and ready method of——"

"Explain the mysteries to me later," Stari interrupted. "All right then, we have an idea of the range. What can we do about a line of sight?"

Carraday pondered. "I'll try and position myself on the crest between the gun and the bridge. You can use me as an aiming mark."

"Good." The old man nodded approvingly. "Jelena will have to act as your runner: it is too far to shout fire orders from there." He grinned and patted the girl's arm. "I hope your wind is good, little one. Between me and Rikardo you may have a lot of running."

He rose to his feet and ducked away from the skyline, beckoning the others to follow. "Come, we must make a start. Have you any other instructions, Rikardo?"

"Yes," Carraday said, "don't shoot me."

He and Jelena worked their way along the ridge of the hill until Carraday judged they were on a line between the gun in its hollow and the target three-quarters of a mile down the valley. He could see Stari and his motley crew traversing the little howitzer to follow him. The sound of the battle was rising to a crescendo as daylight revealed targets on both sides. By the intensified crackle of musketry Carraday guessed that the German infantry were attempting to dislodge the partisans from their positions on the lower slopes.

He was now about eighty yards from the gun, which menaced him with its black muzzle. He tied his handkerchief to the barrel of his Schmeisser and held it aloft. "Lie flat," he told Jelena, "and hope that the old man knows his elevation."

Stari's arm dropped. The howitzer roared and Carraday felt and heard the rush of the shell above his head. Then, to his great surprise, he saw it: hanging like a small black insect against the dawn purity of sky. He was able to follow its slow trajectory as it curved out over the valley and plummeted down towards the target. It sent up a puff of white smoke well short of the bridge.

"Is that good or bad?" the girl asked breathlessly.

Carraday grinned. "For a beginning I reckon it's bloody marvellous. Tell Stari to raise his sights two hundred yards and traverse fifteen degrees to the east. Can you remember that?"

"I think so," Jelena said. She rose to her feet, her lips moving silently in repetition of the message. Carraday watched her as she ran lightly down the slope, her dark hair bobbing under the Italian cap.

Stari listened to her and then waved to show that he understood. The girl was half way back when the howitzer boomed again, with such unexpected violence that she staggered slightly and covered her ears with her hands.

"It is spiteful for so small a thing," she gasped, falling down beside Carraday. "How was that one?"

He watched the smoke drifting up from the trees beside the road. "Tell him five degrees west; and another hundred yards up."

"You had better get this right soon," she breathed with difficulty, "or find another runner."

She set off down the hillside again, holding her right hand over the stitch in her side.

We should have a system of signals, Carraday thought. But it would take too long to explain. He saw the smoke gush from the muzzle of the 75 and turned to observe the fall of the shot. It burst squarely on the road, fifty yards short of the bridge. One of the engineers' vehicles began to burn.

Jelena was labouring up the slope. Carraday cupped his hands and screamed at her: "Tell him to keep firing on the same bearing. I think we have it."

"What?" She raised a hot, flushed face.

"More!" he shouted. "More of the same. Hurry!"

She lifted her shoulders expressively and trotted back into the hollow. Carraday saw the gleam of Stari's teeth as he grasped the import of the message. Then the howitzer began to boom every eight or ten seconds, punctuated by the thud of the breech and the brassy flash of the empty case being ejected to the ground.

Another shot fell short, and was followed by one just over. "Bracketed!" Carraday yelled, brandishing his clasped hands over his head. Ant-like figures were scurrying in all directions away from the bridge.

"Run, you bastards!" Carraday bellowed, carried away by excitement. He ducked as an enemy shell burst just below him on the ridge.

There was the sound of scraping boots and a stocky figure in buff grey slumped down beside him. "*Dobar dan*," Major Ninkovic growled, craning forward to watch the howitzer bursts. "*Da! Da!*" He grabbed Carraday's hand and shook it vigorously.

They were joined by Stari and the girl. The old man was grinning like a schoolboy. "The *Majore* wouldn't believe we had found the target. Who said you were not an artilleryman, Rikardo?"

"Something tells me we were lucky," Carraday said.

"Three shots—only three sighting shots!" Stari proclaimed. "No one could have done better, I tell you."

Carraday smiled. "As long as no one asks us to do it again. We had better rest on our laurels after this."

The howitzer had ceased firing. The crew were struggling with the breech. Major Ninkovic muttered something to Stari and stumped back towards the gun.

"Jammed," the old man explained. "A deformed case, probably. The *Majore* says it happens sometimes when they hit the ground during the parachute drop. He will fix it."

"Did he get through on the wireless?" Carraday asked.

"Yes, the first planes should be here within an hour; perhaps sooner if they can divert those already operating in this area."

"There's plenty of smoke to guide them in," Carraday observed. "Have you witnessed many air strikes?"

"A few," the old man said non-committally.

"You don't sound very impressed."

Stari stroked his nose with his finger and looked sideways at Carraday. "You want the truth?"

"Of course."

"I think these planes of yours make a great noise," Stari said. "Is that not so, Jelena?"

"A most impressive noise," the girl agreed wryly.

"But . . ." Carraday began.

"Yes," the old man continued, "I well remember the occasion when the *Majore* called up the American Air Force to destroy the bridge over the Bosna. Twelve twin-engined bombers in impeccable formation. Bomb doors opening as one. The bombs falling in a cloud . . . you remember it, Jelena?"

"How could I forget," the girl said. "There was not a stone of the church standing afterwards."

"The church?" Carraday looked puzzled. "But I thought the target was a bridge?"

"So did we," Stari said drily. "But what went up in fact was the church in the village five hundred metres away. It was a Serb Orthodox church which had stood empty since the *Ustase* persecutions. The Catholics and the Moslems were delighted at this token of American friendship."

"The Americans are inclined to be a little erratic," Carraday admitted. "Now in our Spitfires . . ."

"Ahem," the old man said, exchanging glances with Jelena.

"Our accuracy is astonishing," Carraday tried again. "I have actually seen——"

"That old man in his *kola* on the Bihac road," Stari remarked reminiscently to the girl. "It was a Spitfire on that occasion, was it not?"

"Undoubtedly a Spitfire," the girl agreed. "I know them by their rounded wings."

"*That* was certainly accurate," Stari said. "An old man on his cart makes a small target."

"Very small."

"One bony nag, one two-wheeled *kola*, one old peasant," Stari persisted. "A small mark, would you not say, Rikardo?"

"We only attack military targets," Carraday snapped.

"Of course," the old man agreed. "You are sure it was a Spitfire on that occasion, Jelena?"

"Without a doubt," the girl said. "Their wings are broad and curved at the tips; very different from the Messerschmitt's. And they have cannon sticking out in front . . ."

"Ah yes, I remember now," Stari added. "It was the cannon which blew up the old man . . . and the horse, and the *kola*. Your Spitfires have very accurate cannon, Rikardo."

Carraday had to laugh. Laughter was the only defence against the old man's irony. "All I can say is that it wasn't I who shot the old man off his cart. These mistakes happen sometimes."

"I believe you."

"One can't always see clearly from a plane speeding at three hundred miles an hour. It's difficult to distinguish between friend and enemy."

"Thank you for warning us," the old man said. "Should we dig holes for ourselves now, Jelena? The English planes will be here soon."

"I will stand behind Rikardo," Jelena told him.

Stari grinned. "And I behind you. I have seen what these Spitfires can do to old men."

Carraday's retort was drowned by the renewed clamour of the howitzer. Major Ninkovic came striding up the slope, looking well pleased with himself. He crawled into their coign between the rocks and studied the battle intently through a pair of captured German binoculars. Suddenly he grunted and drew Stari's attention to something taking place below.

"What's happening?" Carraday asked Jelena. He could read the concern on Stari's face.

"Our men on the lower slopes are being mortared out of their positions. They are giving way all along the line, the *Majore* says."

Carraday had been expecting as much. Lightly armed with Stens and a few captured Mausers, the partisans were no match for the trained German infantry in a pitched engagement. Added to which was their natural inclination to retire and disperse before heavy pressure. It was up to the planes now.

He craned forward, flinching occasionally at the close burst of a shell. The enemy gunners had guessed where the howitzer shells were coming from and were searching the ridge with shrapnel and high explosive. But most of their weapons were of too flat a trajectory to reach the little 75 in its hollow behind the hilltop.

Now he could see the grey-clad German infantrymen advancing in short rushes up the slopes, behind a curtain of mortar fire. The partisans were retiring ahead of them, doggedly at first, then in a disorganized hurry which suggested a rout. They were suffering considerable casualties despite the covering fire from their own Vickers higher up the mountainside.

"Here comes Venco—with a couple of prisoners," Jelena said.

The saturnine young man with the fierce eyes came striding along, driving the two Germans ahead of his cocked Sten. He halted them in a small depression of dead ground behind the crest and stood waiting for the Major.

The prisoners were both young: in their early twenties, Carraday judged. One was blond and of medium height, with a look of frightened appeal in his baby-blue eyes. The other was tall and dark, wearing an expression of haughty disdain on his finely-boned, patrician face. Their hands had been bound behind their backs with twine.

Stari asked them a question in German. The fair boy began to stammer a reply, but was curtly silenced by his companion. The tall German looked Stari up and down, taking in his broken boots, his threadbare clothing, his stubbled face. Then he regarded the old man's companions in the same cold, contemptuous way. "Banditen!" he said, and spat on the ground.

Carraday saw the veins swell in the Major's powerful neck. He controlled himself with an effort, muttered something to Stari and trudged off towards the gun. When Carraday next glanced his way he was supervising the dismantling of the howitzer and its loading on the backs of the mules.

Stari looked at the tall German questioningly, gently, like a kindly schoolmaster trying to understand a delinquent child. "What does one do with these people, Rikardo?" he asked a trifle wearily. "Torture them? The blond one would probably respond to torture and tell us quite a lot. They deserved to be tortured, don't you think, for all they have done to my countrymen?"

Carraday shook his head violently. "I can't approve of torture."

"But they torture us," Stari said reasonably.

"That doesn't mean that we should sink to their level."

"Perhaps not," the old man said, studying the tall German thoughtfully. "Bandits, he called us, Rikardo: because our clothes are not to his liking. Look at the scorn on his face. He cannot believe that a rabble like us will defeat his master race."

He took Carraday by the arm. "Come then. We will refrain from torturing them because we are simple bandits, not yet educated to their civilized ways." As he turned away with Carraday and Jelena he glanced at Venco and made a dismissive gesture with his head.

They had walked perhaps ten paces when the clatter of the Sten burst out behind them. Carraday whirled around but Stari and the girl went on walking as though nothing had happened. The tall German was down and the blond boy was still falling, his blue eyes wide with surprise.

Venco carefully laid down his smoking Sten and drew his knife. He grasped the twitching blond youth by the hair, pulled back his head and punched the point of the blade into his throat. Blood engulfed his hand. He repeated the casual act of butchery with the tall prisoner and wiped his hands and knife on the dead man's tunic. Then he picked up his sub-machine gun, rose to his feet and smiled sardonically at Carraday before strolling off towards the battle.

Carraday felt cold and sick as he hurried to catch up with Stari and Jelena. "You knew that was going to happen," he accused the old man.

"Yes," said Stari, looking straight to the front. "I knew."

"And you did nothing to stop it?"

"No," the old man said. Neither he nor Jelena glanced at Carraday.

"Christ!" Carraday exclaimed. "You're as bad as they are." He passed a trembling hand across his brow. "As for that Venco . . . a damned butcher, that's all he is. What kind of man can do a thing like that?—and smile afterwards!"

The mules were jingling away in single file, their backs humped awkwardly with the bits and pieces of the howitzer. Stari and Jelena trudged behind them. Carraday followed, seething with icy rage.

After a while Jelena dropped back and put her hand on Carraday's arm, as though seeking understanding. He shook her off.

What sort of woman was this, anyway? he thought wonderingly; who can witness two men being murdered with less emotion than an Englishwoman confronted by a mouse.

What sort of children will she bring into the world one day? How bereft will she feel when they sound the cease fire and take her Sten gun and her grenades away from her? How many men has *she* killed?

He walked on, stony-eyed, ignoring the hurt on her face.

They descended into the valley, the patter of small arms fire and the thumping of mortars and artillery fading behind them. They crossed a small river and zigzagged up a loftier hill which brought them once more within sight of the battle. The spectacle of the mule train labouring up the barren slope invited an angry storm of 105mm. shells from the enemy guns unlimbered on the road.

Carraday marched on, uncaring. To cries of *"Pozurite! Pozurite!"* men and mules were scattering in all directions. Jelena ducked as a shell burst nearby and for once Carraday did not feel the usual fearful solicitude for her safety.

The mule carrying the wheels of the howitzer brayed hoarsely and fell on its knees, blood gouting from its neck. Two partisans came running with a spare beast and transferred the load. No one bothered about the wounded mule which remained on its knees, blowing pink frothy bubbles between its big yellow teeth. Carraday shot it through the head before going on.

He was the last to gain the safety of the crest. The Major had found a fresh position for the howitzer, in the shelter of a limestone outcrop. They were fitting the wheels and digging a place for the trail as Carraday arrived.

Stari was propped on his elbows behind a low shelf of rock, studying the Germans through the Major's glasses. Jelena was with him. She avoided Carraday's eye as he slumped down a few feet away.

"Rikardo," the old man said. He too was angry now, Carraday observed.

"Yes."

"You asked what sort of man Venco is: I will tell you."

"I know what he is," Carraday replied shortly. "A butcher."

"He was not always like that."

"No?"

"The Germans made him what he is."

"It's a useful excuse," Carraday said.

Stari shook his head and sighed.

"Why trouble to explain?" the girl asked bitterly. "What do the English know of war?"

"At least we don't make a habit of killing prisoners," Carraday retorted.

"When last was England invaded?" Jelena enquired. "When last were your women raped and your towns and villages put to the torch?"

"Don't talk about such things," the old man advised. "You will shock his pure English mind."

"I will shock him," Jelena said. "I will tell him about Venco."

"Venco! Venco!" Carraday snapped irritably. "I know all I want to know about him. He's a surly, introspective young man who smiles only when he kills."

Jelena said nothing. She rose abruptly to her feet and walked away to help with the gun. Her departure left an awkward silence.

"You have hurt her," the old man said.

Carraday pretended to be absorbed in his study of the enemy convoy.

"We do not do this for pleasure," Stari remarked quietly.

"I know that."

"We did not ask the Germans to invade our country. We were ordinary people before they came."

Carraday remained silent.

"Take Venco," the old man said. "The ordinary son of an ordinary farmer; with a mother and two sisters, and all his life ahead of him."

"He has a natural propensity for killing," Carraday retorted.

"You are wrong," Stari said. "When the Germans came to his father's farm he was a normal boy of eighteen. There had been some partisan activity in the area and they suspected him of being involved. They tortured him."

Carraday listened, unmoved. He had heard so many tales of German brutality that he was becoming inured.

"They stripped him and tied his hands behind his back and beat him with rifle butts," Stari went on levelly. "He could tell them nothing . . . he knew nothing. So they fastened a noose of copper wire around his genitals and dragged him from one side of the room to the other. He fainted. When he recovered consciousness the Germans had gone, taking his family with them. They have never been heard of since. Venco was found that night by our men. His hands were bound and the wire noose was still in position, drawn tight as they had left it. Gangrene had already set in. That's the kind of man Venco is . . . if you can still call him a man."

"I'm sorry," Carraday said. He felt sick.

"We live with these things," the old man continued. "They become normal to us. And then someone like you comes along and reminds us how we used to be—what butchers we have become. You are a disturbing person to have around, Rikardo."

"I'm sorry," Carraday repeated. He wished the girl would come back so that he could ask forgiveness for his lack of understanding. He looked for her but she was standing, a small disconsolate figure, beside the assembled howitzer.

Major Ninkovic came and conversed with Stari before rejoining the gun crew.

"He wishes us to direct his fire," Stari informed Carraday. "If you give me the corrections I will shout them to him."

The first shell blasted over their heads.

"Left ten degrees. Down three hundred yards," Carraday ordered, observing the tiny white puff on the hillside beyond the road.

When he looked around the girl was lying beside him. He took her hand in his and saw her eyes close against the sudden welling of tears. He knew then that despite the Sten gun and the grenades she was as vulnerable as any other girl in love.

Then he saw the first flight of Beaufighters slipping silently over the far mountain peaks and diving like silver minnows into the valley. "The planes!" he shouted, and the old man gave a hoarse yell of exaltation and made wild beckoning motions at the Major.

There were four Beaufighters in line abreast. They came skimming above the tips of the tall forest spruce, the whisper of their quiet sleeve-valve engines almost lost in the racket of the battle. Like probing fingers the smoky trails of their rockets reached out towards the crowded German transport.

Jelena's hand tightened in Carraday's as the sixty-pound explosive missiles burst all along the road, shattering vehicles, bringing down minor cascades of earth and stones from the overhanging banks.

Then the twin-engined fighters pulled up and banked overhead; so close that the partisans on the hilltop could see the grotesque masked shapes of the pilots crouched behind the twinkle of sun-dusted perspex. They waved and shouted madly as the fighters went plunging down again, each machine streaming grey wisps of smoke from its four cannon and six machine guns. The cannon shells sparkled like spilled jewels among the squat black shapes of the German transport.

Still in line abreast the four machines lifted over the mountains and vanished, leaving a dozen new oil fires behind them.

The entire gun crew had deserted their gun and were stretched out on the crest beside Carraday, revelling in the spectacle.

"I take back all I said about the planes, Rikardo," Stari shouted joyfully.

Carraday merely grinned and pointed, for there were eight Spitfires throbbing over the western peaks. They were up at about five thousand feet and to Carraday's companions hardly larger than black dots in the sky. Carraday knew they were Spitfires by their characteristic "sit" in the air; the way an experienced duckhunter can tell mallard from teal or pochard almost as soon as they have winged into sight.

The Germans were not to be taken by surprise again. Black smears of 88mm. flak began to dirty the sky around the approaching fighters as they swung loose battle formation into bombing echelon. Carraday could see how they were working around to the east to come down out of the sun.

"Now!" he said to Jelena, as the first plane imprinted its elliptical wings against the sky and fell away into the bubbling cauldron of light flak.

Actually hearing anti-aircraft fire for the first time, he was staggered at the volume of lead and steel and high explosive being delivered at the diving planes. The big 88's were silent now as the nimble fighters stepped within their ponderous punch. Their task was taken over by the spitting 37's, the vicious four-barrelled 20's, the Spandaus, the Mausers—even the Lugers and Schmeissers as the planes swept low from their bombing dives. The thousands of individual reports fused into one continuous roar of sound like the ripping of a huge sheet of calico. Glowing streaks of tracer imprinted their bright tracery lingeringly on the eye's receptive retina, so that the whole sky seemed an impassable web of fire.

"For the love of God—how do they get through?" Stari demanded, as the fighters swooped and rose unscathed, twisting and turning to shake off the pursuing shells.

"Watch carefully," Carraday told him, shouting to make himself heard above the reverberation of exploding bombs, "and you'll see that nearly all the bullets go behind them. It'll be a bad day for pilots when ground gunners get it into their thick heads that they must fire fifty or a hundred metres in front of a plane —not at it."

"I see," Stari said thoughtfully. "Is that why we never hit the Messerschmitts when they come? They are so close sometimes that one can see the rivets in the skin and the oil leaks around the engine; yet we never hit them."

"Messerschmitts?" Carraday exclaimed. "There are none left here now, surely."

"That's where you are wrong," the old man said. "They come from Bihac and from Karlovac, towards dusk, when all your planes have gone home to roost. Heinkels we get too, and even those slow ones with the bandy legs which scream as they dive."

"Stukas!"

"Yes. It would not surprise me if they come tonight, looking for us. But we shall be in the forest by then."

He stopped talking to watch the Spitfires skimming in at tree-top level, their cannon winking brightly in the leading edges of their slender wings.

"Maria, but they are things of beauty," the girl said breathlessly.

Carraday winced, watching the sparkle of shell strikes along the fuselage of the second machine. It pulled up abruptly, trailing smoke. Fragments broke away from the windmilling propeller. "Oh Christ!" Carraday said feelingly. He did not want to witness any more, but there was a morbid fascination in watching the stricken machine curve over on a rising scream of despair and plunge down towards the hillside.

The sullen wuumph! of the impact was a sound like no other; a sound compounded of torn earth and rending metal, of buckling spars and bursting tanks and the instantaneous shredding of living flesh.

There was the roaring crackle of high-octane fire, fed with oil and cordite and magnesium. It sent its foul breath over the hill-top; a hot acrid stench, with faint undertones of roasting meat.

"The pilot——!" Stari cried, scrambling to his feet.

"Forget it," Carraday growled. He turned on his back to watch the Spitfires winging away overhead. One was trailing the white vapour of coolant from its radiator. You won't get home, you poor sod, Carraday thought.

There was a lull before the next air attack. Stari and the *Majore* got busy on the howitzer again and with Carraday's help ranged it in on the bridge. Wounded and demoralized partisans began to stagger past in two's and three's and then by the dozen and the score. Their hands and faces were blackened with powder stains from their Stens and they looked as though they had seen enough of the tough German infantry for a while. Even the men who would obviously die were being dragged along, gasping and crying in their pain. It was a holy Partisan principle never to let a friend fall alive into the pitiless hands of the enemy.

The next planes were Mustangs, the sun glinting on their uncamouflaged silver flanks and bubble canopies. They came darting down behind their pointed scarlet spinners, six .5's belching, pot-bellied air-scoops hanging open like kangaroo pouches.

Faster even than the Spitfires, they whistled unscathed through the flak, which seemed to be losing some of its venom. But when the Mustangs had gone and four lumbering old Hurricanes appeared it redoubled its fury as though in anticipation of easy prey.

Carraday watched the approach of the Hurricanes with a sinking heart. Contrary to the propaganda-inspired public image he knew them to be poor aircraft, always labouring under a disadvantage. He felt very sorry for the pilots, perched in their fabric-covered fuselages, peering out through the birdcage latticework of their old-fashioned cockpits, trying to coax a few more m.p.h. out of their tired engines. After the Mustangs' flashing attacks they came bumbling in like early-season pheasants towards the waiting guns.

One released its rockets and pulled up over Carraday's head. He looked and saw daylight punched through its wings by the 20mm. shells and a stream of glycol pouring from its punctured radiator. It staggered away to die in the forest over the hill and he took his eyes from it in time to see a second plane spread its flaming wreckage over a hundred yards of rocky hillside. The surviving two pulled away, but turned almost immediately for another attack.

"Crazy bastards," Carraday muttered admiringly. Hurricane pilots always seemed to be a little braver than anyone else. They had to be.

They came in very low this time, jinking from side to side in a vain attempt to substitute manoeuvrability for speed. The guns found their range and latticed the sky with multiple bars of tracer.

Carraday groaned as black smoke belched suddenly from the cowling of the leading plane. It towered like a heart-shot bird and rolled slowly on its back. A small black figure detached himself and fell away. The parachute was still streaming, unopened, when he struck the ground.

The surviving Hurricane turned for home.

"I did not like that," Jelena said sombrely. "They had better send more of the silver ones next time."

But if there was a next time they did not witness it, for shortly afterwards the Germans gained the neighbouring ridge and ranged in on the howitzer with their heavy mortars. With the bombs bursting all around there was no time to dismantle the gun. The trail was hitched to the nearest mules and the stubby howitzer went bumping and jouncing down the slope, with the crew running alongside to lend a steadying hand.

The mortar bombs followed them into the forest and Carraday learnt another of the infantryman's lessons: that tree-bursts high overhead were even more deadly than bombs bursting in open ground. They lost two of the gun crew there and the Major was hit in the arm by a jagged splinter.

There was no rest for them now, for Bradko arrived to report that reinforcements of Alpine troops had been sighted coming down the Banja Luka road.

The cry of *"Pokret!"* went up again and they straggled wearily off towards the north, seeking the wilder forests and the deeper gorges, knowing that German vengeance was never more than one step behind.

A tatterdemalion mob, smoke-grimed and battle-weary, they made heavy work of the rough terrain, with the wounded dragging ever more pitifully in their wake

The wounded walked until they could walk no farther, and were then carried on improvised litters. When the litter bearers discovered that they were carrying a corpse they deposited it at the wayside. If the earth was soft they scratched a shallow grave. On stony ground they contented themselves with a few concealing pine branches. Carraday began to understand why the wolf population of Bosnia had shown such a marked increase in the past three years.

He never ceased to marvel at the fortitude of the women on these marches. The *partizankas* ate less, complained less and endured more than the men. For several miles he helped carry the litter of a girl whose leg had been blown off at the knee by a mortar bomb. For some reason her blood refused to clot and despite all their efforts with bandages and tourniquets they knew that she was bleeding to death. She knew it too, and could still smile.

One of the couriers, a boy of fourteen, was her brother. He walked beside the litter, laughing and making jokes. Carraday was glad that he at least seemed unaware of the seriousness of his sister's condition.

They crossed a clearing where the white crocuses drifted like snow up against the south-facing boulders. The boy knelt and gathered a bunch of them for his sister. He gave them to her and suddenly turned his face away. Then Carraday saw that he had known all along that she was bleeding to death and that the crocuses represented the words of love and affection which a fourteen-year-old boy could never find or express.

She was holding the bunch of white flowers on her breast when she died; and the boy, who had joked and laughed up until that moment, sat down beside the litter and howled like a small lost dog.

This was one of the dead they could not leave under a shroud of pine branches. Carraday and Jelena stayed behind to help bury her, with Venco a hundred yards up the trail to guard against surprise. They fashioned a small wooden cross and placed the white crocuses beside it.

Then Jelena lifted the boy to his feet, hugged him tightly for a moment and led him away by the hand. He followed unprotestingly. Carraday had once seen a newborn calf behave like that: transferring its dependence from its mother's lifeless body to the first warm, friendly thing that chanced to come along.

At dusk, as Stari had predicted, the German planes came looking for them. A Heinkel flew overhead in the failing light without seeing the struggling column toiling through the trees. Then a Fiesler Storch hung about above their heads, thin-bodied and spindly-legged, with a wasplike drone from its small engine. It tracked them through the forest like some malevolent insect and its presence attracted two Messerschmitts which swooped down with glowing exhaust ports and barking cannon to strafe the refugees.

Darkness drove away the enemy planes and brought a northeast wind which banished with its frozen lash all memories of spring. It rained and then the rain turned to sleet which tinkled metallically on rifle butts and stiffened capes. After the sleet came a face-numbing cold.

Stari called a halt and they searched the surrounding forest for wood with which to build a fire. The wood was damp and would not hold a flame. The small clearing was full of people standing silently in the darkness, waiting for the warmth and light they needed to survive the night.

They used all the scraps of paper in their possession. Then they wrenched bullets from their brass cases and poured the loose cordite on the pine needles. The flame hissed hotly for a few seconds and left a spiral of acrid smoke and a dying glow in the ends of the damp twigs. Stari cursed softly and methodically as match after match succumbed to the wind and the cold.

No one else said anything. Each brief spurt of light illumined tired faces and drooping figures: a tableau of ineffable weariness.

Then Carraday felt in the inside pocket of his battledress tunic and pulled out the Bible which his mother had given him: the red leather-bound Bible with the gold-edged pages, and the inscription in her cramped, minatory hand: "Fear God and Keep His Commandments!"

I *have* feared God, Carraday thought, standing there in the darkness with the Bible in his hand. I suppose I've been afraid of Him all my life, in accordance with my mother's teaching.

But the strange thing is that I fear Him no longer. When I can bring myself to believe in Him at all, I pity Him, because He has made such an unholy mess of things and that must surely trouble Him.

I don't suppose my mother would approve of her gift going up in smoke to provide a night's warmth for a few ragged guerillas: atheists, most of them—and communists: her two *bêtes noires*. But here it is: it's been a heavy thing to carry around all these years, in more ways than one.

She was a good woman—my mother. Very stern and pious and unforgiving in her condemnation of what she used to call "the world". I don't blame her for believing that all earthly pleasures are a mockery which divert men's minds from the "real life" beyond the grave. It's a belief that seemed to suit her very well; but it was a hell of a creed in which to rear a sensitive and impressionable son.

He handed the Bible to Stari and the old man stood with the weight of it in his hand, puzzled at first and then comprehending.

"*Hvala*, Rikardo," he said simply.

The flames ran upwards through the crumpled pages and the pine needles and the small twigs, purring harshly as they rubbed their thin red shoulders against the logs above.

Well, it made a good fire, Carraday thought as the logs began to crackle. And it's nice to know that I carried it all these years to some purpose.

It's strange to see something which exercised so much power over me vanishing like that in a puff of heat. I shall feel a little lost without it, for a while. It was more than just a book in my pocket. It was a conscience, and a talisman. I used to feel that I would come to some harm if I lost it. But I no longer feel that way.

Why, even if it were the passport to heaven I would trade it now for the sight of these few faces that I love pressing in upon the warmth that I have given them.

I thought I feared God, but what I feared in reality was life itself. I suppose my mother feared it too, which was why she held herself aloof from it, looking for something better in the world beyond.

But this is the world we find ourselves in: with its pain and its sweat and its tears . . . and its love and its close human companionship.

He looked down at Jelena and she smiled at him and placed her small cold hand trustfully in his.

It may not be much of a world, he thought; but it's where I want to be.

CHAPTER SEVEN

THE British Major came out of the largest and most imposing house in the village and stared at Carraday.

The house was the headquarters of the British Military Mission in that district and the Major was in command. He stared at Carraday wonderingly, resentfully, and then with controlled anger.

Carraday smiled at him. It was good to see a British face again, even if that face belonged to a pompous, polished pipsqueak of a pongo officer like this one.

The Major was of medium height and as slim as a lath. The way he carried himself—as though a broomstick had been rammed up his backside and he was still getting used to the feeling—made him appear taller than he was. His barathea uniform was beautifully tailored and immaculately pressed There was a Yugoslav woman from the village who came in every day and ironed the uniforms of the Military Mission. There was another who cooked their meals and two more who did the dusting and cleaning. They were grateful for the work: it was better than starving.

There was also a Yugoslav youth who polished the Major's boots. They were fine boots and the boot-boy was a very industrious polisher. Carraday could see his own reflection in the toe caps of the Major's boots.

The Major carried a handsome walking stick and he put the point of it on the ground and crossed one creased trouser leg over the other with studied insouciance. Then he twitched his neatly-trimmed moustache once or twice and asked coldly: "Well?"

Carraday, still smiling—for it was good to see such familiar pomposity in a Bosnian village—replied: "Flying Officer Carraday, sir. I was shot down three months ago, south of Banja Luka."

"I see," the Major said.

He looked Carraday up and down and his disapproval showed in his pursed mouth and frosty eyes.

R.A.F.—the look said. The blue-eyed boys. The debs' delight. The scruffy bastards who think, because they drive aeroplanes, that they're a cut above everyone else. It infuriated the Major still more to observe that Carraday, apart from being unkempt and unwashed, had left the top button of his jacket undone in the traditional fighter pilot manner.

"Where have you been all this time?" he demanded.

"Fighting with the partisans," Carraday answered blandly.

A few months ago this Major would have terrified him half to death. Prior to meeting Stari and Jelena, Bradko, Venco and the rest, he'd have "Yes, Sir'd" and "No, Sir'd" this minor martinet; licked his polished toe caps if need be. Now he merely shrugged his Schmeisser into a more comfortable position, crossed his own legs and looked the Major in the eye. It was the Major's glance which wavered.

"You should have got back to your unit a long time ago," he accused.

Carraday did not actually tell him to go and get stuffed. Sometimes a look can be as eloquent as the words.

The Major's eyes became a little bloodshot with rage. Here's a bloody glamour-boy, he thought; marching in as though he owned the place. Scruffy as hell. Hair half way down his collar. Three months beard. Sub-machine gun on his back; grenades, knife, revolver . . . like a damned brigand. Expecting me to help him, no doubt; and not even the courtesy of some respect for my rank. Jesus, I'll show the bastard!

"I haven't time to talk to you now," he said icily, glancing at his watch as though some urgent Military Mission business required his immediate attention. "Report to my office this afternoon at two—no, three," he amended, thinking of his lunch.

He looked Carraday up and down again; a subordinate-shrivelling look. "And get yourself cleaned up beforehand. You're the idlest-looking man I've ever seen!"

He took a pace forward, expecting Carraday to jump out of the way. Carraday did not jump. He shrugged the webbing sling of the Schmeisser into a fresh position and said: "Excuse me, sir."

"Well?" the Major barked. "What is it?"

"When do you expect the next plane to arrive?" Carraday asked.

"Plane? What do you mean?" the Major demanded testily.

"You have a landing strip over the hill," Carraday explained patiently. "I saw it this morning as I came in. When do you expect the next plane?"

In barely controlled tones the Major said: "The arrivals

and departures of aircraft are matters of the strictest secrecy."

"I realize that, sir."

"However, if we're not crowded out with wounded to be evacuated, I'll see if we can fit you on the next one—within three or four days."

"Thank you, sir," Carraday said. As the Major attempted to brush past he added: "There's another thing."

"What the hell is it?"

"I have a woman with me, sir . . . a *partizanka*. Will it be possible for her to accompany me?"

"Is she wounded?"

"No, sir."

"Then it's out of the question. Who is she?"

"My fiancée."

"Your what?"

"My fiancée, sir. I wish to take her back with me to Italy so that we can be married."

The Major controlled himself with a great effort. "Carraday," he said in a trembling voice, "may I remind you that there's a war on. Do you really imagine that you can use a high-priority military aircraft as a sort of honeymoon taxi?"

Carraday kept his temper. He had caught sight of his reflection in the window and it occurred to him that maybe he knew more about there being a war on than this powder-puff Percy. But Jelena's safety was at stake and he had to play it carefully.

"I believe her life to be in danger, sir," he said, wishing it didn't sound so melodramatic.

"What do you mean?"

"They may sentence her to death," Carraday explained. "For —for associating with me."

It took the Major some while to digest this information.

"Have you—er—been intimate with this woman?" he asked chillingly.

"I believe that's the expression," Carraday said.

The Major's lip curled. "So that's why you've been three months in the forest? Shagging the local bint."

Carraday thought of Jelena and kept quiet.

"Of all the bloody irresponsible . . . !" the Major stuttered. "Don't you know that we're working our guts out trying to remain on amicable terms with these people?"

"Yes, sir."

"Now a bastard like you comes along and breaks all the rules. I'll have you court-martialled for this, Carraday."

"I'm not concerned with what happens to me, sir. It's the girl's life I'm thinking of."

"I'm afraid that's something we shall have to leave to the local authorities."

"But, sir——"

The Major cut him short. "We have no jurisdiction over this sort of thing. The girl has committed a crime and will be tried by Partisan law." He glanced contemptuously at Carraday. "It's lucky for you that as a member of His Majesty's Forces you fall under my protection."

"But can't you understand, sir?" Carraday said hoarsely. "She'll be shot."

"You should have thought of that in the first place," the Major replied coldly.

Carraday's right hand had fallen to the butt of his pistol. Jesus, the Major thought, this is a dangerous bastard! The sooner we have him disarmed the better.

"I'll speak to the Political Commissar about it," he said grudgingly. He did not like the look in Carraday's eyes at all.

"Thank you, sir. The girl's name is Jelena Vedajic. Perhaps if you explain that we're betrothed—that she'll be leaving the country with me . . ."

"I'll try," the Major said. "I can promise no more." He was glad that Carraday had taken his hand from the gun.

Carraday walked back down the village street. There were not many houses left. The Italians had occupied the village after the Axis invasion. Then the partisans had driven them out. Then the Germans and the *Ustase* had driven out the partisans.

There were none of the original inhabitants left when the partisans finally returned. They were all lying in a long trench which they had dug themselves under the supervision of the German soldiers. The trench was covered with a thin layer of earth and lime. It was not a good place to get down-wind of now that the weather was warming up.

Most of the wooden cottages had been burnt, with the sick and the bedridden in them. If you kicked about among the ashes you came across pieces of bone, charred and yellowed by the heat.

The stone houses were still standing, their walls inscribed with defiant slogans: *"Zivio Tito! Zivio Stalin! Zivio Redeci Armada!"*

And daubed on another house in huge white letters: *"SMRT FASCIMO—SLOBODA NARODA!"* Death to Fascism—Freedom for the People!

Zdanka was sitting in the sun against the wall with a man whom Carraday did not recognize. She had removed her cap with its red metal star and the sunlight glinted on her cropped blonde hair. At the sight of Carraday her broad Slav features twitched in the semblance of a smile.

That's bad, he thought. When Zdanka smiles—that's bad. He felt a chill of foreboding.

He went on down the street, looking for Jelena. But it was Stari who hissed at him from behind a broken wall.

"Rikardo! . . . here!"

Carraday glanced around with assumed casualness. No one seemed to be watching. He vaulted the tumbled stones and sank down behind.

"What is it?"

The old man's face was grim. "Jelena . . . they've arrested her."

"Who has?"

"The men of the Commissar of this district. Zdanka has been telling tales and when you were at the Mission three men came and took her away . . . for questioning, they said."

"What does that mean?"

The old man shook his head despondently. "It is bad, Rikardo."

"Will they sentence her to death?"

"It would not surprise me."

"Can't *you* do anything?" Carraday appealed. "The men respect you: you are their leader."

"No," Stari said, "Tito is their leader. He and the Communist Party make the laws and the Commissars carry them out. I have no authority."

"But the men . . . ?"

"The men will not go against Partisan law, Rikardo. I know that only too well. One of the rules forbids looting. Once, in the early days, I saw two boys of sixteen shot for stealing grapes from a peasant's vineyard. The men who were detailed for the execution wept at what they had to do—but they carried out their orders. It will be the same with Jelena."

His eyes searched Carraday's face. "Did you speak with the English *majore*?"

"Yes."

"Did he offer to help?"

"He said he would try . . . but I don't think he'll try very hard. I am to see him again this afternoon."

"And if that fails?"

Carraday's face hardened. "Then I'll rescue her myself—or die in the attempt."

For the first time Stari smiled. "I was hoping you would say that, Rikardo. I was hoping very much you would say that. All the way here I was watching you and wondering: How much does he love Jelena? Enough to want to marry her? To take her back to England? To risk his life for her? Or just enough to sleep with her in the forest? You must forgive me, Rikardo; but old men become cynical. I thought perhaps when you were with your own people again, when the plane came from Italy and home seemed near, you might find it easy to forget a little *partizanka* who showed you some affection. But that is not so, is it, Rikardo?"

"She is the only woman for me," Carraday said quietly.

"Then it's all very simple," the old man remarked. "We will rescue her together."

Carraday was deeply moved. "I don't expect you to implicate yourself in our troubles."

"This is a matter that touches me too," Stari said. "The longer I live the closer I feel to a few people, and the more distant from the mass. You and Jelena are prominent among those few. What respect would I have for myself if I allowed her to go to the firing squad?"

He and Carraday shook hands impulsively.

"If we manage to rescue her—what then?" Carraday asked.

"I have heard a story in the village," the old man said. "They say that the British have been allowed by Tito to move several squadrons of fighters from Italy to Yugoslavia; to a place called Prkos, near Zadar on the Dalmatian coast. Would your unit be amongst them, Rikardo?"

"What kind of planes?" Carraday asked.

"Spitfires," Stari answered, "and some of those slow ones that burn so well when the flak hits them."

"Hurricanes," Carraday guessed.

"Yes, I believe so. It is a place where American bombers crash in large numbers: when they are too badly damaged to face the

Adriatic." His shrewd eyes twinkled. "If your unit is there we shall find friends of yours, eh, Rikardo?"

"Yes."

"Friends who will help us; hide us from the commissars . . . smuggle us away in some plane going to Italy."

"By golly, yes." Carraday grinned. "How far is it to this place?"

Stari pondered. "The way we shall have to walk it, avoiding the Germans and a mountain here and there—say two hundred kilometres."

Carraday's face fell. "That's a hell of a long way for a woman."

The old man chuckled. "If you are concerned about Jelena: she will walk both of us off our feet." He placed his hand on Carraday's arm. "Anyway, don't worry. Perhaps it will not be necessary. Try your English *majore* again. He may fix everything. We will only undertake the long walk as a last resort."

This time the Major deigned to take Carraday inside the sacred precincts of the Military Mission. He was gratified to see that Carraday had washed and tidied himself up. But the beard annoyed him.

"Couldn't you have got hold of a razor?" he enquired testily, seating himself behind the heavy wooden table which served him as a desk.

"I'm afraid not, sir," Carraday apologized. In fact he had rejected the idea of shaving in case he had to take to the forest again. There was a lot of warmth in a good beard.

"I'll have to lend you one," the Major said. "Can't have you in the mess looking like that."

"Thank you, sir." Carraday changed the subject. "Were you able to do anything about the girl?"

The Major leaned back in his chair and pressed his fingertips together. He was glad now that he had insisted on Carraday leaving his Schmeisser at the door; regretful that he had not demanded the same procedure for the grenades and the pistol. The fellow really had no right to swagger around looking like a Balkan cut-throat. He would have to be sat on—hard!

"I'm afraid I haven't had much satisfaction in that quarter," he admitted.

Carraday was watching him closely. The Major began to feel uncomfortable under the gaze of those steady blue eyes.

"I want you to realize what a tricky business it is dealing with these—these Partisan chaps," he said pompously. "They're not exactly gentlemen, you know."

Carraday raised an eyebrow slightly and said nothing.

"My job is to co-operate with them and keep them friendly to the Allied cause," the Major continued, becoming angry. "And I might tell you my job isn't made any easier by randy bastards like you."

"No, sir," Carraday said meekly.

"I've thought the whole thing over," the Major said, "and I've decided not to interfere in the matter any further. You've brought this upon yourself by your own irresponsibility. As for the girl— she's probably no better than she ought to be. I'm not going to jeopardize the success of this Mission on her account."

There! he thought, sitting back in his chair. That's told the bastard off. He was glad that Carraday was taking it so quietly: sitting opposite him with his hands relaxed in his lap and a thoughtful expression on his face.

All bluff, the Major thought. The beard and the sub-machine gun and the knife and the grenades . . . all bluff. All piss and wind, like most of these glamour boys. Just needed a bit of old-fashioned discipline to put him in his place.

"I want to see you spruced up before this evening," he ordered. "You can borrow a razor from my batman. Get your hair cut too. And you might as well burn those filthy togs and draw some army battledress from the stores." His moustache twitched. "If you're going to share our quarters until your plane comes you might as well try and look like an officer and a gentleman."

Carraday smiled at him, surprisingly mildly, and lapsed back into thought.

"Get rid of all that bloody hardware too," the Major rapped. "You'll have no further need for it under my command."

He noticed how submissively Carraday was taking it all and relented somewhat. "We dine at eight, by the way."

"At eight," Carraday repeated mechanically.

"I've built up quite a reasonable cellar since I've been here," the Major said conversationally. "The pre-war *Blatina* is excellent. Not to be compared with a first-growth Médoc, of course, but —well, an interesting little wine."

"I'm looking forward to trying it," Carraday said. He stood up and added meekly: "Thank you, sir."

"That's all right, Carraday," the Major replied, mollified.

Mustn't be too hard on the fellow, after all. Been in the Air Force all the time: never had the advantage of a pukka military training. Probably quite a good chap at heart. Get him into a proper uniform; shaved, washed, hair cut . . . be almost human.

"Remember, dinner at eight," he repeated. Important to stress the idea of punctuality. Smartness and punctuality—first principles of good discipline.

Carraday smiled at him and shrugged his shoulder through the sling of his Schmeisser. As he turned to go through the door into the street he made a rather cryptic remark: a remark which caused the Major to stand with a puzzled frown for a few moments, wondering if he hadn't been too easy on the fellow after all.

"Up the Army," Carraday said, and walked slowly and purposefully down the street.

CHAPTER EIGHT

AT eight o'clock to the second the Major snapped his cuff back over the face of his wristwatch, rose to his feet and stalked, fuming, into the dining-room.

Carraday had not arrived.

Confound the fellow, the Major thought. Well, that finishes him as far as I'm concerned. A trip back to Italy and a court-martial. That's what he's asked for and, by God, that's what he'll get. And I hope they shoot his bloody girl friend . . . well, no, not exactly. But that's what the two of them deserve.

With his four fellow officers he sat down at the scrubbed deal table and proceeded to go through the ritual of a formal mess dinner. Disposed before him, in respectful attitudes, were a captain, two lieutenants, and another captain who was a doctor. The doctor was slightly despised because he had attained his rank through his medical qualification and not by reason of a proper military background.

He was a slight, balding man, skilled and conscientious, who—in the right company—could display a wide general knowledge and a puckish sense of humour. Now he looked slightly cowed because at any moment the conversation might turn to the subject of schools.

The doctor felt vulnerable and guilty whenever schools were discussed because once, in a moment of alcoholic weakness, he had

let it be tacitly understood that he too had attended one of the
revered and expensive private educational establishments which
by some quirk of British nomenclature were known as "Public"
schools.

Although the incident had occurred two months previously, on
first joining the Major's staff, he remembered every detail of it
with painful clarity. A few seemingly casual questions by the other
officers had elicited the information that the doctor came from
Southborough, in Kent, and had gone to school nearby. Where-
upon the captain, who was familiar with that part of the world,
had asked: "Tonbridge, I suppose, old boy?" and the doctor had
smiled and inclined his head slightly, a gesture which implied:
"Of course; where else?"

To this day the doctor did not know why he had allowed himself
to drift into such deceitfulness. It would have been so easy at the
time to say: "No, not Tonbridge—Tunbridge Wells."

But he was a newcomer, both to this mess and to the Army, and
still sensitive about the kindly but patronizing look which comes
over the faces of Public School Englishmen when confronted by
one of the lower social orders who have not enjoyed the same
educational and cultural benefits.

And the silliest part of the whole business was that he knew
that the other officers knew that he was lying, even on that first
evening in the mess. He had betrayed himself by a hundred
nuances of speech and behaviour, so subtle that no foreigner
would have been aware of them: nuances which nevertheless
enabled his companions, congenitally skilled in sifting class dif-
ferences, to classify him within a few minutes of making his
acquaintance.

They guessed, without a direct word on the subject, that the
doctor was of lower middle-class extraction and grammar school
education. These suspicions were confirmed by his facility for
"getting on" with the other ranks. It was obvious to all that the
doctor would have been more at home in the sergeants' mess (two
sergeants ate together in the small room beside the wood shed), or
even with the privates in the kitchen. The Major had been forced
to reprimand the doctor on several occasions for not "holding
himself aloof" from the other ranks. It was bad for discipline, he
insisted.

But the doctor found it difficult to hold himself aloof from
men whose genitals he examined weekly for crabs and who con-

sulted him confidentially about such complaints as bowel stoppages and nocturnal emissions. Some of the men were quite disturbed about the latter and imagined that something had gone wrong with the works. The doctor was able to assure them that it was a normal phenomenon, not unrelated to the fact that anyone caught with a *partizanka* was liable to court-martial or the firing squad. If they found it inconvenient, he advised them, they could tie some small hard object in the small of the back, this having proved efficacious in waking the slumberer from erotic dreams.

Of course there was always the humorist who expressed a preference for the dreams—if he couldn't have anything else, that was.

Yes, the doctor reflected unhappily, it was very difficult to hold oneself aloof from the other ranks. On the other hand it was only too easy to remain withdrawn from the Major. If the Major suffered from crabs or constipation or nocturnal emissions he had preferred to keep his own counsel. Perhaps, the doctor thought, cheering up a little, the Major suffered from all three—hence the rigid back and the stiff upper lip.

This reflection led the doctor into a diverting speculation . . . how much of human behaviour and human history was influenced by trifling physical ailments. Perhaps Wellington's dour defence of Torres Vedras was merely the stubborn irascibility of a gouty man. Perhaps Napoleon left too much to Ney at the Battle of Waterloo because haemorrhoids made it uncomfortable for him to sit a horse. Who knew? Perhaps the Major's constipation would one day cause him to act brusquely towards the local Commissar. And the Commissar would complain to Tito and the Anglo-Americans would be thrown neck and crop out of the Balkans and the seeds sown for the next World War.

It was an entertaining line of thought and helped the doctor forget his trepidation that the conversation would turn to their respective Public Schools. In fact so pre-occupied did he become that he almost committed the unforgivable gaffe of passing the *Blatina* from left to right, and with his left hand of all things!

It was at this stage of the meal that there was a thunderous knocking at the outer door and the Major's orderly appeared, very flustered, to announce that the Commissar himself had arrived.

The orderly was in a great state of perturbation: terrified both by the violent Slav fury of the Commissar and the Major's certain displeasure at being disturbed at his evening meal.

"'ees in a real state, sir, 'ee is," the orderly gasped, shifting his weight from one foot to the other. "Carrying on something awful!"

He was indeed carrying on, with flamboyant gestures and torrents of Serbian swear words. Even the Major trembled inwardly, for he was not accustomed to such overt displays of emotion and feared that some major catastrophe had occurred. This Commissar was a renowned partisan leader who had been with Tito on Mount Durmitor and notched up an impressive record of blood-letting and revenge. The Major was grateful, for once, that the two of them had to communicate through the modulating medium of an interpreter.

But as the story came out he was able to indulge his own annoyance. Soon they were stamping up and down together, the Commissar, all Balkan passion, the Major coldly angry in a properly-controlled English way; the interpreter shuttling in between carrying his vials of wrath.

Carraday had absconded. Bearded, unwashed, unregenerate, he had taken to the mountains; spurned the Major's generous offer of a razor, a seat in the officers' mess and a free trip back to Italy.

And what was worse, he had taken the *partizanka*, Jelena Vedajic, with him: removed her from custody at the point of a gun. He and a sinister old man whom the English brigand had suborned to his wicked purpose.

Did the Major know that the girl was pregnant? Yes, she had admitted it without shame—with pride, in fact—when threatened with a medical examination.

Pregnant by the English imperialist! Pregnant in defiance of all Comrade Tito's strict edicts! Pregnant and doomed to the firing squad when the forces of the law caught up with her, as they undoubtedly would.

The Major plucked agitatedly at his moustache. "Please inform the Commissar that His Majesty's Government sincerely regrets the inconvenience caused to the National Army of Liberation," he instructed the interpreter.

These soothing emollients only provoked a fresh outburst:

Did the Major know that after binding and gagging the guards the culprits had helped themselves to military stores? The Commissar tore open his breast pocket and produced an impressive list.

Five hundred rounds of 9mm. ammunition; bandages and sulphonamide powder; a dozen "K" rations; six tins of meat and
vegetables——

"It will all be replaced," the Major interrupted hastily, "as
soon as the next plane comes in."

"And what about the chief culprit—the British officer?" the
Commissar demanded, his roaring tones translated into the interpreter's trembling falsetto.

"He will be tried and punished according to British Military
Law," the Major said sternly.

"*Ne!*"

That was not good enough. The National Liberation Army
would deal out its own summary justice. With a significant leer
the Commissar passed his finger across his throat.

"I say, you can't do that, old chap," the Major objected.
"Carraday *is* a British subject, after all."

The Commissar spat on the wooden floor, stamped his booted
foot and crooked his right hand around the butt of an imaginary
pistol. "Bam! Bam!" he exclaimed and strode out into the street.

What an extraordinary, melodramatic individual, the Major
thought as he returned to his dinner. At the door of the mess he
paused, reflecting that it was his duty to get on the wireless and
circulate a description of Carraday and his companions to the
other Military Missions in the country.

Then he thought: No, damn it all, let's at least give the fellow
a sporting chance.

He opened the door and went into the mess.

Carraday, Jelena and the old man did not pause until they had
walked eight miles.

They started off in a southerly direction, seeking out the patches
of unmelted snow and leaving obvious tracks. Then, on a stony
hillside, they veered to the right and headed due west.

They were well-rested and in hard physical condition. Stari set
the pace with a rangy, tireless stride. His white hair, below the
faded cap, gleamed in the moonlight like the aureole of a saint,
making him easy to follow.

Jelena came next and Carraday brought up the rear. Now and
again he reached out to place his hand caressingly on the nape of
her neck; or when she was climbing rocks ahead of him he could
not resist the temptation to smack her well-rounded little bottom.

He needed these physical reassurances to prove to himself that they were safely together again—well, not safe maybe; but together anyway. Being together was what mattered.

It was probably a good thing that the old man was there to act as chaperon. If they had been alone the caressings might easily have developed into something more urgent, and that would have slowed them down. As it was they devoted their energy to following the saint's halo, bobbing confidently ahead of them in the moonlight.

When Stari considered them safe from immediate pursuit he drew them into a coppice where they dumped their heavy packs and settled down by the light of a torch to examine Carraday's map.

Getting to the coast involved penetrating the German lines, but Stari did not seem to consider this particularly difficult as long as they kept moving westwards. The enemy had withdrawn from the Dalmatian coastline and anchored his right flank on the Dinaric Alps. Bihac and Gospic were still in his hands but from all accounts the line on that side was thinly held.

"We can avoid the Germans," Stari told them, "but not the partisans. They hold all the mountains and we're bound to bump into them from time to time. We must act with confidence and always tell the same story. Do you understand?"

Jelena and Carraday nodded.

"We are two couriers sent by our unit to guide you—a crashed airman—back to your squadron at Zadar," Stari said. "We were picked for our knowledge of English."

"Sounds convincing," Carraday agreed.

"If they ask for our Commander's name, it is *Majore* Ninkovic," Stari continued. "He is well known and since we left him near Krupa he will know nothing of our recent difficulties . . . should they check up on our story." He shrugged and smiled philosophically. "Even if he *has* heard he may well tell a few small lies for old time's sake. He and I were good friends."

They lay down with their heads on their packs and slept for two hours. Then Stari had them on their feet again for the next trek. Cautiously, with dawn breaking, they marched through rugged surroundings to the banks of the Sana River, which they crossed with difficulty north of the Jajce–Bosan Petrovac road. Then, in the afternoon, they climbed into some of the wildest country Carraday had ever seen: a region of dense spruce forests and bottomless ravines, where roaring streams vanished without trace into mysterious limestone caverns deep in the bowels of the earth.

Aeons of erosion and subsidence had played all sorts of devil's tricks with the porous armature of the mountain range. One of the strangest was the creation of immense funnel-shaped depressions—*jambas,* Stari called them—from whose gloomy depths grew the tallest of pines, stretching upwards for the light.

It was bitterly cold and the snow still lay thickly on the ground under the trees. They were almost five thousand feet above sea level.

Crossing a small clearing, moving slowly with mounting fatigue, they were halted by the gleam of oiled steel among the trees and the familiar challenge: *"Stoj!"*

"Partisani!" Stari called, raising his clenched right fist.

They were inspected by several rough-looking individuals who sidled suspiciously from the forest, their Sten guns at the ready. A few words from Stari and Jelena put them at their ease and they were soon swapping greetings and information.

Carraday contented himself with a hearty *Zdravo* and left it to his companions to do the talking. They conversed amicably for a while and then one of the men turned and pointed to some destination over the next hill.

"Hvala," Stari thanked him and led off again, with Jelena turning to wave and call *"Do videnja"* in her musical voice.

"If it is all as easy as that," she remarked, when they were in the forest, "we shall have nothing to worry about. They did not even ask who you were, Rikardo. I think they mistook you for another *drug."*

"If he takes off his wings and his badges of rank he can pass as one," Stari said. "It might be a good idea." He searched one of his pockets and produced a razor blade. "Sit down here, Rikardo, and let Jelena do it for you. She will cut the threads more neatly than you or I."

"Where were they directing us?" Carraday asked as he reclined on a fallen three trunk and submitted his uniform to Jelena's deft fingers.

"To the next village. One that was recently liberated from the enemy and contains good stocks of food and drink."

"Won't it be risky to go there?"

"I think not. There is no wireless here—I verified that—and we have travelled faster than any of the Commissar's couriers are likely to have done. We should conserve our own food whenever possible. Besides"—he grinned and wiped the back of his hand across his cracked lips—"I could do with a drink."

"The drink is the main attraction, if the truth be told," Jelena teased. "I saw his eyes light up as soon as the *maraska* was mentioned."

"The *maraska* is certainly worth investigating," Stari said, "though I do not believe in its existence. Where would the Germans have found a stock of *maraska* at this stage of the war?"

"What is this drink?" Carraday asked.

"A liqueur—a superb liqueur—made from the morello cherries which grow on the coast. You would probably know it as maraschino. The principal distilleries were at Zadar . . . have you visited Zadar, Rikardo?"

"I have flown over it," Carraday said. "It's one of the places I vowed to return to after the war; and Dubrovnik as well. Dubrovnik is very beautiful from the air."

"Dubrovnik is a jewel," the old man affirmed. "But students of antiquity tell me that Zadar is more interesting. It was ancient before the Romans came. Is it true that the war has reduced it to ruins?"

"It is certainly damaged," Carraday told him.

"All those beautiful distilleries," the old man grieved. "St. Simeon must have been asleep."

"St. Simeon? I don't understand."

"He is the patron saint of the town. I was there once in October, on St. Simeon's Day. The streets were thronged with peasants making the pilgrimage to his shrine. Each one was given a small piece of cotton wool which had been rubbed on the saint's coffin and thereby endowed with the power of curing toothache. Religion is a wonderful thing, is it not, Rikardo?"

"Marvellous," Carraday agreed. "But I think I would prefer a dentist for the toothache."

"Ah, but most of the local peasants have never heard of a dentist," Stari explained. "Many have never been attended by a doctor. The women still deliver their children in the traditional way, kneeling alone on the ground. Sometimes, if the birth is a difficult one, an old woman of the family will whip the mother with a viper skin, crying: 'Almighty, help the child to come out, as you helped the snake to shed its skin.' " He shrugged and smiled cynically. "If the child does not come out and the mother dies it is, of course, the will of God. Religion is a great comfort to my people, Rikardo."

They went on across the high ridge and in the soft glow of early evening saw the lights of the village beneath them. The Germans, for some reason, had abandoned it in too much of a hurry to indulge their usual passion for destruction. It was a fine thing to see so many houses with roofs on them, and so many window panes and wooden doors intact. There were even some old people and some children, giving the place a wonderful air of permanence.

The *gostiona* was crowded with partisans enjoying the good things which the Germans had left behind. The men wore parachute scarves and the girls gay blouses of the same brightly coloured material. They were smoking English cigarettes—"V's" and Players—and the atmosphere was thick with smoke and the heady fumes of plum liquor. The "Death to Fascism" slogans were already up on the walls and the innkeeper had draped the partisan flag—a Yugoslav tricolour superimposed by a red star—over one of the wooden beams.

But alas, there was no *maraska*. All the stories had originated with two bottles which had disappeared on the first night of the reoccupation. So they—Stari and Carraday—consoled themselves with *raki*, and Jelena drank a *spricer*—a glass of soda water laced with dry white wine.

The *raki* had a burnt, bitter taste: good on the palate after the cold clean air of the forest. They had another, and another, while they listened to the singing.

This singing was different from any Carraday had heard before. It had a ring of triumph in it: the fierce, martial spirit of an emotional people in the full tide of victory. He found it intensely moving.

Then the bottles and the stone jugs passed from hand to hand, and the mood changed and throbbed with sadness and nostalgia.

A *partizanka* in a green blouse climbed on the bar and sang to the accompaniment of a single-stringed violin. Even Carraday, who could understand only a few of the words, knew that she was singing of home and the lover who would return no more. There was silence while she sang and he saw tears on more than one rough, unshaven face.

The roar of approval when she stepped down, almost lifted the shingled roof of the *gostiona*. Men raised their empty glasses above their heads and smashed them on the stone-flagged floor.

"They are in *sevdah*," Jelena explained, using an expression which synthesized all the intensity, ardour and melancholy passion of her Slav countrymen.

The single-stringed *gusle* began to throb again, insistently this time, and they cleared the floor and danced the *kolo* with their arms on one another's shoulders and their booted feet drumming the flags. Carraday danced too, a little drunk and lightheaded, until Jelena murmured breathlessly: "Enough," and drew him out into the street.

They followed the cobblestones between the cottages until the roar of voices in the *gostiona* became muted and might have been the susurrus of distant water. The sky was clear and the long curve of the Plough pointed faithfully to the North Star.

They kissed up against the wall of a house in the main street ... the touch of lips and gently probing tongues very familiar now and setting off all the usual male and female reflexes.

Carraday worked his hands into the front of her blouse, to the unbelievable softness and warmth of her breasts, and then Stari —who could move very quickly and quietly for an old man— tapped him on the shoulder and said: "Maria Madonna! Do you want to go before the firing squad in every village between here and the Adriatic?"

Carraday reluctantly withdrew his hands and scowled at the old man who was—as usual—right.

"Come along," Stari ordered brusquely. "I have found a peasant woman who will give us a meal, and a place on her floor for the night."

He waited while Jelena buttoned her blouse and then they went back up the street to the pink house on the corner opposite the inn. The woman, who was a Moslem, served them with *kapama*—a dish of mutton and green herbs, covered with curdled milk sauce, and did not demand an unreasonable sum of kuna in payment.

Jelena and Carraday dossed down beside the fire and were eyeing one another through half-closed eyes when the old man, who could be a very tiresome old man at times, intruded himself between them, arranged his white head comfortably on his pack and growled: "I have arranged for the woman to wake us at dawn."

Then he smiled to himself and said, *sotto voce*: "Sweet dreams, my passionate ones."

CHAPTER NINE

THEY left early in the morning, before there were many people in the streets: walking boldly and openly so that anyone could see they were heading northwards. Then, when the forest closed around them, they turned to the west once more.

They could not travel fast now because the country was unknown to them and strongly held by the Germans. The old man was as cunning as a seven-summer fox at this sort of intrusion; avoiding all the obvious traps and some that were not so obvious.

Finally, in the early afternoon, they came to a road which they had to cross, as it ran north-south athwart their line of travel.

The old man lay and studied the road for a long while, almost an hour, from an outcrop of rocks on the crest of the hill. Jelena and Carraday lay beside him in the sunshine, which was becoming warmer every day and driving the snow into sullen grey mounds under the shadiest trees.

It was pleasant to rest with the sun's heat cupped between one's shoulder blades, but they wondered why the old man made no move, for it was obvious to anyone that the sandy, potholed road was innocent of any traffic.

Then Stari said "Aha!" in a soft undertone and pointed up the track, where it hairpinned on the mountainside and swung back above its own tortuous course.

They followed the line of his gnarled finger and after many seconds of searching Carraday's vision was focussed by a scintilla of light gleaming from a gap in the stone wall at the sharpest of the hairpin bends.

"What is it?" he asked, for it had lasted only a moment or two and could easily have been a chance ray of sunshine bounced from a facet of the quarried stone.

Stari, whose old age had compensated him with a stereoscopic long-sightedness, said quietly: "They have a spandau up there, in a gap of the wall. Can you see the barrel, Rikardo?"

"I'll take your word for it," Carraday replied. He felt cold at the thought of what would have happened had Stari not been there to warn them . . . a few steps across the innocent emptiness of the roadway and then the last sound they would ever have heard: the harsh rasp of the German machine gun spitting out eight hundred bullets a minute.

"What do we do now?" he asked.

"We wait," Stari said, settling himself more comfortably on the hard ground. "They will probably leave at dusk."

They lay and waited. One of the German machine-gunners came out from behind the wall and urinated over the drop. A small convoy of four wood-burning trucks went through, chugging along over the potholes with an armed guard sitting on the roof of each cab.

Late in the afternoon an armoured car patrol appeared from the south; three cars in all, one of them a massive eight-wheeler with a short-barrelled 75mm. gun. They halted beside the spandau detachment and took them aboard.

"We have seen the last of them," Stari said, when the dust had drifted, golden as pollen, down through the tops of the firs. "These German swine become nervous when darkness approaches and scuttle back to their fortified camps." He scrambled to his feet. "Come, we are safe now."

They worked their way down the rocky slope but were stopped short of the road by a rusty wire fence and a notice which proclaimed in faded lettering: *ACHTUNG MINEN.*

"Probably bluff," Stari remarked. "They can't have enough mines to protect every yard of the road."

But he seemed hesitant to cross the few yards of suspect earth. Instead he leant over the wire and studied the ground with meticulous attention.

"There has been no digging here for some while. Look carefully, Rikardo. Sometimes, when the rain has washed them clean, you can see the three little steel prongs of the *Schützenminen*—the anti-personnel mines. Are you familiar with the accursed contraptions? They jump five feet in the air and spray you with steel balls. Three hundred and fifty in each mine . . . I know: I took one to pieces once and counted them."

They all searched the ground but could see nothing.

"Let's go," Carraday said, throwing a leg over the wire.

"No, wait!" Stari pulled him back. "A few extra precautions will do no harm." He stooped and picked up a round boulder. "Take cover behind the outcrop."

Crouching with them he heaved the boulder through the wire.

It bounced forward on to the road. "And another," Stari grunted, rolling a second heavy stone.

Neither had any effect except to displace some loose earth on the high bank.

"Bluff!" Stari exclaimed. "All bluff."

He stood up and clambered over the wire and walked confidently down into the roadway. Carraday and Jelena followed, a little more gingerly.

Planted at the roadside was another sign. Larger than the first, freshly repainted, it held out a warning to all German travellers: *ACHTUNG! BANDITENGEBIET.*

Stari put his hands on his hips, threw back his head and laughed. "Beware! Bandit territory," he translated. "So they do not feel safe—even on the main roads."

He threw his shoulder against the post and snapped it off at the ground. "Go on, you two, while I drag this into the middle of the road. It will make them even jumpier to know that certain of the bandits have passed this way."

Carraday disregarded the double line of barbed wire and went boldly ahead, followed by Jelena treading in his tracks. They turned and waited for Stari on the far side of the supposed minefield. He came shuffling along in his patched-up boots, a broad grin on his weatherbeaten face, his untidy white hair curling up around the brim of his captured headgear.

It was at that moment that the *Schützenmine* jumped.

The old man stepped over it, somehow triggering its sensitive steel prongs as he brought his rear foot forward. It leapt out of the ground behind him and its two-second fuse exploded it at shoulder height in a flash of red flame and spurting black smoke.

Carraday saw the old man blown forward off his feet. But the supreme horror of the moment was Jelena's shuddering cry as she buckled over her collapsing left leg.

He threw himself down beside her, shouting her name. Her hands were clamped on her thigh and the blood was pulsing between her fingers. The old man lay on his face, unmoving.

"What is it?" Jelena gasped. "What happened?"

"Mines!" Carraday groaned. "There were mines planted there all the time."

His only thought now was to put a stop to the terrible flow of blood. He tore away Jelena's panic-stricken hands and found the rent in the cloth through which the steel had entered. One savage rip with his forefinger and the wound was exposed.

It penetrated the fleshy part of her thigh. He felt around the back and came across the hard lump of the ball just under the skin. That at least would be easy to remove.

But what the devil had it severed on its way through her leg? He tried to staunch the bleeding by pressing the heel of his hand on the blue-edged aperture, but the blood still gushed out, hot and slippery.

Then the first numbing panic passed and he remembered his first-aid training. He slipped his hand up her trouser leg into her groin and clamped his thumb accurately on the femoral artery. The flow of blood slackened.

"Is it bad?" she whispered.

"I don't think so," he replied. He took her right hand and guided it to the pressure point. "Place your fingertips here . . . a little lower. Can you feel the pulse? Then press hard."

The steel bullet would have to stay where it was for the present. He cleansed the entry wound and felt slightly reassured. It was a small hole, clean and free of laceration.

He dusted it with sulphonamide powder, placed a pad over it and drew the pad tight with a bandage. The pressure of the pad reduced the bleeding to a trickle, even when Jelena released her hold on the artery. For good measure he gave her a shot of morphia from one of the little ampoules in the first-aid kit. He was withdrawing the needle when Stari moaned.

Carraday ran to the wire. The old man saw him coming and cried warningly: "Rikardo—keep out! There are more mines here."

He raised his head painfully and glanced around. "Where is Jelena?"

Carraday jerked his thumb. "Back there . . . wounded in the leg."

"Ah, curse me for my carelessness," Stari groaned. "Can she move?"

"Yes—with my assistance."

"Assist her then. Get her into the forest. If the Germans heard that explosion they will be back here at any moment."

"First let me get you out of there," Carraday said, beginning to climb over the wire.

"Get back!" the old man hissed, his face contorted with helpless anger. "For the love of God, Rikardo—use your head. You are the only one who can save Jelena now."

"But you . . ." Carraday began.

"I am finished," Stari gasped. "My back feels broken and God knows what else besides. Look, my friend, and you will know that it is no use worrying about me."

He lowered his head so that Carraday could see his back. It was a sickening sight. The *Schültzenmine* had lashed him from nape to calf with a flail of steel shot. The miracle was that he still had any life left in his body.

Carraday felt the coldness of tears on his cheeks. He said: "I can't leave you. I will not leave you. I would rather we all died here together."

It sounded melodramatic but he meant it. Not for himself—not even for Jelena—would he leave this man, this companion, this best friend, to perish alone on the mountainside.

"Then you are a fool," the old man said roughly. "Have you learnt nothing in all the months you have been with me?"

"I have learnt never to leave a wounded comrade," Carraday replied stubbornly, approaching the wire again.

"Rikardo," the old man said, playing his trump card, "listen to me. Jelena is carrying your child."

"You're lying," Carraday exclaimed hoarsely.

"I'm speaking the truth."

"Why didn't she tell me?"

"She would have told you when you were safely in Italy . . . when you had asked her once again to marry you. She is a proud girl—and sentimental."

Carraday stood there with his hand on the top strand of rusty barbed wire, dumbfounded and irresolute.

"That makes a difference, doesn't it," the old man said gently. "Now go, Rikardo. Take her into the forest and look after her well. I entrust her to you." He managed a smile. "Have many fine children and name one for me. Do they have a name like Gregorich in English?"

"Gregory," Carraday said, fighting the tears.

"I like that," the old man said weakly. "Have a son and call him Gregory after me. Now go—please!—I implore you. I will not suffer long."

His hand came up from his belt, clasping a grenade. He held it to his mouth and pulled the pin with his teeth. "Take her,

Rikardo. When you are in the forest I will let the lever go and place this under my chest. It will be very quick . . . a better end than I deserve after my long and sinful life."

His voice strengthened and regained something of its old authority.

"Turn around, Rikardo. I am still in command here. Now march . . . and remember all I have taught you. You have a long way yet to go."

Carraday lifted Jelena to her feet and with her arm across his shoulders stumbled for the shelter of the trees. She did not ask any questions: she knew better than he the stern realities of guerrilla war. But when the forest closed around them and they heard from behind the muffled thump of the grenade she whispered: "Oh, Stari Papa!" and turned her face against Carraday's chest.

CHAPTER TEN

THEY did not travel far from the road that night. After going a few hundred yards Jelena fainted. Carraday picked her up and carried her, but even her light weight—added to the burden of their guns and ammunition and stores—proved too much in the gathering darkness.

Finally, shaky at the knees, he found himself staggering down a steep declivity when all his directional instincts told him that he was breasting the slope of the next mountain. He stopped, placed Jelena on the ground, and examined his surroundings. Then he realized that he had stumbled unwittingly into a *jamba,* one of the strange funnel-shaped hollows which millenniums of weather had bored into the soft limestone.

The timber here was very dense, fighting for the restricted circle of sky. It struck him as a good place to stop for the night, where their fire would be concealed below the level of the surrounding terrain.

By the light of the fire he operated on Jelena's leg. She was fully conscious again but the injection of morphia had deadened the area round the wound and she made no protest when he slit her flesh with a razor blade and gently squeezed out the steel slug like a stone from a pulpy fruit. The bleeding was less severe now and he was able to reassure himself that the main artery was intact and that the severed veins were clotting and sealing themselves off.

She had lost a lot of blood and was feeling sick and faint, but he saw no reason why with rest and care she would not make a rapid recovery. Then he reflected grimly that rest and care were the last things she was likely to get in their present circumstances.

After their meal they huddled together beside the dying fire and fell into a sleep of utter exhaustion. Carraday woke only once during the night, aroused by the shrill clamour of a fox challenging the moon. He gathered Jelena more closely in his arms and lapsed back into dreamless slumber. By now he was developing a sixth sense about danger and could usually tell, by an atavistic prickling of the hackles, when it threatened.

This peculiar apprehension assailed him when he awoke in the morning. They had overslept and the sun was already gilding the tips of the firs. Carraday lay with his hands clasped behind his head, reluctant to disturb Jelena who was still sleeping so peacefully, and yet wondering what it was that had aroused him with such a strong sense of unease.

Then he heard a sound that chilled him with fear . . . the barking of a dog. It came again, on a note of whimpering excitement: the sound of a dog hot on the scent and straining at its leash. His mind flashed back to the broken signboard left in the roadway, the old man's body in the minefield, and the fresh blood trail leading into the forest.

He placed his hand across Jelena's mouth and shook her awake. One look at his face convinced her that something was amiss. She did not ask any questions but pulled the bolt of her Sten out of its safety socket while he bundled their few possessions into his pack. As he shoved his arms through the straps they heard the growl of men's voices on the very lip of the *jamba*.

He took Jelena's weight on his arm and they stumbled downhill. It occurred to Carraday, as the ground fell away ever more steeply under the soaring pines, that they were fleeing into a trap: a funnel-shaped trap from which there was no escape. But at least in the broken limestone formation of the *jamba* floor they might find a better defensive position in which they could sell their lives dearly when their pursuers caught up with them.

That was all they could hope for now: to shoot down a few Germans before they were butchered themselves.

They slithered down an almost sheer six-foot drop and found themselves on the lowest level of the pit. Around them grew the tallest pines that Carraday had ever seen, rising fifty feet and

more, like Grecian columns, before the protrusion of the first
branches, then mingling their foliage densely as they struggled
for light and air.

They could hear the subterranean gurgle of water. The ground
rang hollowly under their feet. But of a good defensive position
there was no sign. Carraday cursed himself for his stupidity. It
would have been better to fight it out at their bivouac than retreat
into this dank, gloomy hole where they could be finished off by a
few grenades lobbed from above.

Then Jelena jogged his arm and pointed and he saw the cave.
Its mouth yawned blackly from the opposite side of the *jamba*.
He grabbed her around the waist and they staggered for it as fast
as they could go across the rough and pitted floor of the limestone
bowl.

As they plunged into the darkness the first grenade exploded
hollowly behind, sending its jagged shards of metal ringing against
the portals of the cave.

Carraday released Jelena and struck a match. He held it for a
moment above his head and then dashed it to the ground. His
mind retained a plan of the cave, imprinted on his retina by the
brief flare of light.

The cavern they were in went forward for five paces and then
bifurcated: the left-hand fork deviating at only a small angle, that
to the right taking a sharp twist into darkness behind a jagged-
toothed construction of stalagmites and stalactites. Carraday
grabbed Jelena and leapt for the fanged opening. So accurate was
his memory of the scene that they passed through without colliding with a single obstruction and were able to pause again and
draw breath, out of the line of fire from the cave mouth.

A second match threw its light feebly into a vaulted cavern so
immense that only the faintest glitter of snow-white lime crystals
betrayed its farthest walls. Beyond there were probably other
caverns, for the whole mountain was a vast honeycomb.

As a defensive position it was the most perfect thing that Carraday could have prayed for. Anything fired or hurled from outside
would continue harmlessly down the left-hand fork. Yet from
behind the barricade of stalagmites Carraday could, in darkness
and security, command the lighted entrance of the cave.

The relief from a conviction of certain death was so overwhelming that he threw back his head and laughed. The sound
echoed eerily in the cavern, arousing a squeaking torrent of forest

bats which streamed past his face with a papery rustle of wings.

The dog barked close outside and a voice shouted: *"Schnell! Schnell!"*

"Come on in, you bastards," Carraday said softly. He pushed Jelena back out of harm's way before dropping prone behind a stalagmite and covering the entrance of the cave with his Schmeisser.

There was a lot of noise outside: the clumping of many boots and the low-pitched growl of voices. They were coming down from the sides, not showing themselves against the lighted circle of the cave opening. Carraday knew that he was dealing with disciplined, calculating men: soldiers who in three years of savage warfare had learnt all there was to know about hunting down guerrillas. He loosened several grenades from his belt and placed them on the ground beside him.

The noise outside diminished. Their assailants had taken up their positions on either side of the cave mouth and were awaiting further orders. One voice dominated the rest and was followed by a brisk: *"Jawohl, Herr Leutnant!"*

Here it comes, Carraday thought. He felt Jelena's hand on his back as she crept up beside him. "Keep down!" he whispered urgently.

An arm swung against the daylight and a German stick grenade came whirling into the cave. The force with which it was thrown carried it down the other fork. Before it exploded Carraday heard the sounds of several more striking the stone floor. He put his hand on the back of Jelena's head and pressed her down as the cavern reverberated with crashing detonations. Acrid fumes burnt the back of his throat.

Shadowy figures appeared in the smoke curling from the entrance of the cave. *"Feuer!"* came the sharp command and a storm of sub-machine gun fire lashed against the stone walls.

Carraday waited, smiling a little.

The firing ceased and the figures closed in on the entrance. Carraday pulled the pin from a grenade, let the lever fly off, counted two and with a quick underhand flick of the arm rolled the bomb into the open.

Someone had time to cry: *"Lieber Gott!"* before the roar of the grenade drowned his voice. Carraday rolled a second bomb and was rewarded by a chorus of groans and curses and the stampeding of feet.

They must have been gathered pretty thickly around the mouth of the cave, he thought, chuckling grimly. Perhaps I should have used a third grenade while I had the chance, but we have only eight or nine in all and the rest of the day ahead of us. How many more hours of daylight will that be? About six or seven . . . they won't hang around in the forest once dusk begins to fall.

I wonder what they'll do now. Call the whole thing off? No, not the Germans. Pretend to go away and leave a few snipers in the trees to shoot us when we venture out? Or send for some more effective weapons . . . a *Panzerfaust* or a *Flammenwerfer*?

The bazooka won't help them much; nor will the flamethrower for that matter. If it gets too hot where we are we'll simply back up into the main cavern until they stop squirting. I suppose the sensible thing for them to do would be to lay a charge of gun cotton and seal off the mouth of the cave. That wouldn't be very nice—for us.

But there's plenty of water in here and with the food we've got I guess we could last a couple of weeks. In that time we might be able to dig ourselves out . . . or even find another opening. This mountain is as full of holes as an Emmenthal cheese.

Thinking of cheese made him hungry. When we get out of here —out of this cave, out of this bloody awful country—we'll do a lot of eating, he promised himself. I'll take Jelena to the "Imperiale" in Bari: the food was good last time I was there. We'll have a bottle of Spumante too. What fun I missed by being a teetotaller.

There are a lot of drinks I have yet to try. Clarets and burgundies, hocks and moselles. If I get out of this alive I'm going to do a lot of eating and a lot of drinking and a lot of love-making too. The simple things; the satisfying things. Life really is simple when you reduce it to its essentials.

He took off the girl's cap and ran his hand over the soft, silky back of her head. Her teeth gleamed in the darkness.

"They are being very quiet," she said.

"Yes."

"Perhaps they've gone."

"No," he said, "they haven't gone. Not the Germans."

"Then what?"

"What would you do in their position?" he asked.

She pondered. "If I had the time I'd send for a flamethrower."

"That's what I was thinking," he said. "I wonder how far——?"

He did not have time to complete the sentence for at that moment someone flung a bundle of blazing, oily waste into the cave and by its ruddy light the entrance seemed jammed with men. Ahead of them leapt the dog—a great shaggy Alsatian—with a growl rumbling in its throat.

Carraday did not deliberately aim at the dog. It crossed his line of fire as he emptied the magazine of the Schmeisser at the figures crowding the mouth of the cave: dark uniformed figures emitting the red muzzle-flashes of their own automatic weapons.

The Alsatian gave a single yelp of agony, reared on its hind legs and fell, kicking. The attackers in the cave mouth withered away as Jelena's Sten added its clamour to the stuttering of Carraday's weapon. A couple of grenades completed the rout.

Several forms were sprawled in the mouth of the cave. Another crawled away, dragging a shattered leg. Carraday was not taking any chances. He fitted a new magazine and fired a burst into each of the fallen men before the oily rags flickered out. The wounded soldier covered his head with his arm and cried: *"Nein! Nein!"* each time the gun barked.

"Verflucht!" someone swore, and dragged him to safety.

Carraday felt a trickle of blood on his cheek. A bullet had struck the stalagmite above his head, showering him with jagged flakes of stone. Otherwise he and the girl were untouched.

"I don't think they'll try that again," he said calmly. "How do you feel?"

"Hungry," Jelena replied.

"That's the stuff. How's the leg?"

"Stiff . . . and painful." She made a groping exploration. "The bandage feels dry."

"Good! I was afraid the effort of getting down here might start the bleeding again. Can you reach the pack?"

"Yes."

"Open a tin of something. I'm starving."

She struck a match and he could hear her rummaging about in the haversack. "Meat and vegetables—how does that sound?"

"It'll do," he grunted, not taking his eyes from the cave mouth.

It was cold and greasy and it stuck to the roof of his mouth, but between them they could have eaten twice as much.

"Give me the empty tin," Carraday said, grinning wolfishly.

He flung it towards the cave entrance and saw it go twinkling out into the light. There was a sound of hastily retreating footsteps, a few moments incredulous silence, then hysterical laughter which ceased instantly at a barked command:

"*Ruhe!*"

Nothing happened for a long while. Carraday's eyelids began to droop with the strain of watching.

"What's the time?" Jelena asked.

He consulted the luminous dial of his watch. "Nearly two o'clock."

"They are still there .. I can hear them moving every now and then."

"Yes."

"They must be waiting for a flamethrower," Jelena said with conviction. "If it were not so they would pack up and go home. They know by now that they can't get us by ordinary means."

Carraday grunted noncommittally. The more he thought about it the less he liked the idea of a flamethrower. The force with which the burning liquid was propelled would cause it to splash in all directions; even ricochet around corners. A small quantity on the clothing could inflict fatal burns.

If the Germans brought one into action he and Jelena would have to retreat into the main cavern and fight it out from there.

"Can you walk?" he asked her.

She struggled to her feet and tentatively tested her wounded leg. "Yes—a little."

"Take these matches and explore the cave," he instructed. "Find a good position for yourself where you can keep this opening covered. I'll stay here in case they try anything."

Glancing over his shoulder occasionally he saw the glow of lighted matches receding farther and farther into the gloomy fastnesses of the cavern. It was even vaster than he had thought. From the back they would certainly be out of range of a flame projected from the opening in which he now lay.

After a while he heard Jelena's limping step returning. "Well?" he asked, as she dropped down beside him.

"There's no way out of here," she said, breathless from the exertion of walking on her wounded leg. "But there are enough holes and ledges and stalagmites to hide a battalion. Near the back, on the right-hand side, is a sort of gallery . . . thirty or forty feet above the floor. It slopes down at the rear end and one can climb it without difficulty. I have never seen a better place. We should go there now."

"Can you climb up by yourself?"

"Yes."

"Then get into position and cover me when I come. Give a whistle when you're ready and drop a lighted match from above. I'll bring the haversack."

When the girl had gone he lay and listened carefully. There was renewed activity outside and some calling to and fro across the *jamba*.

New faces on the scene, Carraday thought. Perhaps Jelena was right about the flamethrower.

An idea occurred to him and he took a grenade and placed it at arm's length on the floor of the entrance cave. It might "cock off" in the heat of the flame and give the enemy operator an unpleasant surprise.

At that moment there was a sound like tearing cloth and a deafening explosion which flung him back, dazed and winded. He groped for his gun and struggled to his knees. The ripping noise came again and was followed by a roar in the other branch of the cave and the rumble of falling rock.

Carraday gathered his wits sufficiently to grab his belongings and retreat deeper into the cavern.

A *panzerfaust*, he thought dazedly. They've brought one down the opposite side of the *jamba* and it's lobbing its bombs into the cave mouth from above my angle of vision. The second shot must have ricocheted off the floor and gone down the left-hand fork before exploding. The first burst on impact . . . it nearly got me, that one.

There was another flashing detonation at the mouth of the cavern. The whole mountain seemed to reverberate like a drum.

Jelena whistled urgently. A lighted match came floating down from the gallery above.

Carraday wasted no time. He struck a light of his own and followed its pool of radiance over the broken floor of the cavern.

"Keep walking," Jelena called, and he saw the dark shadow of the ledge curving down to meet him.

Carefully he edged up against the dripping walls. The gallery widened near the top, under a canopy of glittering limestone pendants. Jelena was laying in a hollow close to the edge, behind a saw-toothed rampart which, in aeons of time, would rise to meet the remorseless drip of calcium-saturated water from above. It was—as she had said—a perfect place from which to fight a defensive action.

The bombardment of the cave mouth went on and on as he slumped down beside her. Carraday's mind recorded sixteen explosions in all. Then there was an eerie silence.

"If they've got a flamethrower they'll use it now," he said.

The words were hardly out of his mouth when the outer cave filled with hissing red flame. It lapped like a breaking wave around their previous position, hurling flaming droplets twenty feet into the main cavern.

"Maria Madonna!" Jelena whispered in an awed voice. "We are well out of that!"

The dragon's breath of fire swirled brighter and brighter as the operator advanced into the cave. It came in jets; each roaring discharge overtaking the dying flames of its predecessor. Suddenly a hundred-foot tongue of flame hissed into the main cavern itself.

Jelena raised her Sten.

"Don't shoot," Carraday said in a low voice. "He's only poking the nozzle around the corner. Wait until he exposes himself."

The flame swivelled right and left, searching hungrily. It died and half a dozen grenades exploded in quick succession, winking malevolently in the darkness.

"Now they'll come," Carraday said. He raised his gun in readiness.

The flame gushed out again, silhouetting in stark relief the figure of the operator, tank on back, standing in the centre of the opening, flanked by two soldiers with sub-machine guns at the ready.

Carraday aimed at the fork of the operator's straddled legs, knowing that the muzzle jump of the Schmeisser would spray its bullets up the length of his body. The flame went out instantly as he pressed the trigger and there was the hollow sound of the half-empty fuel tank striking the stone floor. The escorting soldiers fired back and drew upon themselves a burst of chattering fury from Jelena's Sten. There was a sobbing scream—and silence.

Carraday rose to his knees and hurled a grenade. It burst accurately in the mouth of the cavern.

"I somehow think that's the last of that," he said grimly.

There was a lot of shouting from outside the cave, but no one ventured in. Then the shouting ceased and there were no sounds except the drip of water, the squeaking of bats and the silken rustle of their wings.

It was only three o'clock but daylight was fading already from the mouth of the cavern. Jelena and Carraday passed the time by reloading empty magazines. Both the Sten and the Schmeisser had special lever devices for forcing down each bullet against the powerful pressure of the magazine spring.

From experience they did not fill the magazines completely, but inserted only twenty-five or twenty-six cartridges in each. Filled magazines had a nasty habit of jamming at the wrong moment.

They ate a few biscuits and took it in turns to doze. Not until Carraday's watch indicated nine o'clock did they make a move.

Carraday went first, leaving Jelena up in the gallery to cover him while he explored the mouth of the cavern.

The *flammenwerfer* operator lay staring upwards with sightless eyes, pinned by the weight of the tank on his back. One of his escorts had fallen beside him, stitched from shoulder to shoulder by the darting red needle of Jelena's Sten. Of the second escort there was no sign except a trail of blood leading outside.

Carraday crept to the cave entrance and stood with the cold air drifting across his face while he listened intently for many minutes. He could hear nothing but the safe, natural sounds of the forest: faint animal and bird noises as an obbligato to the constant sough of the night wind. He went back inside and called Jelena.

Out in the open they paused while Carraday adjusted the heavy pack on his back in preparation for the long march. He gave his arm to Jelena and would have taken a step forward had he not felt something pressing, ever so gently, calf-high, against his trouser-leg.

His groping hand encountered a string stretched tautly across their path.

"Don't move!" he warned Jelena. "I think they've left us a booby trap."

He felt his way gingerly along the string. It passed at right-angles around a short, forked stake driven into the ground. Then it led for fifteen or twenty yards in the direction in which they would have walked . . . to the pins of a pair of grenades attached to the base of some saplings.

Simple and ingenious, Carraday thought admiringly. If we'd emerged normally from the cave we'd have jerked the pins from the grenades, and then walked right on to them during the four or five seconds the time fuses were running out. The dear old Hun! You have to hand it to him.

He carefully dismantled the booby trap and added the grenades to his own armoury. Then cautiously, feeling for any other manifestations of Teutonic nastiness, he and Jelena climbed out of the *jamba*.

The sky was dark, with a film of cloud obscuring the stars.

"This way," Carraday said confidently, leading off in what he thought was a westerly direction.

Jelena checked him. "No, you are mistaken. *This* is the way." She tugged him towards the right.

"Nonsense. I know this is the west."

"And I know just as well that it's the south," Jelena insisted stubbornly.

Carraday released her and turned around, trying to orientate himself. "Now you've got me all confused. I don't know where the hell we are."

"This way," Jelena asserted, pulling him at forty degrees to her original direction.

"For heaven's sake!" He had to laugh. "If I listened to you we'd go around in circles all night."

"All right"—he could sense her shrug—"you suggest something."

Carraday had a flash of inspiration. He rummaged in his pockets and produced Pawlings's fabulous fly buttons—magnetized—rectum—for the concealment of!

"Give me a light," he growled.

While Jelena held a match he placed one metal button on the back of his hand. Then, with a dramatic flourish, he balanced the second button on top—and awaited results.

The top button fell off.

"What does that prove?" Jelena asked politely.

"It proves," Carraday said with admirable patience, "that I had them arranged the wrong way around."

While Jelena struck a second match he reversed the order of the magnetized buttons.

The top button fell off.

"I don't want to hurry you," Jelena said sweetly, "but the night is passing."

"Listen," Carraday grated, "these things *work*! Do you imagine they issue them to a hundred thousand Allied airmen for fun?"

"Perhaps they are just ordinary buttons," Jelena suggested reasonably, "for replacing those that get lost. It would not be easy to escape across enemy territory if one's trousers kept falling down."

Carraday said nothing .

"They look like ordinary buttons," Jelena said.

"These are not ordinary buttons," Carraday replied, searching the ground around his feet. "They're made like that to fool the Germans."

"They fooled me," Jelena remarked.

"Obviously."

"Perhaps they fooled you too."

"If you would stop talking so much and strike another match. . . ."

"I'm sorry. There it is under your left heel."

Carraday examined the buttons very meticulously in the light of the match. "Look!" he said triumphantly. "If they are ordinary buttons then why does one have a little protuberance and the other a little hollow?"

"If you turn them the other way," Jelena replied, "you will see that the protuberance becomes a hollow, and the hollow becomes a protuberance. They are exactly the same."

"Nonsense," Carraday said, more loudly than was necessary. "They are specially constructed so that one can balance on top of the other . . . like this!"

The top button fell off.

Jelena took a deep breath. "I believe you, Rikardo. If we stay here long enough we shall undoubtedly succeed in balancing one button on the other. It is only a matter of patience . . . and time. But what, in the name of the Holy Virgin, will that tell us?"

"It will tell us the magnetic north. Perhaps your feminine mind has not yet grasped the principle of these two buttons. One—the top one—is magnetized. When properly balanced it will revolve until this line points towards the north——"

"Which line?"

"This one here."

"It looks more like a scratch."

"That's to fool the Ger—— Good God, woman! Hold the bloody match steady!"

This time, miraculously, the top button balanced on the lower button.

"Watch now," Carraday hissed, hardly daring to breathe.

With exasperating slowness the top button revolved, swayed drunkenly to and fro, and came to rest.

"There!" Carraday proclaimed, flinging out his arm.

"And there!" Jelena said, pointing in another direction at the North Star which had come out unnoticed from behind the clouds.

Carraday used an unprintable word and flung the buttons as far as buttons could be thrown.

He and Jelena travelled for some distance in silence.

"You were right about the buttons," Jelena said in a small voice. "They were undoubtedly a device for indicating the north."

"Mmmm," Carraday replied.

"They were not so very far wrong, after all. Only—say, fifty degrees."

"A lot of use that would have been."

"At least we would not have gone back in the direction we came from," Jelena said.

"Blast the buttons!" Carraday snapped.

Jelena laughed. "Kiss me, Rikardo. One day I will sew magnetic buttons all the way down your fly and you will be able to find the north unerringly just by spinning on your heels."

He kissed her. He could see that their marriage quarrels would be easily resolved.

He wondered if he should tell her that he knew about her child. Then he thought: No, I will let her break the news to me in her own good time. But I'll remember to treat her with extra tenderness because of it.

By two in the morning they had gone perhaps four miles. Jelena never complained but her walk became more and more laboured, despite his arm around her waist. Finally she stumbled and fell and when he put his hand on her leg he found the bandage wet with fresh blood. It was obvious they could go no farther.

They made a fire and cooked themselves a hot meal. Jelena was as pale as a ghost with exhaustion and blood loss. But the wound was clean and showed no sign of infection. They fell asleep in one another's arms and did not wake until the sun was high in the sky.

Leaving her to rest Carraday went scouting. He ranged widely in all directions but could find no sign of recent human intrusion.

The forest was given over to the fox and the boar and the wild deer, whose tracks he found in abundance.

Below an overhanging cliff, well screened by vegetation, was a small cave. Carraday approached it cautiously, thinking that it would make an ideal refuge while Jelena was recuperating from her wound.

Some wild creature had been using the cave recently. The moss on the entrance stones showed signs of wear and there were long, fresh scratch grooves on the bark of a nearby tree. The cave itself had a strong animal smell.

A bear, he thought, hesitating at the entrance with his gun in his hands. Bears were supposed to be reasonably harmless, but that might not apply to one that believed itself trapped in its lair. How did you explain to several hundred pounds of frightened, resentful bear that you were taking over its residence for a while?

"Hey—bear!" Carraday called loudly, standing back from the mouth of the cave.

There was no sound from inside.

Carraday threw a stone and jumped aside. No reaction. He slung his Schmeisser and struck a match. The cave was a small one, no bigger than a fair-sized room, and it was empty. Perhaps the late tenant had completed his hibernation and taken himself off to other parts. Carraday hoped so.

He went back and fetched Jelena. Her wound had stiffened and he had to carry her all the way. At the mouth of the cave he paused with her in his arms and said: "Chez Carraday . . . how do you like it?"

She was very pale but she managed a smile. "What do the French say?—*il n'y a pas de petit chez soi*. It was very clever of you to find it."

"That's what I thought."

"Forgive me for asking, but when do you expect the owner back?"

"I hoped he was away on vacation."

"Unless my nose misleads me, he was in occupation only this morning."

"Will he be violent, do you think?" Carraday asked. "I'm not very familiar with bears."

"Nor am I . . . but I'm afraid we'll know more about them by nightfall."

"Shall we take the chance?"

"Of course." She kissed him on the throat. "Our first home . . . you must carry me across the threshold."

He carried her inside and lowered her gently to the ground. "Try and make yourself comfortable. I'll cut some branches for a bed."

She clutched nervously at his arm. "What if the bear comes home?"

He laughed. I have a lot to learn about her, he thought. She's such a strange mixture of the feminine and the unfeminine. She'll shoot it out with battalions of Germans, but she's scared of bears. Maybe of mice, too.

"Are you scared of mice?" he asked her.

"No—nor of spiders. But of bears—yes!"

"Show him your teeth and growl," Carraday advised. "And if that fails you have your Sten."

"I couldn't shoot a bear . . . they have such gentle faces."

"Then fire a shot into the roof of the cave. He won't stop running for twenty miles."

Carraday went out and cut armfuls of soft, new pine branches. Their sharp, tangy scent almost banished the smell of bear.

The stream in the gorge had brought down cords of driftwood and flung it carelessly along the banks. While Carraday was gathering wood he saw the trout rising in the deep, slow pools and turning—green and silver faceted—over the gravelly shallows in the sunlight coming down slantwise through the tops of the forest trees.

He took a hand grenade from his belt and fingered the pin. Then he thought: No, it would be ill-luck to spoil the peace of this beautiful place.

Sitting beside the fire at the mouth of the cave, he and Jelena unravelled a length of parachute cord for a strong, thin line. A safety pin and a strip of tin made a serviceable lure. Carraday carried Jelena down to the river and she sat on the bank in the sun's warmth while he fished.

The trout were fat and greedy and totally unaware of hooks or men. They followed the glittering lure two and three at a time. Then one, bolder than his fellows, came sliding like an olive-green torpedo towards the surface and carried the lure a foot into the air with him as he lunged.

Carraday tightened the line and the trout tail-walked across the pool, fanning the spray in silver showers. He threw the barbless hook from his jaws and as it fell and shimmered down through the crystal water another trout, larger than the first, hit it with a shock which went right up Carraday's arm.

This time the hook held and the trout lay on the bank, opening and closing his coral gills and sending the long tremors of exhaustion shivering down his rainbow flanks.

They caught three more and took them back to the cave and laid them in the red coals of the fire.

After nightfall the bear came back to the cave: an old brown bear, almost as cumbersome as a grizzly, with silver hairs on his muzzle and his ears. He padded up carefully and suspiciously on his massive, long-clawed feet. He sat upright on his haunches and sniffed the alien smells of human beings and woodsmoke.

But the sounds that sent him back into the forest, surly and bewildered, were the sounds of whispers, of laughter, and of kisses.

CHAPTER ELEVEN

IT was dawn and they stood on the high crest of the mountains above Obrovac and saw the sea for the first time. The *jugo* was blowing: the soft south wind of spring; shaking the white cherry blossoms from the trees on the *polje* below them.

An old man came past on the dusty road, leading a horse and a creaking two-wheeled cart.

"*Zdravo drugovi,*" he murmured in greeting, and indicated that they might climb into his *kola* and ride down to the plain.

The bony horse plodded slowly and they felt the warmth of the sun as it lifted over the Velebit mountains.

They saw the long inlet of sea coming in past the mouth of the Zrmanja and beyond it the island of Pag, as intricately cut as a piece of jigsaw puzzle.

Carraday was bearded like a Cetnik and as hard and brown as a peasant from the Black Mountain. Jelena, with an apricot bloom of health on her tanned cheeks, hid her three-month pregnancy in a deceptive slenderness. Of her wounds nothing now remained but two farthing-sized scars as a foil to the perfection of tapered thigh.

The blue sky was sonorous with the murmur of American bomber fleets on their way to Austria and Hungary. To this grave symphony was added the shrill accompaniment of Spitfires taking off from the landing strip east of Zadar, beside the blue lake. They swung over the plodding *kola*, engines high-pitched in climbing revolutions, cannon thrusting forward into the airstream. Carraday followed them with his eyes as they faded into the haze over the mountains.

He smiled at Jelena, and then at the old man who had also been watching the fighters.

"*Engleski!*" the old man said resentfully, as his ancestors had probably said: "Romans! Turks!"

It would be a good thing, said the old man's brooding eyes and pursed mouth, when the conquerors had gone and he was left to till the soil in peace.

The farms they were passing were sadly neglected . . . tumbled stone walls, broken gates, orchards rank with weeds and grass. But the women—the bowed survivors of the holocaust—were labouring again in the fields, pecking away at the barren earth with their heavy hoes.

Four women, harnessed together like oxen, pulled an ancient wooden plough. Wars came and went. Conquerors had their brief day and vanished under the wheels of time. But the soil was always there: unchangeable in its demands and its rewards.

Carraday and Jelena said goodbye to the old man near the river and hitched a lift in an old wood-burning truck which was going to Dubraja. Then they set out across country towards the aerodrome which was quite close now, a frenzied hive of activity as the fighters took off and returned from their missions against the crumbling German front south of Karlovac.

They walked side by side with the easy stride of mountaineers. The heat of the sun was trapped between the mountains and the sea. Lizards with gently pulsing throats lay as though crucified on the burning stones.

The aerodrome was surrounded by armed partisan guards. Every bush seemed to harbour a pair of watchful eyes and the short ugly muzzle of a Sten. Wondering at the precautions, Jelena and Carraday stopped and spoke to a young *drug*.

"Are these not our allies?" Jelena asked quietly.

He sneered; very arrogant in his new English battledress, with his enamel red star on his forage cap and his Sten gun slung over his shoulder. Yes, the capitalists had been of some use. But now the war was almost over and they must be kicked out before they could hinder the Socialist revolution. They and the Fascists. Long live the glorious Army of Liberation! *Zivio Tito! Zivio Stalin!*

Other partisans were beginning to gather around, glancing suspiciously at Carraday's faded battledress. He touched Jelena on the arm and they walked on, hurrying without appearing to hurry, until they were within the perimeter of the British camp.

It was past noon and the American bombers were straggling back overhead, their perfect cohesion of the morning shattered by fighters and flak over the target. The crippled ones began to spiral down for emergency landings and Carraday understood why there was such a fantastic dump of wrecked machines piled up at the northern end of the runway.

Soon the circuit area was full of wounded Fortresses and Liberators, firing red Very lights in token of their plight. Some were too badly shot up to attempt a landing and were headed for the sea on their automatic pilots before being abandoned by their crews. The parachutes came drifting down the wind like puffs of cherry blossom.

There was keen competition among the R.A.F. ground crews to reach the parachutists first and claim their nylon parachutes as the spoils of the chase. Aid for the dazed fliers themselves seemed to be a secondary consideration.

The apparent chaos was obviously old stuff to the aerodrome staff. Fire tenders and ambulances were ready to greet each new arrival as it slithered, crunched or spun to a halt. There were tractors to drag the damaged machines off the runway and a huge mobile crane which picked up bodily those whose wheels and undercarriages had collapsed under the strain.

A Liberator with a missing front wheel touched the runway on its main undercarriage, ran a few hundred yards and then pitched slowly forward on its perspex nose. There was a scream of tortured metal as the tail rose to the vertical, transporting a terrified gunner sixty feet into the air. With agonizing hesitancy it hung there for several seconds before toppling over on its back with a crash.

A Fortress, its hydraulic system shot away, swung off the runway and went charging through an R.A.F. encampment, picking up several tents on its prop blades.

The chaos in the circuit was increased by a squadron of Spitfires, low on fuel, which flew around waggling their wings in mute appeal. Every now and then one would peel off and try to squeeze in between the crashing bombers, to be met by an indignant barrage of red rockets from the harassed ground controller.

The American planes which had landed safely were drawn up in rows on the west side of the field. The ambulances plied between them, taking off the wounded.

There was a Liberator named "Life" which had probably been donated by the popular journal of that name. A flak-scarred, oil-leaking wreck, it looked as though it would need a further generous contribution from the publishers to get it into flying shape again.

There was a Fortress called "Mickey Mouse" and another called "Saucy Sue". The latter carried a twelve-foot-tall painting of a naked blonde on the tail fin. Some inspired markmanship by a German gun crew had pierced the blonde exactly where she might normally experience pleasure.

The crews of the American planes were good-looking young men. They spilled out of hatches and doors, flung themselves on their knees and kissed the dusty earth. They shouted and embraced, or walked around with dazed expressions, like men in a dream.

"Tough mission?" Carraday asked one who was standing alone, as lost as a child in a crowd.

"Jesus yes!" the airman said, and burst into tears.

Carraday remembered the *pokrets* . . . the wounds, the frost-bite, the disease—and the patient, stubborn faces of the peasants. He avoided Jelena's eye.

In the R.A.F. section affairs were being conducted with proper British phlegm.

Chubby "erks" in oilstained overalls tinkered with the innards of Rolls-Royce Merlin engines. Stolid, intent on their tasks, they required an extraordinary crash or display of fireworks to arouse them to comment.

Then an occasional "Cor!" or "Fugging shambles, innet?" sufficed to show that they were aware of events around them.

A tall officer with a permanent smell of ordure under his nostrils stalked past, rationing himself to one quick glance of disdain for the two unkempt partisans.

Then an officious M.P. came bustling up, all bulging battle-dress and white webbing, mouthing indignation from a sweaty red face:

"'Ere, you with the fuzz-face and the tommy-gun! Bugger off back to your own lines!"

He was met by a pair of level blue eyes and a voice whose unmistakable authority rocked him on his heels:

"Stand to attention when you address an officer!"

Having established his ascendancy Carraday demanded, and got, the information he required regarding the whereabouts of his own squadron.

The mess marquee was the faded canvas one he remembered from Termoli. The same badly-painted sign outside. The same clutter of flying helmets, goggles and yellow Mae-Wests around the entrance. The same conviviality of youthful male laughter and talk from within.

Carraday bowed politely to Jelena and led the way inside. A stunned silence greeted their entrance. The tables were set for lunch but most of the off-duty pilots were gathered about the makeshift bar at the end of the marquee, drinking—since they were flying again shortly—tinned pineapple juice and some iced cokes they had scrounged from the American detachment on the field.

"Who's this shaggy-looking shower?" Jake Mancier, the Canadian, asked in a carrying voice, jogging his companion in the ribs.

Cobber Catrick turned slowly with his glass balanced in his hand. "A bloody Yugo," he commented in his broad Australian accents. "What the hell does he want?"

"A drink, by the looks of him," Jake said. "Let's throw the bastard out."

Cobber took another look at the fierce, bearded stranger: at the sub-machine gun, the grenades, the knife, the pistol. "Throw him out yourself," he replied. "I'll hold your jacket for you."

Then he whistled softly between his teeth. "Hey, take a pike at the babe!"

Jelena had stepped out from behind her companion. She stood there, calm, beautiful and confident, with her hand on Carraday's arm.

"Oh brother!" the Canadian breathed. "What wouldn't I give for a piece of that."

"Ask them over for a drink," Cobber suggested slyly. "Maybe we can get whiskers drunk and dump him somewhere."

"Good idea," Jake said, grinning. "Tip the barman the wink to lace the bastard's drink while I go and call them over."

He approached Carraday and said courteously: "Good afternoon."

"*Dobar dan,*" Carraday responded, keeping a straight face.

"Do you speak English?" Jake enquired.

"*Engleski?*" Carraday made a disparaging gesture. "*Ne razumum.*"

"Perhaps you and your lady-friend would like a drink," Jake suggested, indicating the bar and making elbow-lifting motions with his arm.

Carraday nodded brusquely. "*Hvala!*"

They walked over to the trestle counter. "Can't understand a bloody word," Jake commented to Cobber, smiling meanwhile at Carraday with feigned politeness. "Surly bastard, too."

"Stuff him," Cobber commented. "What's he want to drink?"

"Beer?" Jake asked Carraday.

"*Da,*" Carraday grunted. He gestured at Jelena and held up two fingers. "*Dva!*"

"Two beers," Jake instructed the barman. "And slip a good stiff tot of vermouth in the one."

The beer was Canadian, from cans. Carraday held his tankard aloft and called loudly: "*U vase zdravlje!*"

"And the same to you, with knobs on," Jake responded. His eyes strayed to Jelena, lingering on the smooth brown skin, the hazel eyes, the red mouth with its slightly sensual pout. "Jeeze, I'd give three months pay for half an hour with this bint!"

"Me too," Cobber replied, "but for God's sake don't let whiskers know what you're thinking. He looks as though he'd have the ballocks off you for sixpence."

"Tough-looking sod," Jake agreed.

He smiled at Carraday and gestured with his tankard. "Up yours!"

"*Zivio* Churchill," Carraday replied, clicking his heels.

"Good old Tito," Cobber said, not to be outdone.

"*Zivio Redeci Armada!*" Jelena entered the game with zest.

"And bless your little round smackable derrière," Jake retorted. For a moment he thought the girl had blushed. She certainly was a doll.

"Jake," he said, pointing at himself.

"Jelena," she told him. She placed her hand possessively on Carraday's arm. "Rikardo."

"And Cobber," Jake completed the introductions. "I wonder how he came by his R.A.F. battledress?" he asked his friend.

"Probably bumped off the previous owner," Cobber grunted. "He looks capable of it."

"You're telling me!" Jake leant forward and indicated Carraday's jacket. "Where d'ja get this, bud?"

"*Ne razumem.*" Carraday looked puzzled.

"English uniform," Jake said, fingering the lapel. "What happened to the owner?"

"Aha!" Carraday chuckled grimly and ran his finger across his collar.

"What did I tell you?" Cobber yelped. "He cut the poor bloke's throat!"

"And I should cut yours too," Carraday said calmly, "for spiking my drink."

Jake choked and spilt pineapple juice down the front of his jacket. "Oh, my God!" he gasped. "It's—it's—no, it can't be!"

"Carraday!" Cobber shouted. He was going to add "Twitty" Carraday, but the "Twitty" would have sounded so incongruous when applied to this bewhiskered bandit that he amended it to: "Rick Carraday!"

"Where the hell have you been all this time?" Jake demanded. "We thought you'd bought it!"

The uproar brought other members of the squadron clamouring around to offer their congratulations. It was Jake and Cobber's turn to look embarrassed when they discovered that Jelena could speak fluent English.

"I say . . . Oh, my gosh!" Jake stuttered. "I am sorry about that." He blushed to the roots of his hair. "You will forgive me, won't you?"

"Up yours," Jelena said sweetly, raising her tankard.

A roar of laughter completed Jake's discomfiture.

"Squadron Leader's coming, gentlemen," the corporal behind the bar hissed warningly, stifling the hilarity.

"Brathwate!" Jake said in Carraday's ear. "Got his promotion when Dickie Dawson was posted. Oh brother, what a pill!"

Carraday turned like a bristling dog. His old persecutor's name conjured all the humiliations of the past.

Come on, you bastard, he thought. I'm ready for you now.

Brathwate stood in the entrance of the marquee. Carraday glared at him through narrowed eyes. Then his face relaxed and a little vertical line of puzzlement appeared between his brows. Suddenly he smiled.

Well, I'll be damned, he thought. So *that's* Brathwate! That skinny twerp with the narrow nose and the ungenerous little mouth. That effete apology for a man with the shifty eyes and the air of carrying more rank than he can hold.

Brathwate! The terror of the fags. The elegant sixth-former with the supercilious voice and the condescending manner. Good God! If you took him on a *pokret* he wouldn't last two days. Why, Stari or Bradko could have eaten a couple like him for breakfast.

The impulse was too strong: he threw back his head and laughed.

"Who are these people?" Brathwate demanded. There was a querulous note in his voice. He could sense the antagonism his presence aroused and it put him on the defensive.

"Have a drink, sir?" Jake said.

He smiled as he made the invitation, knowing that Brathwate would take the breach of protocol as a personal slight. A subordinate was not supposed to offer his commanding officer a drink.

Jake compounded the insult by waiting just a shade longer than necessary before adding "sir", and then giving it undue emphasis.

Brathwate flushed. This was the sort of thing he had had to put up with since taking command of the squadron. No flagrant breaches of discipline—those would have been easy to deal with—but a series of pinpricks to remind him that he was generally disliked and that his only authority was the slender advantage of an extra ring around his sleeve.

"Would someone be so kind as to introduce me to our guests?" he requested icily.

To his own great wonderment Carraday found himself feeling sorry for the man.

"You probably don't recognize me behind all this undergrowth," he said, "but I'm Richard Carraday."

"What!" The exclamation was wrung from Brathwate. Then he recovered his composure and said chillingly: "You've been a long time getting back, Carraday."

"Yes," Carraday agreed, and added with gentle mockery: "The train service is rather bad."

Everyone laughed—except Brathwate.

"I didn't ask you to be funny, Carraday," he snapped. His glance went to Jelena. "And who, may I ask, is this young woman?"

"Miss Jelena Vedajic," Carraday said. "My fiancée."

"Your what!" Jake exploded. "No wonder you were so long in the bush, you randy old sod!"

Carraday was forced to submit to a round of congratulatory hand-shakings and back-slappings in which Brathwate did not join.

"I shall require a full written report of your activities since you were shot down," he told Carraday. "There'll be other formalities as well, including a Medical Board to determine whether you are fit for further flying duties. I believe the quartermaster has your kit. See that you're looking more like an R.A.F. officer when you report to my trailer at"—he consulted his watch—"four o'clock."

"Yes, sir," Carraday responded formally. He could feel the weight of the organization pressing down on him again. He was once more a cog in a machine: a huge impersonal machine with no regard for individual lives or emotions. Even Jelena was beginning to look a little lost and frightened.

"Since we have no facilities for feminine guests," Brathwate continued, turning his fishy eyes on her, "I assume you'll make arrangements for Miss Vedajic to lodge with the partisan detachments guarding the aerodrome." His depreciatory glance flicked over her travel-stained clothes and the assortment of weapons which suddenly seemed ludicrous and mock heroic in the chilly atmosphere of the British mess. "No doubt she'll be more at home there."

You're the same cold-blooded swine, Carraday thought. The difference is that I'm no longer frightened of you. If it ever came to the choice between you and Jelena your life wouldn't be worth a buckled farthing.

"Miss Vedajic has left the Yugoslav army," he said levelly. "I intend marrying her as soon as possible. Until then she's under my protection."

Brathwate's mouth tightened. "I'll have no camp followers in my establishment, Carraday. See that you make other arrangements as soon as possible. And be at my trailer at four . . . shaved, washed and properly dressed."

He turned and stalked from the marquee.

CHAPTER TWELVE

AT three o'clock Carraday was sitting in his tent, ridding himself of the last vestiges of beard. Jelena curled up beside him on the camp stretcher. She looked depressed.

"That Squadron Leader of yours, he is the cold one, yes," she remarked despondently.

"He's a rat," Carraday growled.

He was rather disconcerted by the sight of his pale face in the mirror hanging on the tent pole. Rikardo the brigand lay in the sweepings on the floor. Flying Officer Carraday looked out of the reflecting glass. The metamorphosis was disturbing.

"He did not like me," Jelena said disconsolately.

"Don't let that worry you," Carraday replied. "He doesn't like anyone . . . and nobody likes him."

"He has eyes like a dead trout," Jelena remarked. "He looked at me and his eyes said: 'Pshaw! This trollop will tarnish my beautiful discipline. Away with her!' Is that not so, Rikardo?"

"That about sums it up," Carraday agreed.

"I will be a nuisance to you here; I can see that," Jelena mourned.

Carraday did not reply. He was concentrating on removing the last patch of roughness from his upper lip. He wiped the lather with a damp towel and felt his baby-smooth face reflectively.

"I will be a big nuisance," Jelena persisted. "Perhaps you would like me to go back to the mountains?"

"Perhaps," Carraday teased.

Her lower lip began to tremble. Carraday put down his shaving things and took her in his arms. He kissed her on her soft and vulnerable mouth and asked: "What's the matter?"

She tried to hide in his shoulder. Suddenly she seemed small and in great need of protection.

"I'm frightened," she whispered.

"You!" he exclaimed. "You frightened? Don't be absurd. What's there to be frightened of?"

"That man with the cold fish eyes . . . and other things."

"What other things?"

"Going to a strange country . . . getting married. I will be—what you say?—a flop."

"Nonsense."

"It's true. I know nothing of these things. All I know is child-hood—and war. I have never been a woman. I have forgotten what it is like to wear a dress. I do not know how to make up my face, or do my hair, or cook, or sew . . . you will be ashamed of me."

He took her by the shoulders and shook her gently. "You little idiot. With all your beauty and courage: there isn't a man in the world who wouldn't be proud of you."

He was still kissing her when there was the sound of hurrying footsteps outside and Jake put his head into the tent.

"Scram," Carraday murmured. "Can't you see we're busy?" Then he took a closer look at Jake's face and rapped: "What's up?"

"Trouble," Jake said, entering the tent.

"What sort of trouble?" Carraday demanded, releasing Jelena.

"I don't quite know. Brathwate ordered the I.O. to get in touch with the Yugoslavs and ask them to take a partisan girl off his hands. According to Pawlings they came right back with a report that you fit the description of a couple wanted by the authorities . . ."

"The slimy bastard!" Carraday breathed, thinking of Brath-wate.

"All hell's a-popping," Jake said. "Pawlings reckons there's a crime sheet against Jelena as long as your arm. Violating the moral code of the Army; desertion from her unit; theft of stores and ammunition . . ." He grinned admiringly. "Jeezes, you haven't wasted much time, have you? What'll they do to her?"

"If they catch her, they'll put her up against the wall," Carraday said grimly. He handed Jelena her Sten and began to throw things into his rucksack.

"What are you doing?" Jake asked.

"Getting out of here," Carraday snapped.

"Where will you go?"

"I haven't decided. Down the coast, probably . . . try and steal a boat somewhere."

"You'll never make it," Jake said. "The place is crawling with partisans. Every time I step off the taxying paths I see one skulking under the nearest bush."

"We'll just have to try," Carraday said, tight-lipped. He slung his Schmeisser over his shoulder and took Jelena by the arm.

"Wait," Jake said. "I've got a better idea."

"Spit it out," Carraday rapped impatiently. "We haven't much time."

"The Jugoslavs can't arrest you," Jake said. "Now if we hide Jelena . . ."

"Hide her where?" Carraday demanded. "Brathwate will turn the place upside down looking for her."

Jake was eyeing the girl speculatively. "Say we disguise her as an 'erk'. Cut off her hair, put her in uniform. Bit of grease on her face . . . who the hell's going to know the difference?"

A smile spread slowly over Carraday's face. "Jake, you're a genius. Do you think you can manage the uniform?"

"Sure I can. Old Rawlings in the stores will do anything for a bottle of vermouth."

"Go to it then, but for God's sake hurry! I'll get rid of her hair in the meantime."

Considering that it was a nail scissors and razor cut, and the haste with which it was accomplished, the result was highly commendable. R.A.F. mechanics were inclined to be a bit scruffy about the ears anyway.

Jake came hurrying back with a kitbag full of new blue battledress, forage cap, boots and underclothing. "Like me to help you change?" he asked ingenuously.

"My privilege," Carraday told him. "You can stand in the open and keep guard."

"You are a mean bastard," Jake said, returning outside.

While Jelena discarded her shabby old uniform, Carraday gathered up all the hair clippings for future burning.

"How do you like the passion-killers?" Jake asked through the canvas.

"I see what you mean," Carraday answered ruefully, staring at Jelena in her long white cotton underpants with the row of buttons down the fly. "Never mind, sweet. Nylons and frillies for you when we reach Italy."

He helped her into her battledress and handed her the mirror. "There! How do you like that?"

"Mary Mother!" she exclaimed, surveying the wreck of her hair. "Give me the scissors."

With Carraday holding the mirror she managed to tidy things

up a bit. Her firm chin and high cheekbones made her an extremely handsome young airman. The forage cap and a little grease completed the disguise.

"Bloody marvellous!" Jake exclaimed, peering in through the flap. "Good thing the jacket's full enough to hide the—er—er . . ."

"That's enough from you," Carraday said. He thrust the kitbag of old clothing and hair clippings into Jake's arms. "Buzz off to the incinerator with that lot."

"What about Jelena?"

"Any suggestions?"

Jake nodded. "Better let her come with me. I'll ask Rawlings to keep her out of sight in the stores marquee. We'll shuttle her from place to place if there's a search."

"Roger." Carraday glanced at his watch. "I have to report to the C.O. in ten minutes. See you later."

He was not surprised to find three armed *drugovi* standing to attention outside Brathwate's trailer. The escort to take Jelena away, no doubt.

"Come in!" Brathwate snapped, when Carraday climbed the short flight of wooden steps and knocked on the door.

He was sitting at his table. In a chair beside him reclined a heavily-built man in khaki battledress. The cap reposing on his knees bore the red star insignia.

"Ah yes, Carraday," Brathwate said ominously, as Carraday drew himself to his full height and saluted. "We've been waiting for you."

He turned expectantly to his burly visitor, who was examining Carraday from under craggy eyebrows. "This is the officer in question, Captain Krugevac."

"According to my description he had a beard," the Captain growled, in guttural but fluent English.

"He arrived with a beard," Brathwate confirmed. "I ordered him to remove it . . . not knowing anything of the circumstances, naturally."

"I would like to question him," the Captain requested, watching Carraday with a hawk-like gaze.

"Please carry on." Brathwate smiled thinly and settled back in his chair.

"Where have you come from?" The Yugoslav officer's voice cracked like a whip.

Carraday smiled with veiled insolence and gestured vaguely towards the east. "Over there."

"Where? Be more exact, please."

"Over the hills and far away," Carraday said. "From a place with a long name ending in 'ic'—or was it 'ska'? I really can't remember."

A tiny pulse began to throb in the Captain's temple. "To which partisan unit were you attached?"

"I'm not absolutely sure," Carraday said casually, "except that it had once been part of the something-or-other Proletarian Brigade."

"There are many such brigades," his interrogator snapped. "What was the name of the leader?"

"I wouldn't know how you spell it," Carraday replied. "But it sounded something like Row-dog-anky-skanky . . . or could it have been skanky-anky?" He smiled helpfully. "Most people called him Ivor."

"A common name," the Captain said, making a note in his pad. "Can you describe him?"

Carraday beamed. "Of course, I was with him every day for months. I can describe him *very* well. About medium height, brownish hair, dark eyes, sunburnt face, hair parted in the middle . . . Oh yes, and he sometimes grew a moustache—when shaving was difficult . . ."

"This description would fit eighty per cent of my countrymen," the Yugoslav officer said impatiently.

"Well, he was a typical partisan," Carraday said. "I think that was the secret of his popularity."

"Anything else?"

"He came from Belgrade," Carraday added.

"Ah, a Serb!" The Captain fastened on the first piece of concrete evidence.

"No, I don't think he was a real Serb," Carraday said. "He once told me that his mother came from Slovenia . . . and I'm not sure that his father wasn't a Croat . . ."

The Captain suddenly ground the point of his pencil through the top pages of his pad. "I am sorry, Squadron Leader: I can get no useful information from this man. May we have the girl, please?"

Brathwaite nodded. "Carraday, bring Miss Vedajic here immediately."

"I'm afraid I can't," Carraday said blandly.

"That's an order!"

"You're half an hour too late. She's gone."

"What do you mean?"

"Gone . . . left me. It's all most terribly sad." Carraday put on a doleful expression.

"I don't understand. I thought you said she was your fiancée?"

"She was," Carraday said, "but she changed her mind."

"Are you lying to me?" Brathwate demanded. "What reason would she have to change her mind at such short notice?"

Carraday shrugged. "You know what women are. She'd had qualms about our association for some while, it seems. She didn't think that a true daughter of the Liberation could live happily in a foreign country—especially a cold and unfriendly place like England. She wanted to return to her comrades of the Proletarian Brigade and help build up a Socialist state. Her last words to me were: 'Death to Fascism! Liberty for the People!'"

"Ah!" the Captain said, obviously touched.

Brathwate glowered suspiciously. "Which way did she go?"

Carraday's arm wavered through an arc of forty-five degrees.

"I wish to know *exactly* which direction she took," Brathwate snapped.

"Between the bomb dump and the airmen's latrine," Carraday answered, looking him straight in the eye. "On a course of zero nine zero, magnetic."

"My men will track her down," the Captain announced, rising to his feet. "That is"—he shot a baleful glance in Carraday's direction—"if she really has left this camp. Otherwise—I should like to make it clear that you are on Yugoslav national soil, and that our forces have certain rights of entry and search. Remember that, gentlemen."

"You need not worry," Brathwate assured him hastily. "I intend to have this camp searched myself."

"That would be wise," the Captain said in an ominous voice. "My superiors would not be pleased to hear that you, our allies, have taken to harbouring war criminals. *Do videnja,* gentlemen."

He descended the wooden steps and strode away at the head of his men.

Brathwate rounded on Carraday. "Come on, out with it. You don't expect me to believe that cock-and-bull story."

Carraday studied him reflectively. If only I could trust you, dear companion of my youth, he thought. But you're such an *officious* swine. If Wing Headquarters said: Hand the girl over —you'd hand her. You'd never risk your precious position for a little thing like personal loyalty. No, my friend, the less you know the better.

"It may sound unconvincing, sir, but it's the truth. I'm absolutely brokenhearted."

Brathwate relented a little. "Never mind, Carraday—ahmm!— all for the best. These foreigners, you know: unreliable people. Go home and get yourself a nice English girl one day. Far better —far better."

"I suppose you're right, sir."

"Absolutely, absolutely. Didn't like her from the start, to tell you the truth. Too bold by half . . . and all those ridiculous grenades and things. Melodramatic! Unfeminine! She would never have settled down at home."

"No, sir."

"All right, Carraday. Let's hear no more about it. You may return to your quarters."

"Thank you, sir," Carraday said ironically. "Thank you very much indeed."

CHAPTER THIRTEEN

THE Wing Commander's face was grim. He glanced around the assembled pilots, cleared his throat and came straight to the point:

"Gentlemen, I may as well tell you; we are being thrown out of Yugoslavia."

An incredulous murmur went up.

"It's a rotten way to end the war," the Wing Commander continued, standing stiff and straight beside the empty briefing board, "but there it is. It's not your fault. You've done your job and you've done it well . . . damned well!"

"The ungrateful bastards!" someone growled.

The Wing Commander ignored the interruption. "Some of you may think that this has come about because of our refusal to go on attacking German road convoys in Istria after the official cessation of hostilities, as a result of which those convoys were able to escape into Italy and surrender to the Allied armies there, but the real reason—I understand—is a dispute over the occupation of Trieste."

A series of muffled explosions cast drifting smoke shadows across the sunlight streaming through the open flap of the marquee. The Americans were setting fire to their dumps of stores and fuel.

The sounds added urgency to the Wing Commander's voice: "We've been given forty-eight hours in which to evacuate. That's impossible, as you know. A great deal of our equipment will have to be abandoned or destroyed. The important thing is to ferry our aircraft away. The ground crews are working non-stop to get every Spitfire possible into flying shape."

He allowed himself a brief smile. "Some of them will be pretty ropy, I'm afraid . . . unpatched holes, leaky hydraulics, unserviceable brakes and air speed indicators. It can't be helped. If you're tempted to turn back when you're out over the Adriatic just remember that you may be a guest of the Yugoslavs for longer than you bargain. Bail out, if the worst comes to the worst, and let the kite prang in the sea. We'll see that you're picked up."

"B—— that for a joke," Jake whispered to Carraday, who had been summoned with the rest.

"Now, we shall need every pilot," the Wing Commander went on. "A few of you may even have to be ferried back for a second trip, depending on how many aircraft we can get into the air. As far as your kit goes: you'll have to leave most of it behind for the ground crews to bring by ship. But I've given instructions for the cannon shells to be removed from the wings. You'll be able to pack a few personal belongings in the empty ammunition bays."

He unfolded a large-scale map and pinned it to the board.

"We have orders to ferry our Spitfires to Brindisi. Now that's a long way across the sea. In view of the dicey state of some of the aircraft we'll head straight for Pescara and then fly down the coast. I want you to mark and memorize the positions of emergency landing fields along our route."

There was a general reaching for maps and pencils. "I hope there's plenty of skirt in Brindisi," Cobber said out of the corner of his mouth.

"You have four hours in which to pack your kit and have something to eat," the Wing Commander concluded. "We'll assemble here for a final briefing at 14.00 hours. All right, gentlemen; dismiss."

They walked out into a scene of frenetic confusion. Great clouds of black smoke were billowing upwards from the American lines. The stench of burning rubber and oil permeated the air. Bofors anti-aircraft guns were being hauled out of their pits by sweating crews. Mechanics armed with axes and saws were hacking the tail assemblies from Spitfires which could not be made serviceable in time. They glowered at the passing Yugoslavs as they worked.

The partisans, emboldened by the scene of dissolution, were flocking into camp from the surrounding countryside. They swaggered, armed and arrogant, through the British lines; shrugging off the ineffectual protests of the camp guards.

The looting had already started. Red-starred guerrillas began to stream past, carrying inflatable dinghies, Very pistols, wireless equipment and even .5 Browning machine guns stripped from the wrecked Fortresses and Liberators parked at the end of the field.

"Hey, that's one of ours," Cobber shouted, catching sight of a *drug* marching off with a parachute slung over his shoulder. "Stop the bastard!"

The partisan looked around at the circle of indignant faces, gestured indifferently and threw the parachute down in the dust. No one tried to restrain him as he walked away with his hand on the butt of his Sten.

Captain Krugevac came marching along the perimeter track at the head of a platoon. He recognized Carraday and halted his men.

"So, my friend—you are leaving us?"

"You know bloody well we are," Carraday growled.

The burly Yugoslav officer smiled sardonically. "Would it surprise you to hear that we did not catch your little companion after all?"

"Bad luck," Carraday rejoined.

"She is of no importance," the Captain said contemptuously. "A foolish girl who places her own selfish happiness before her patriotic duty. No importance at all! But my orders are to apprehend her and"—his expression hardened—"I like very much to carry out my orders."

He glanced at the turmoil around him and the corners of his mouth twitched.

"Something tells me, comrade, that we *will* find her. The best time to look for ants is when the ant nest is overturned . . . not so?"

Carraday shrugged and turned away.

"*Zbogom*!" the Captain shouted after him. "Goodbye, my friend. Think of me—think of us!—when you are in Italy."

"Hey, that guy means business," Jake said worriedly. "You'd better warn Jelena not to show her nose until the stores truck is safely embarked on the ship."

Carraday frowned. "And what happens if they search the trucks before they pull out of camp? They're capable of it, you know. Listen, Jake, I can't take the risk of leaving her behind."

"There's no alternative . . . you've got to fly a Spitfire out of here this afternoon. Pity we're not on bombers, then you could smuggle her aboard."

"Do you think the Americans might have any aircraft leaving?"

Jake shook his head. "If they have you can be certain they'll be crammed to overflowing with their own personnel."

An idea occurred to Carraday: a crazy, impossible idea for crazy, impossible circumstances. "Do you reckon I could fit her in my Spit?"

"Not a chance," Jake said. "The cockpit's hardly big enough for one."

"It's been done before," Carraday reminded him. His eyes began to sparkle as the idea took hold. "I tell you, man, it's possible. Jelena's only a slip of a thing. I'll chuck out my parachute and dinghy and sit right forward on the edge of the seat. She can slide in behind me. Then I'll still be able to see the instruments and operate the controls."

"You'll prang and break both your bloody necks," Jake said doubtfully.

"So?—at least we'll be together. Anyway, I'm not going to prang. Life's too damned good and I've got a feeling there's lots more of it to come." He threw back his head and laughed. "Oh lord! Can you imagine Brathwate's face when we step out at Brindisi!"

"He'll blow a fuse," Jake chuckled. "One of his precious squadron aircraft being used as a honeymoon taxi. Brother, what a joke!"

Brathwate, turning on the wooden steps of his trailer, saw Carraday and the tough Canadian doubled up with laughter and wondered sourly what was amusing them.

At 14.30 hours, having attended the final briefing, Carraday strolled out towards his Spitfire, parked in line with the rest of the squadron machines.

He wore a Mae-West and a helmet, but instead of a parachute he carried a foam-rubber cushion. He had remembered that the edge of the metal bucket seat would be very hard.

There was a mechanic at the battery starter, and another screwing down the panels of the ammunition compartments over Carraday's personal kit. A third mechanic—a slim, rather effeminate mechanic—was assiduously polishing the transparent canopy. Carraday's aircraft seemed to be the only one getting this extra treatment.

A score of partisans, bristling with weapons, had come to gloat over the departure of their former allies. They sniffed around the parked Spitfires like suspicious dogs.

"All ready?" Carraday asked the airman with the screwdriver.

"Yes, sir!" the mechanic replied emphatically, giving Carraday a broad wink.

"Good," Carraday said.

He stepped up on to the wing of the Spitfire, brushing past the airman who was doing the polishing. An observant onlooker might have been shocked to see that he pinched the posterior of the airman in passing and that the airman, with gross insubordination, momentarily protruded the tip of a pink tongue.

Carraday opened the side flap of the cockpit and climbed in, arranging the foam-rubber cushion on the bare metal seat. Unlike the other pilots who were settling down in their Spitfires on either side, he did not fasten his straps, but merely plugged in his radio leads, primed the engine and waited with his fingers on the twin starting buttons.

Down the line of aircraft starters whirred and the big four-bladed propellers began to turn, slowly and jerkily at first and then abruptly blurring into shimmering nothingness as the engines coughed black smoke and bellowed into life.

Carraday pressed the starter buttons. Red flame belched from the exhausts and the rush of the slipstream modelled Jelena's uniform to her body as she clung to the open cockpit. Her blue forage cap was plucked from her head and sent whirling towards the watchful partisans.

"Jump in!" Carraday ordered, throttling back and grabbing Jelena by the arm. He closed the side flap with his left hand as she wormed her way in behind him.

The Spitfires were taxying out one by one, swinging their tails from side to side as the pilots ruddered to peer past their bulky engines.

Carraday pulled the seat straps over Jelena and himself and drove home the locking pin. The mechanic had already disconnected the starter trolley. Carraday released the pneumatic brakes and eased the throttle forward. Jelena had her arms around him and all her warmth and softness were pressed firmly into his back.

This is very nice, Carraday thought happily. This is quite the nicest way to fly. He found that he had plenty of room to operate the stick and the rudder bar.

In the rear-view mirror above his head appeared a furious, gesticulating figure: Captain Krugevac at the head of his squad of men.

"Too late!" Carraday yelled into the slipstream. He kicked the rudder and swung the tail towards them; locked the brakes, whipped back the stick and pushed on the throttle.

A thousand-horse-power wind bellowed and crackled past the cockpit, blowing the Captain off his feet and enveloping his men in flying dirt and stones.

"*Do videnja!*" Carraday shouted. "Or should I say *Zbogom*? This is goodbye, after all, and not au revoir."

He throttled back and went snaking down the taxying path towards the runway. The planes ahead of him were already airborne. Carraday paused cross-wind, hurriedly checked his switches and trimmers, then looked around at Jelena.

"All set?"

She was smiling; flushed, excited, very lovely despite the cropped hair. "Yes, Rikardo."

"Here we go!" he said.

He turned the Spitfire into wind. A thrust on the throttle brought the tail up off the ground almost before the wheels had started to roll. The Spitfire balanced there in her flying attitude, poised on her spindly little undercarriage, with the huge prop blades whizzing a scant few inches above the ground. Then she took off down the long, straight runway with an exultant howl.

The grass verges blurred and the elliptical wings began to feel the air. Carraday let the needle of the A.S.I. flick well past the hundred mark before he lifted her off. He retracted the undercart and pelted upwards in a climbing turn to port, following the other aircraft of the formation.

He caught up with them as the coast slid by underneath. There was the ancient city of Zadar, its war scars healed by the haze. Then the islands—Ugljan and Dugi Otok; rocky scars on the pellucid blue of the Adriatic.

And the sea . . . the open sea: stretching unbroken to Italy. The islands and the coast swinging away—he hoped for ever— behind the trailing edge of the wing. He reached up and closed the canopy, shutting out the roar of the buffeting wind.

He pulled off his helmet and leaned back so that Jelena could press her soft cheek to his, kiss him on the throat and whisper things that he had heard a hundred times before but would never tire of hearing.

He was not keeping very good formation and someone, Squadron Leader or Flight Commander, was probably yelling over the R.T.: "Bolo Blue Four—what the bloody hell are you up to?"

Carraday could not hear him and wouldn't have cared if he had. The war was over. He had Jelena and a pocketful of money: crisp American dollars from his escape kit and a pay-book worth three months back pay. They were going to Brindisi and he had heard that Brindisi was a pretty good place. It was down in the south and there would be lots of sun. There would be a good beach and a cheap villa overlooking the sea. For a honeymoon Brindisi was highly recommended.

Brathwate would probably kick up a fuss but Carraday felt confident of handling him. He would remind Brathwate, very gently, that within a few weeks or months he would have to put aside the protection of his rank and return, with Carraday, to civilian life. It would be much better for the future shape of his high-bridged, aristocratic nose if he kept on good terms with his subordinates during the brief time they still had together in the Air Force.

Meanwhile the engine was purring as only a healthy engine can; signifying its contentment with all the happy little faces of its dials and instruments. Temperature normal; pulse-rate excellent; oil pressure admirable. Fuel needles all clicking merrily against the Full marks. A very smooth, reliable Rolls-Royce engine . . . nothing but the best for the Carradays.

Jelena was purring too; yes, distinctly purring, with her soft mouth brushing his cheek. This is quite a woman I'm taking home with me, Carraday thought. I wonder what she'll look like in a dress? She has very good legs . . . small in the ankle, and firm in the calf and thigh from all the mountain climbing.

Will she always look undressed without a Sten gun? I hope not. Sten guns are definitely not de rigueur in Kent. At least they weren't when I left.

The green fields and the cherry orchards of Kent. The hop gardens and the squares of new wheat. The bells ringing from the grey Norman churches and the white swans flying along the Stour. How small and tidy everything will seem to her after the mountains of Bosnia.

But peaceful, too . . . I'm sure she'll appreciate the peacefulness, once she gets used to it.

I think I'm squashing her a little. I must be careful of that. Women in her condition aren't meant to be squashed.

I'm glad we started the baby. Some day when it's grown up—I can't think of it as a he or a she yet—perhaps it might be amused to hear how it was conceived: in the snow, on a parachute, between a Schmeisser and a Sten.

I hope it's a broad-minded baby!

THE BOAT

Walter Gibson

A true chronicle of the sea

"The Boat" is published by
W. H. Allen & Company

*To my wife Mary, my daughter Ree
and my son Colin Roy but for whom
this story would never have been told.*

My thanks are due to Macdonald Daly, the
writer, whose untiring efforts shaped my war
experiences into their present form, and to
David Emsley for his constructive criticism and
unfailing encouragement.

AUTHOR'S NOTE

MY name is Gibson, Walter Gibson, late of the Argyll and Sutherland Highlanders, with whose 2nd Battalion I served for seventeen years, in India, in China, and in Malaya.

This story was completed on March 2, 1952—that being the tenth anniversary of the morning on which I climbed into the boat.

I wrote this chronicle, of the days of horror which I and Doris Lim, the Chinese girl, endured together in the boat, because from all over the world had come letters demanding that I should do so.

Late in 1949, my story, in briefer form, was told in a British Sunday newspaper.

As a sequel it was published, though still more briefly, in nearly all the tongues of the world, in newspapers and magazines in Europe, the Empire, the United States, China, Japan, and South America.

Reader's Digest translated it into French, German, Spanish, Dutch, Italian, Danish, Swedish, and Japanese.

And from all these countries, in all those tongues, came requests from people who wanted to know more.

It is given to few, thank God, to drift for a month beneath a pitiless blazing sun, across a thousand miles of ocean, with nothing but a few handfuls of food and a few mouthfuls of water to sustain them in that time.

It is given to fewer still to be the only white survivor of such an ordeal.

And never again, I pray, may it be given to one man, as it was to me, to be the only white survivor of 135 souls who on that morning, March 2, 1942, looked to the boat for salvation.

Four days before, the Dutch K.P.M. steamer *Rooseboom*, of 1000 tons, with a crew of Dutch officers and Javanese seamen, had left the port of Padang in Sumatra, carrying more than five hundred evacuees, most of them British, from Malaya.

Singapore had fallen to the Japanese. The evacuees included soldiers of many ranks, officials, policemen, traders, miners, planters, women, and children.

The *Rooseboom* was taking them, crowded in her cabins and

on her decks, to Ceylon and safety—there, it was hoped, for the regiments broken in the Malaya debacle to be formed again.

At midnight on Sunday, March the first, the *Rooseboom*, halfway to Ceylon, was torpedoed. She sank in a few minutes. Only one of her boats was launched and kept afloat. Towards it swam and paddled survivors. Eighty of them scrambled or were lifted into the boat. More than fifty others clung to the side.

It was twenty-eight feet long, the lifeboat, and only eight feet at its widest part. The number of people it had been built to hold was twenty-eight.

For over a thousand miles, taking twenty-six days, she drifted across the Indian Ocean. Drama, tragedy, heroism, murder, pathos, and self-sacrifice went with her day by day.

In the end, when the boat pounded on a coral island less than a hundred miles from the port of Padang from which the *Rooseboom* had sailed, only four people survived.

Two were Javanese sailors whose final dreadful deeds aboard the boat made them unworthy of the life which was restored to them. The third was a Chinese girl, Doris Lim, who had worked for British Intelligence against the Japanese.

And I was the other.

I had fought with the Argyll, in the bitter Malaya campaign from last ditch to last ditch, of December, 1941, and January, 1942. I had survived a six-week escape flight through the jungle after the battle of Slim River. I had crossed to Sumatra in a sampan and had joined up there with fellow Argylls and other troops before boarding the *Rooseboom*.

I had been asleep, on a mattress on the *Rooseboom's* deck, when the torpedo struck.

But let me begin at the beginning . . .

CHAPTER ONE

THE docks and harbour of Padang, the Sumatran port, presented a grim sight in the days which immediately succeeded the fall of Singapore.

The town itself was crowded with people who had escaped from Malaya. The Japanese were bombing systematically.

The *Rooseboom*, usually engaged on the coastal run between Sumatra and Java, was en route from Batavia to Ceylon and safety when she was ordered to pick up evacuees at Padang.

Now, deep down in the water from the load of humanity she carried, she drew away from the quayside, and we could see the half-submerged ships, victims of the Jap raid, which dotted the entrance to the harbour.

But even so I found myself caught up in the spell of the sunset's beauty—for the dying rays fell on a lush growth of tropical vegetation on the dozens of islands round about us, and there are few more beautiful harbour approaches in the world than Padang's Bremerhaven.

Behind me a voice said: "It's lovely, Hoot, isn't it?" and I turned to find Willie MacDonald at my elbow.

Sergeant Willie MacDonald was an old friend of mine. He had been wounded with the Argyll carrier platoon at Dipang, but had remained on duty until the battle was over. He had come out of hospital to join in the fighting on Singapore, and had escaped to Sumatra.

"Aye, it's lovely, Toorie," I answered him. "The folks at home would give a bit to see this, wouldn't they?"

"Gie me Inverness," said Willie. "*And* the Caledonian Canal."

It was a scrap of conversation I will never forget—the words of a brave Highlander, many years away from home, but with his heart still in the silver city he was never to see again.

The atmosphere aboard the *Rooseboom* was a strange mixture of relief at leaving the perils of Malaya and Singapore behind, and of tension at the ever-present prospect of bombs and torpedoes.

A Jap plane had been over the port not long before we left, and we scanned the skies anxiously, and had our two Bren guns mounted.

The troops were packed liked sardines, and sleeping on deck almost atop of one another.

But after two nights had passed without event, and the Dutch captain had issued a bulletin that we were now out of bombing range, tension lessened, everyone became more friendly, and the atmosphere was very nearly carefree.

Senior Army officer aboard the ship was Brigadier Archie Paris, who had commanded the division against hopeless odds during the Malayan campaign.

He and the brigade major, Major Angus MacDonald, member of a famous Argyllshire family, heir to a £200,000 estate, had escaped from Singapore in a yacht owned and sailed by a young officer of the Argylls, Captain Mike Blackwood. Blackwood, red-haired and blue-eyed, was a tremendously keen yachtsman. He had won several races while we were stationed in Singapore before the campaign.

He, the brigadier, and Major MacDonald were all engaged in the hand-to-hand fighting as Singapore fell.

At one stage about fifty Jap tanks threatened to penetrate into the rear of Singapore town.

But Mike Blackwood, with an anti-tank rifle and only one or two men, took up positions at the road block and engaged the leading tank at point-blank range. He gained precious time for defenders back in the heart of Singapore.

The brigadier himself was known to us of long service in India as a fine soldier.

He was a powerfully built, handsome officer, his face deep tanned through his years of service, his iron-grey moustache always neatly clipped, his eyes shrewd and quizzical.

Always a great all-round athlete, of exceptional strength, he took tremendous pride in his physical fitness, and on many an occasion was able to outmarch men many years his junior.

On the *Rooseboom*'s third evening out from Padang, Brigadier Paris invited a number of officers to have a drink with him. He gave what he called "the obvious toast" . . . safe arrival at Colombo. "Forty-eight hours more," he said, "should find us in happier and and more comfortable circumstances."

But five hours later, just ten minutes short of midnight, the torpedo struck.

I had fallen asleep on a mattress on the deck, beside Willie

MacDonald. I woke to find myself lying sprawled in the scuppers, half through the rails.

There was a weight pressing on my face and chest. As I pushed it off, I realized that it was all that was left of MacDonald.

Around me was indescribable noise. Screams, shouts, groans, the noise of escaping steam and in-rushing water, with above them all the bellowing of a bullock which we had taken on as rations.

I staggered along the deck, which was already sloping steeply. The port boats, I saw, had been destroyed.

The captain and crew were attempting to lower one of the two boats on the starboard side. Around the other was a milling crowd—and as I watched something broke, and the boat crashed bow first into the sea, catapulting dozens of people with it.

I ran to the side. Oddly enough, though I was to find later that my collarbone was broken, a piece of metal lodged in my shin. and my eardrum burst by the blast, I felt no pain.

The deck rail was almost awash. As I threw myself into the water and came to the surface, the one thing I remained conscious of was the continuing noise.

The predominant note of the bullock's frenzied bellowing had given way to a high-pitched monotonous wail from some native seamen somewhere away out in the darkness.

Voices were shouting, "Where are you, Mac?"—"Is that you, Jock?" There were choking cries for help.

Somewhat to my left, a soldier's voice, inevitably, started "Roll out the Barrel". Near me a naked man clung to a piece of floating debris. I swam towards him, and shouted, "Do you mind if I share your piece of wood?"

"By all means, old man," he replied.

He was Assistant Commissioner Roger Owen Davis of the Malay Police. He was to live only twenty-four hours in the lifeboat. He was to slump down, exhausted, on the evening of the first day, and be crushed to death in the night.

Assistant Commissioner Davis was a son of the Reverend Gerald Davis. He had been intended for the Royal Air Force but a defect was discovered in his eyesight, and he was transferred to the colonial service. He was an exceptionally good Chinese scholar, and much of his work lay in following up Communist and Japanese spies in the Malay States. The Japanese marked him down as a "dangerous person", and in 1937 he was decorated by the King for gallantry in a clash with bandits. He had a chance to escape from Singapore to Australia, but was anxious to continue his war service in India and the Far East.

Davis and I must have clung for an hour to the piece of wood before we saw, some distance away, shadowy in the moonlight, the blurred figures of people standing up in a lifeboat.

We kicked out and made slowly towards it. The scene was pandemonium. The boat had been damaged as they launched her, and there was a gaping hole in her port bow.

Men scrambling aboard her pulled the hole below water, so that she filled almost to the gunwales.

As we arrived, the Dutch captain and his officers were shouting to the crowd about them to give them a chance to get her repaired.

We stayed there, dozens of us, treading water, while they plugged the hole with shirts, socks, singlets, shorts. Then a Royal Army Ordnance Corps man climbed in and patched over the hole with a piece of tin.

A shout came from the captain: "Any women and children out there?"

Yes, there were three women, no children.

"Any wounded?"

Yes, four or five of them.

Then, one by one, we were pulled aboard—and it was only as a sharp pain through my shoulder, when someone seized my arm, that I cried out, "By God, I'm wounded too!"

Numbly, still dazed by what had gone before, we waited for the dawn.

The boat was so crowded—as I have said, it was built to hold twenty-eight, not the eighty who now occupied it—that most of us were standing shoulder to shoulder, face to face, or back to back. It was impossible to change position.

Then, as dawn crept up and lit the scene, we saw others who were dependent on the boat—some fifty of them, clinging to the lifelines on the sides.

Around us, within a radius of half a mile, were the bobbing heads of still more survivors.

The boat itself was down nearly to the gunwales in the water.

I looked around me for familiar faces.

I was in the stern. I could see Brigadier Paris. He was wearing only a khaki shirt, the pliers-and-hammer badge of the R.A.O.C. on its arm. A warrant officer had handed the shirt to him as he climbed, naked, into the boat.

Close by, his hand on the tiller, was the stout red-faced captain of the *Rooseboom.*

He was wearing a white shirt and trousers, with his epaulettes still in evidence. He and his chief officer and chief engineer—both, like him, Dutchmen—were the only men in the boat who were really adequately covered.

I, for instance, was still in the khaki shorts in which I had been sleeping when the torpedo struck.

There were three women in a group in the stern.

One, pleasant-faced and motherly looking, in khaki shirt and slacks, I recognized as Gertrude Nunn, wife of Mr. R. L. Nunn, who had been Director of Public Works in Singapore.

There was a large, stout, fair-haired woman of thirty or so, in blouse and skirt, carrying a handbag. She was the wife of Dirk, the Dutch chief officer.

The third was a slim, pretty Chinese girl, clad in a coloured skirt and shirt, her feet bare.

Perched up in the bows, beyond a packed group of white men (mostly soldiers), I could see a group of about a dozen Javanese seamen; in their midst their serang, or bosun, a white-haired old fellow with a fringe of beard on his chin. A kindly-looking man . . .

CHAPTER TWO

WE welcomed the first dawn. There was, indeed, one wild delirious moment when we imagined that the morning star was the lights of a ship coming over the horizon.

But how, in the days which followed, we were to curse and hate that brassy, blazing, burning horror, the sun.

It was the sun which, more than any other factor, drove our fellows to crazed, demoniac acts and ends. It branded unbearable wounds on our unprotected bodies, scorched out of us the moisture that was life.

On the first morning, however, the sun was merely light and heat, after a shivering shock-shattered night. It let us, for one thing, take stock of our position. It let us see how *unbelievably* crowded our cargo of humanity really was.

We were standing so close that, for night after night that followed, no man could lie down to sleep. He must doze upright, his head leaning on the shoulder or breast of his opposite number.

To slump down was to risk being pressed into the bilge water which was always lapping in the bottom of the boat and there to suffocate or drown.

A count revealed that our company numbered 135 in all, including the people around us in the water.

Within an hour or two, certainly, the number was less—already there were some who could hold on no longer, who just loosened their grasp and drifted away.

We took tally of our food and water. With sinking hearts we heard the total announced.

There was a case of bully beef, containing forty-eight twelve-ounce tins. There were two seven-pound tins of fried spiced rice which the Dutch call nassigoreng. We had forty-eight tins of Colombo condensed milk, and six Bols gin bottles full of fresh milk.

Some of the soldiers had their water bottles, but nearly all had filled with salt water during the hours in the sea.

The Dutch captain regarded the meagre store bitterly. He had stocked this boat carefully with food, water, emergency gear, and medical kit. In the mad scramble in the darkness, when the boat had all but foundered, almost everything had floated away into the night.

Brigadier Paris stood up in the stern sheets and called for attention.

He was more exhausted at that moment, probably, than anyone in the boat, for he had been drawn down with the *Rooseboom* as she sank, and he had come to the surface—"God knows how," he said—with bursting lungs and a stomach full of water.

Now he stood there, very erect, legs bare beneath the shirttail, and addressed his troops as if on a parade ground.

"The captain," he said, "will be in command of the boat. I shall be responsible for discipline.

"We were due in Colombo at dawn on Tuesday. This is Monday. When we don't turn up by Thursday, they are bound to send something out to look for us. That being so, the captain has decided that it will be wiser to stay here, in the vicinity of the sinking. Something should reach us by Friday.

"Our position is pretty sticky. But I look to you all, as British soldiers, as men who have acquitted themselves well on the peninsula, to retain your soldierly qualities until help arrives."

He told us that we would receive a tablespoonful of water at each sunup, a spoonful of milk and water at night.

A tin of bully beef would be shared between twelve people each day. From her handbag, the Dutch mate's wife produced, of all surprising things, a tablespoon, which, for all the time our water lasted, was to act as our measure.

She was carrying, too, some thirst-quenching tablets, which she shared. It was the sort of gesture which gladdened our first hours.

Later she showed some of us the useless Dutch bank notes, thousands of guilders, which formed the greater part of the rest of her handbag's contents.

Officers to whom the brigadier could delegate some of his responsibilities included the two lieutenant colonels—J. P. Acworth of the Indian Army and R. E. Palmer of the Royal Engineers; two majors—Richard Dent of the Indian Army and Noel Corrie of the Engineers.

Acworth swiftly showed himself a strong character. He was a cleanly-built, balding man of forty-five or so, with a striking Guardee moustache.

He took charge of the rationing, and announced that, to lessen the rigours of overcrowding, every man who was not injured must take a compulsory spell of four hours each day clinging to the lifelines in the water.

The brigadier himself took one of the first spells in the water. While he was there two sharks made their appearance—first of many that we saw at various stages—but we yelled and beat at the water to drive them off.

During one of the spells in the water, too, a young soldier was stung by some kind of fish and pulled aboard in great agony. He died an hour later.

Towards the evening of the first day there was a dramatic arrival in our midst.

We were joined by Lieutenant Colonel Douglas, of the Indian Army Ordnance Corps, who had swum from a raft some hundred yards away. His nerves, we could see, were strung to the breaking point.

He told us that with him on the raft had been a white woman, her leg blown off by the explosion; a lance corporal of the Argylls (by whose description I at once recognized Jock Gray, one of the men who had trekked with me through the jungle after the

Battle of Slim River) and Major Angus MacDonald,* the brigade
major I have mentioned before.

MacDonald took with him from the ship, said Douglas, a flask
which he thought contained water. Actually it was brandy—and
MacDonald had spent the day on the raft drinking it in an
attempt to assuage his thirst.

The effects, in the heat, were disastrous. "Angus MacDonald is
raving mad," said Douglas. "I had to leave him. He was trying
to push me off the raft."

We gave Douglas a spoonful of milk and water. Vaguely—for
there were so many other things to occupy my attention—I could
hear his voice rising excitedly as he continued his tale.

Then, as darkness fell, the voice rose to a shout. Douglas would
speak one sentence in English, the next in Urdu. It was a crazy,
high-pitched babble.

Suddenly there was the noise of a scrimmage. He had struck
out at all around him. I heard voices say, "Put him over before
he tips the boat up."

There was a splash.

Colonel Douglas struggled to the side and gripped the gunwale.
Someone fended him off with an oar. He slipped away back into
the darkness, shouting a crazy stream of Urdu curses.

Early next morning, the man I have always thought was the
bravest of all amongst us stepped forward with a suggestion. It
was Major Noel Corrie.

It would ease the well-nigh unbearable overcrowding, he told
the brigadier, if he and some volunteers could construct a raft
on which they might be towed behind the drifting boat.

Corrie and about twenty of the men, including two or three
of the Javanese seamen, swam around collecting debris with
which to construct their raft.

When they had completed it, it was a shaky structure, twenty
by twenty feet, tied together with pieces of cord, strips of cloth,
and sisal fibre they had salvaged from the sea.

They used the sisal, too, to make a towrope which they attached
to the stern of the boat. Then the twenty of them climbed aboard,
and the raft sank until they were waist deep in water.

Corrie must have known that there could be only one end to
the course he had taken.

---

* Seven years later I gave evidence in the court action in Edinburgh which
decided that Major MacDonald must be dead.

Man by man, through the three days that followed, members of his little band slipped off and disappeared. At last there was only Corrie himself, dazed with exhaustion, his upper body blackened by the sun, his legs bleached by the water.

Numbers in the boat had dwindled too, and the brigadier ordered Corrie to return.

He was pulled aboard, more dead than alive, and his gallant, piteous little craft was cut adrift.

He died that night.

The three women, meantime, had drawn together. There they were, three of their sex in a cramped, sweating, groaning congregation of men—the Jocks and the Cockneys and the lascar seamen.

Already little codes of behaviour had materialized. A small space had been cleared so that the women were reclining against the thwarts, half sitting, half lying.

At times, when needs of the toilet had to be attended to, the brigadier would give the order, "Everyone look to the bows," and we would gaze ahead and give the women their spell of privacy.

Now that there was room to move, with men doing their four hours in the water and others on the raft, Mrs. Nunn went about among the wounded, tending their hurts.

Her husband had died as he pushed her to safety. She told me the story, dry-eyed and with pride, as she tied my arm behind me in a rough rope sling, seeking to alleviate the grating pain of my broken clavicle.

They were in their cabin when the torpedo struck. Within seconds, water began to pour across the floor.

Mr. Nunn lifted his wife and pushed her through the porthole —one of those wide, square portholes used in that type of Dutch coaster.

She came to the surface. He did not follow.

They had been a devoted couple. Friends have told me, since, many stories which help to explain the inspirational influence of Mrs. Nunn in the lifeboat.

Before her marriage, as Gertrude Higgs, she was a celebrated contralto singer. She sang at the Promenade concerts, with the Royal Choral Society and at many other big concerts in Britain and abroad.

Her husband, in addition to being Director of Public Works

in Singapore, was a group captain in the volunteer air service.

He had served as a civil engineer in Trinidad, Nigeria and British Guiana, and so rapid had been his rise that he was expected to become a colonial governor.

They were on holiday in England when war was declared. Mr. Nunn was recalled to Singapore. His wife, whose loyalty and devotion were a by-word among their friends, flew out to be with him.

They left Singapore a day before it fell, but their ship, the *Kuala*, was bombed and sunk before it had gone very far.

Mr. Oswald Gilmour, who was deputy municipal engineer in Singapore, has told how Mrs. Nunn then refused to leave her husband.

Survivors from the *Kuala* struggled to reach the island of Pohm-Pohm, where Mr. Nunn took charge.

He arranged the order of rescue—first, women and children and wounded, then civilians, then Singapore's Public Works Department Unit, and last the Services and himself.

A launch arrived, and set about taking off as many as it could.

Some women with hospital experience volunteered to stay behind and look after the wounded who were left.

"Mrs. Nunn," says Mr. Gilmour, "got down as far as the embarkation spot, and then asked me to find her husband for her. He came along, and she said to him: 'Rex, I don't want to go if you are not coming.' She evidently persuaded him to allow her to stay, for she did not leave the island until she was able to accompany him."

When the final batch of survivors was taken from the island by junk and motor launch, Mr. and Mrs. Nunn were the last to go. They were brought on to Padang—and the *Rooseboom*.

The name of the Chinese girl who sat with Mrs. Nunn and the Dutch mate's wife was, I learned, Doris Lim.

She spoke English with a marked American accent, relic of the American convent in Shanghai whose sisters had brought her up.

She had worked for British Intelligence in Northern China. She had escaped from Tientsin just before the Japanese occupation. She was again just a jump ahead of them out of Shanghai and then Hong Kong.

In Singapore, she had taken a post as assistant to a Chinese news cameraman.

Her experiences in the escape from Singapore were very similar to Mrs. Nunn's. The ship in which she was evacuated was bombed and sunk just a couple of miles from the spot where the Nunns' ship also went down.

Doris was the only woman among the passengers who escaped to an island—from which she, in her turn, was brought on to Padang—and the *Rooseboom*.

She looked very young, and very pretty as well, by European or Oriental standards, as she sat there in the lifeboat. Her complexion was particularly noticeable—with a fresh bloom to it, unusual in a Chinese girl.

But, during the early days in the boat, she spoke hardly at all. She would sit gazing ahead of her with the unsmiling stoicism of her race.

And perhaps it was that fatalism, that refusal to be stampeded into despair, which led to our staggering, she and I, ashore on our island a thousand miles away.

CHAPTER THREE

AT least half our number, on that morning when we took a count and found that there were 135 of us, were raw young troops of the 18th Division, just out from home.

They were the boys who had been sent in a last-minute bid to bolster up the crumbling Malayan defences, but who had been diverted when it was seen that the fall of Singapore was inevitable.

They were all conscripts, with no background of Indian experience—nineteen-year-olds, twenty-year-olds. There must have been seventy of them. They were, and it was only natural, the first to crack. They sat silent, motionless, despondent.

We "old sweats" wisecracked and kidded them in an attempt to put heart into them.

"Cheer up, sonny," we would say, "it won't be long now. Just keep thinking about that beer in Colombo."

We kept making them go over the side for a swim. We felt this was terribly important. It would keep them cooler and take their minds off things.

All the soldiers, doing their compulsory four-hour spells clinging to the lifeline in the water, had to take turns by night as well as day.

Mrs. Nunn had become our Florence Nightingale, our Mother

Superior. She was always making her way about trying to cheer up the unhappy boys.

Their conversation with her was always the same. "Do you think anything will come? It isn't hopeless, is it? We're bound to be rescued, aren't we?"

And Mrs. Nunn would always reply, "Of course—don't doubt it. The one important thing is that we should keep a grip on ourselves."

There was one boy who impressed me greatly at this time, a young company quartermaster sergeant (from Ordnance or Engineers, I cannot recall which). He was only about twenty-one, but he had about him a timbre and a toughness that was lacking in the others. What a Regular he would have made, I kept thinking.

He would speak to me about his girl. "She's a lovely thing," he would say. "I wonder if they've told her by now. She'll be wondering what's happened to me!"

"She won't have to wonder long," I would reply. "Send her a cable from Colombo."

There were still plenty of us who continued to be cheerful and optimistic, and this in spite of the fact that, from the second day on, hunger and thirst and the cramped quarters began to tell.

The thirst was worse than the hunger.

Hunger's gnawing pain seemed to reach a climax fairly soon, and then we forgot about it.

But thirsty—I was always thirsty. For a day or two one could make saliva, but afterwards one's throat was always as dry as a board. One always seemed to be trying to swallow, always licking one's lips—and with each day the effort to do so became more painful.

I was more fortunate than most in that the sun did not bother me—partly because of my years in India, when I had often worn nothing but shorts, partly because of my black Highlander's colouring and consequent pigmentation.

Others began to blister from the first day. It was the fair-haired Dutchmen who suffered most. People began to tear off what little clothes they had, so that they might dip them in the salt water and place them on their heads. Yet even this seemed to be a mistake, for the salt water would run down the blistered skin of their faces and make the pain worse than before.

The Dutch captain picked up his sodden, useless charts and

used them as a head covering. Doris Lim and Mrs. Nunn used their shirts, sitting naked from the waist up.

All of us, at various stages in that first week, became prey to hallucination.

The first victim was a most unlikely one—a colour-sergeant of the Gordon Highlanders, a little dried-up nut of a man who had had fifteen or sixteen years Far East service, and who was "Tich" to all of us.

One morning he said: "It won't be long now, till the flying boat gets back."

"What flying boat?" I asked him.

"The one that came last night," he said—and I felt my heart jump in hope.

Then he continued, "The one that took the women and wounded off."

And looking towards the stern I saw the Dutchwoman, and Mrs. Nunn, and the Chinese girl lying back against the thwarts, and knew that "Tich" was the first of us to see mirage.

Almost all of us, at some stage, would imagine we saw a ship.

A soldier leaned over the side and drank from the sea. "It's fresh," he cried. "The water's fresh."

It shows our state of mental receptiveness that we struggled over to join him, wildly believing that what he said was true. Some, indeed, further gone than others, drank and said, "He's right. It *is* fresh."

We had begun to dream—fierce, vivid dreams of food and drink and friendly gatherings. We would compare these dreams and nearly all of them had such points in common.

Then we would wake to the creak, creak, creak of the dried timbers as the boat swayed in the current.

For years afterwards I could not rid myself, in the Jap prison camp or back in Singapore, in London or in Scotland, of the fearsome feeling that this was just another dream, and I would wake again to that creaking sway.

Almost everyone was experimenting with the drinking of sea water.

At first, when the youngsters were detected scooping it up in their hands from over the side, we tried to stop them. Acworth, still the strongest character, made it an order that they must not drink from the sea.

But during the night there was much surreptitious drinking,

and gradually people ceased to care. The effect on those who drank large quantities was to send them into a coma, from which they never emerged except crazed and suicidal.

Those who drank sea water in tiny quantities, however, seemed to suffer no really bad effects. From the beginning I myself gargled with the salt water and cleaned my teeth with it.

At the end of the first week I started to drink sea water in very small quantities—just a tiny scoopful in my hands when the thirst became unbearable.

Yet I found main relief for my parched throat through gargling without swallowing the water, and somehow, through the days that followed, it became a fetish with me to perform these tasks, of cleaning my throat and teeth with regularity.

Almost up to the end, just as long as I had strength to lift my arms and rub my fingers over my teeth, I maintained the ritual.

It was on the third day that people were first detected drinking their urine. Some youngster started it, and, turning to his mate, said, "It's okay."

It became imitative. I did it myself. At first the taste was nauseating, but then someone suggested that we mix the urine with salt water. We did so and it didn't seem so bad.

Later, the taste became so acid that one felt as if one were drinking gasoline. I quickly gave it up.

Slowly the spirit of comradeship with which we had set off began to vanish. We found ourselves watching our fellows— covertly, suspiciously.

From the beginning there had been a careful watch on the rations. "But who," we began to think "is watching the watchers."

Some of us became particularly watchful of a group from another regiment, five of them, who sat huddled together up near the bows, talking in undertones and looking round furtively at the other occupants of the boat.

There had been some suggestion, early on, that they were deserters. They had been stationed somewhere on some island near Singapore, and they had been heard, before the *Rooseboom* sailed, to speak of the possibility of getting a small boat and sailing over to Dutch territory together.

Now, as they sat there, all small men, all malevolent, keeping themselves to themselves and greeting all approaches from others with some obscene rejoinder, one sensed that they were up to no good.

Many of us had already gone. One of the first was Major Richard Dent—"Dicky" to everyone.

On the first day, as he did his four-hour spell in the water, he grinned up to us and said, "It's just like a Mediterranean cruise, isn't it?"

But he was one of those officers, and there are many of them in India, who never expose their bodies to the sun, and now he was among the first to suffer the worst agonies of sunburn.

He just vanished in the night.

We saw another indication of how things were going when a sergeant major, who had been given a life-belt for his spell in the water because he could not swim, refused on coming back to the boat to hand it over to another non-swimmer.

He clung to the life-belt as if it was his last link with his world. Officers ordered him to hand it over, and in the end it was forcibly taken off him.

That night we could hear his voice raised in the darkness as he proclaimed his grievance. We heard someone strike him. Next morning he had gone.

That was the way it was happening. People just disappeared in the night, and we met their departure with a dull acceptance. No one asked any questions.

At the back of our minds, already beginning to work to the theme of "If it's not the other fellow, it'll be me," was the feeling that every man fewer meant more room in the boat

The third night saw the biggest cut in our numbers so far. A storm blew up, the sea was very high, and we shipped a lot of water. We baled frantically, with such utensils as we had, but there were many who panicked.

Out in the night we heard the sound of screams and shouts, and in the morning twenty people were missing.

It was then, I think, that we really began to realize what the five men in the bows were up to.

They had formed themselves into a murder gang, determined that, if everyone else had to go, they would still live.

Next morning rations were cut. A tin of bully beef was now shared between twenty people. The two spoonfuls of water per day became one.

Each day's shareout became an ordeal. It was like the feeding of a band of ravenous wild animals.

Acworth had ordered that the rations be brought up to the

stern, where officers were positioned, so that we might watch them ourselves. All eyes centred on us, for hour after hour. We evolved a system to see that no man tried to come back a second time for a share.

Acworth stood in the stern pouring the precious drops of water into the spoon. Men would cry out, "You haven't filled the spoon. I haven't had a full share."

Acworth ordered me to stand beside him, checking up on the faces of the men as they drew their rations.

If I said that a man had already had his spoonful, Acworth was adamant in his refusal to give any more. Many cursed him, and screamed that they had had none.

The Javanese were the calmest at such moments. For the first day or two, they had refused to take any water. We had to say to them, "Come along there, you've got to have it."

It was as if they sensed the feeling against them which existed among some of the men. Because there *was* a faction which said, "To hell with the blacks—why should we suffer for them?"

That mood changed swiftly when the men began to look to the Javanese as their main hope of salvation.

We were bearded and black. It was hard to say which was white man and which was Javanese. The sun seemed to beat down more fiercely than ever on the brassy ocean.

For two days the blond first officer had been lying in a coma, his face burned and blistered and swollen to unrecognizable shape, with his head in his wife's lap. She sat there, speaking to no one else, crooning Dutch words of comfort to him.

On the fourth night we heard him utter a stream of Dutch sentences. We heard her say "Nae, Nae" as she sought to dissuade him. He had told her that he was going for help.

Suddenly he broke away from her, shouted to us in English "Going . . . going to swim . . . find help." Then he sprang over the side and swam away, quite calmly and with some unsuspected reserve of strength into the darkness.

His wife did not weep. She sat, for nearly another day, in an attitude of resignation, keening and moaning softly to herself. Then, at sunset, there was a movement in the boat and she was overboard.

I was standing beside one of the lascars as it happened. I watched her drift away, and I felt that I *could* go after her, that I *should* go after her. But I did not go.

That was how it was, with me as with everyone else. We were beginning to find out how little man-made codes count when man is facing the ultimate.

One incident about this time tore me with an anguish of a kind I thought I had ceased to be capable of.

A soldier I had known for years, a fine fellow, a Scotsman, one of our best athletes and most uncomplaining soldiers, went overboard for a swim to freshen himself up.

He allowed himself to get just a fraction too far out of range of the drifting boat. He found he was not catching up with it when he tried to return.

He was swimming with an overarm trudgeon stroke, and I saw him change to breast stroke.

Slowly he fell further away from us as his stroke weakened. We lay, even those of us who watched him, too spent to think of any measure which might aid him.

Then, across his face, as it emerged from the water at the end of a stroke, I saw the expression of determination change to an unforgettable one of utter despair.

I saw him realize that he was going to drown.

I watched his bobbing head until it must have been two hundred yards away, with nothing all around it but the sea.

It was half an hour before a big wave hid him from view and when we looked again he was not there.

CHAPTER FOUR

As the first week drew to its close, Brigadier Paris sank back into a torpor, speaking to no one, getting weaker with every hour.

After the effort of his speech to the troops, made soon after he had fought his way to the surface, he had said little. Lieutenant Colonel Acworth had been the directing force.

But the brigadier had a guardian: Mike Blackwood, the young officer who had sailed him out of Singapore in his yacht.

Captain Mike Blackwood had joined us on the afternoon of the second day. He had been swimming from the time the ship sank.

Because he was red-haired, and had that freckled pigmentation which cannot take the sun, his face and shoulders were a raw mass. The lower part of his body was bleached by the water to a strange blue colour.

But his good spirits were astounding.

Soon after coming aboard, he said, "I'm afraid it's up to you and me, Gibson, to look after the brigadier."

I had known him well in India. In the summer of '39, just before the brigadier's departure to Malaya, there was a training course designed to find men "capable of commanding a company on active service". Mike Blackwood, not long out of Sandhurst, finished top. I, then a lance corporal, finished third.

Now, with almost unbelievable fortitude, for the pain of his sunburn must have been worse than anyone's, Blackwood performed little duties for the rapidly weakening Paris—even to the extent of saving part of his tiny water ration for him.

It was a shock when the brigadier suddenly raised his head and turning to Blackwood, said (quite lucidly, quite quietly, very pleasantly), "I say, let's go along to the club for a drink."

Blackwood answered him as conversationally as if they had been strolling down St. James's. "Let's make it later, sir," he said.

Within an hour the brigadier was thrashing violently about the boat, his mind completely gone, while Blackwood and I sought to hold him down.

By morning, which was the Friday on which he had hopes of rescue from Colombo, Brigadier Paris was in a last coma.

Mike Blackwood announced his death to the troops. Men stood silent as we slipped him over the side, and Blackwood repeated such passages of the burial service as he could remember.

The brigadier was the only one, of all those whose lives ended there, for whom we could summon up the strength to have such a service.

Poor Mike Blackwood survived his friend by only a day. He slipped unconscious to the bottom of the boat, and we found him drowned in the lapping six inches of bilge water.

Earlier in the night he did a very typical thing.

He turned to me and said, "I should not have told you, Gibson, but in the circumstances it is in order, I feel, to mention it now —it can't make any difference to either of us. The brigadier had recommended you for the D.C.M."

Mike had been in charge of records, and I can imagine the conflict in his mind as he lay beside me in the boat—should he do that unforgivable thing, from a regular soldier's point of view, reveal a confidence? Or should he speak a heartening sentence to a man with perhaps only a few hours to live?

Within two hours of the brigadier's funeral, the Dutch captain was stabbed by one of his own engineer officers.

The old man was dozing, his hand still on the tiller, when we heard a shout, a sudden splutter of Dutch invective. Before anyone could get to him, the engineer had jumped at the skipper and buried a knife in his ribs.

Apparently he had been sitting nursing a grievance, blaming the skipper for our troubles. No one even knew he had a knife in his belt.

"Grab him," shouted Acworth, and someone flung himself on the engineer as he tried to snatch the few remaining rations, before jumping overboard.

That was a strange feature of every suicide. As people decided to jump overboard, they seemed to resent the fact that others were being left with a chance of safety.

They would try to seize the rations and fling them overboard. They would try to make their last action in the boat the pulling of the bung which would let in the water.

Their madness always seemed to take the form that they must not go alone, but must take everyone with them.

The engineer who had stabbed the captain failed to get to the rations, but tore himself loose and jumped overboard.

He, too, was still strong enough to swim away, and I have since reflected that all the Dutchmen, except the murdered captain, went swimming off—the mate, his wife, the engineers.

Mrs. Nunn bathed the captain's wound with salt water. He just lay there saying, in English, "Finished, finished, finished . . . it is the finish." Then he would murmur the same thing "Kaput . . . kaput . . ." in his own tongue, and every now and again we caught the English word again—"finished."

He died that night, his head in Mrs. Nunn's lap.

I was now guard of the water bottles. There were only two left, and one of them only half full.

I dozed with them under my body. In the night I was awakened by a shout, and then the voice of Mrs. Nunn, "He's trying to steal the water."

There was a hand feeling under me. I grabbed.

It was the chief engineer, sole surviving Dutchman. Crying something angrily in Dutch, he flung himself into the water.

Now, strangely, the Javanese, who hitherto had seemed afraid of the soldiers, assumed a new manner.

It was as if they knew that they, the only seamen left aboard, were now superior to the landsmen.

Their manner took on a subtle difference.

The serang came up to the stern and took over the tiller.

None of the white men did anything to resist this assumption of authority. Rather, indeed, did we encourage it.

Our manner changed, too. We became subservient to the Javanese.

They took it in turns to manage the rudder, and we found ourselves consulting them.

"Are we far from land, Serang?" we would ask. And always his reply was the same, "Tedah Tao" "I don't know."

Every evening someone would imagine he saw land. "Is that not land, Serang?" we would shout.

On the seventh evening, the Sunday, we finished the last bottle of water.

Palmer was in command now, but for all the effort that he could make, it was an empty title. He sat there, hunched up and weak, his face birdlike, the cheekbones standing out.

Then we saw Mrs. Nunn, talking with him, and Palmer roused himself to speak, in a voice little above a whisper, to the boat's company.

"I don't think there is much hope for us," he said. "I'm afraid we must reconcile ourselves to it that if something doesn't turn up pretty soon, it will be too late. Mrs. Nunn has suggested that we commit ourselves to God. She would like to conduct a service."

Somehow, heaven knows how, we had a Bible, water-logged and tattered. Whom it had belonged to, Jock soldier from some Highland village, young public-school lieutenant, or the convent-reared Chinese girl, I will never know.

Mrs. Nunn stood up, her face blackened by the sun, her voice —like the voice of us all by now—cracked and whispering through thirst and weakness. She opened the Bible and began to read aloud.

We all seemed automatically to turn towards her. This strange, mixed bag of tortured, desperate human beings.

We sang with her "Abide with Me" and "The Lord is my Shepherd." We said the Lord's Prayer.

We felt, each and all of us, drawn almost physically towards Mrs. Nunn.

Months later, I talked with a psychiatrist in the prison camp about it.

"You were all," he said, "overcome by that urge which seizes every man in time of danger—the urge to return to the safety of the womb. Mrs. Nunn to all of you personified the mother."

The story, I know, must now be impressing as nothing but unrelieved tragedy—a chronicle of hours in which the only milestones seem to be the deaths of men or women.

But that was how it was.

There were, perhaps, fifty or sixty of us left when the service was held. Thereafter men went quickly. Palmer . . . Acworth . . .

Colonel Acworth, like so many, just vanished in the night. The calmness and efficiency with which he had sought to maintain discipline and morale in the boat were typical of him.

The "supplies" role he had adopted, in rationing out the food and water, had come naturally to him, for he was Assistant Adjutant Quartermaster General to the 11th Indian Division when Japan entered the war.

It was grimly, during the Monday, the eighth day, that I realized that if any discipline was to be retained I must be the one to maintain it.

Up in the bows, malignant and threatening, sat the five deserters.

Mrs. Nunn died that day.

She knew that she was going to die. She spoke towards the end, in endearing terms, of her husband.

"I'm glad," she said, "he went with the ship and did not have to suffer with us here."

She just slipped quietly into unconsciousness, Doris Lim, naked now, beside her bathing her lips with salt water.

I knew the dread things that had been happening to others who had died, and whose bodies had remained in the boat, and I said to Doris Lim, "Get her over the side, quickly."

We slipped her over before the evil band in the bows knew that she had died.

It was just about this stage that the murder gang, as I have always thought of them since, came out into the open.

While others watched, helpless and apathetic, they jumped from behind on the young C.Q.M.S. of the 18th Division who had so impressed me in the early days, and drew a jagged bully beef tin across his throat.

There was no doubt as to their intentions. They had, as we knew, tried to drink the blood of people who had died, and had found it impossible.

Now they were trying butchery.

The youngster tore himself free, and staggered towards us for protection. He lay there dying, painfully and lingeringly.

I said: "For God's sake, put him overboard."

To me then came Warrant Officer MacKenzie, of the Indian Army Ordnance Corps. "Don't you realize what is happening?" he said. "Don't you know that we are all going to be killed. Those men intend to commandeer the boat."

I did not feel brave at that moment. But I pulled myself together and addressed the whole company in as strong a voice as I could muster. I told them what we suspected.

"You crowd," I said, pointing to the five, "are dumping people overboard for your own ends. Do you think you can get away with that?"

Their ringleader leaned forward aggressively. He was a small man, about my own height, not bad looking.

He had, I remember, a coarse Liverpool accent. He was a type of which one finds thousands in the Army—cross-grained, tough, malcontent. When you are a drill instructor, you must break them before they break you.

"We'll bloody well put you over as well if you don't shut up," he said.

I think I muttered something about us being in the majority. But I did shut up. I was scared. This was no barrack square. I could not know how many I might rely upon to back me up.

I waited. Next time MacKenzie came to me, I said: "It's them or us. There's only five of them. How many men can we rely on if we try to rush them and put them overboard?"

MacKenzie moved about among the others, and when darkness came down he told me that he had a majority, twelve to fourteen men, ready to deal with the murder gang.

It was the showdown. I thought to myself, Well, here it is. I had seen so many go over and not come back. We moved down the boat, converging on the five men up near the bows.

They sensed, of course, what was on. It must have been obvious what our purpose was.

All this time, I remember, the Javanese sat placidly in their places. They, too, must have known what was afoot, but they remained blank-faced and phlegmatic.

The atmosphere was electrical. One little tough shouted: "Here they come" and from behind him pulled out a bottle and held it by the neck.

Drummer F. Hardy of the Argylls, a little chap, no more than five feet three inches in height, who had been one of our heroes in the Malayan fighting, sprang forward. The bottle crashed down on his head. Two of the murder gang grabbed him and pushed him overboard.

Then we were at their throats. We struggled and stumbled and rolled wrestling at the bottom of the boat.

We did not seem to put them overboard one by one so much as to rush them overboard in a body.

Three, as they came to the surface, got their hands to the gunwale and tried to drag themselves back.

It was a confusion of pleadings and curses and choking half-smothered obscenities.

Relentlessly we battered at their fingers with the rowlocks. We were down to the elemental now. It was, we told ourselves, a dozen times that night, either them or us.

Drummer Hardy, the victim of this gang, had been formerly batman to Brigadier I. MacA. Stewart, commanding officer of the Argylls, and had earned an undying place in the history of that regiment not only as the last man to cross Johore causeway into Singapore after the retreat from Malaya—but by the manner of his crossing it.

Brigadier Stewart, in his history of the regiment, says that Hardy was a man who would never run, either when Jap planes came over or when a demolition party was hurrying to join the main body. "Japs were only Japs, and it was undignified for an Argyll to take any notice of them."

On the morning when 30,000 men crossed the causeway from lost Malaya into doomed Singapore, Hardy and the C.O. were the last to leave.

The battered remnants of the Argylls had held the final bridgehead. The Australian rearguard had crossed the causeway, then the Gordons. The Argylls followed, steady and heads high, to the strains of "Hielan' Laddie" and "A Hundred Pipers," played by their own two remaining pipers.

"The sappers," says Brigadier Stewart, "were waiting impatiently to set off their demolition of the causeway, and it was imperative that the last party should hurry over before the Japs came.

"I encouraged Drummer Hardy to run, but as I have said, he would never run properly, not even on jungle paths when nobody was looking—not when Japs were about.

"In this dramatic stage setting, almost alone on three-quarters of a mile of open causeway, in the clear light of a tropic dawn, with the Japs coming and with the defenders of Singapore looking on, he became mutinous at such an indignity.

"Nothing I said had any effect. He just walked slowly all the way over."

CHAPTER FIVE

It is when death comes slowly and inevitably, when nervous tension cannot be sustained, that men crack.

There have been, since the war, experiments on rafts and lifeboats to see how long men can last with bare means of sustenance. But how can these experiments tell the full story, when the men in the boats know that they are never in any real danger?

Doctors and officers will visit them at intervals to see how they are getting on; newspaper photographers will fly overhead; they have only to signal and they will be back on land sipping beef tea.

In the real, long-drawn-out emergency, with hopes of rescue growing fainter with each succeeding day, it is the mind which cracks before the body. The body can always summon the last flicker of energy. But it has to be dictated by a refusal to accept death, a determination not to die, a *knowledge* that one was not meant to end like this.

Hundreds of times through the years that have passed since, I have been asked (by fellow prisoners, by psychiatrists, by Jap interrogation officers, by friends at home), "Why is it, do you think, that you lived, when every other white man died?"

Hundreds of times I have puzzled over the reasons in my own mind.

I feel that I started with advantages over most of the other soldiers in the boat.

I had been a regular, on foreign service, for thirteen years. I was toughened to the climatic conditions of the East. I had served in some pretty hot places in India, particularly in Northern Command.

My broken collarbone was a blessing in disguise. Because of it, Paris and Acworth told me that I must not do any spells in the water during those early overcrowded days.

There is no doubt that the four hours a day clinging to the life-lines told heavily on the reserves of strength of all who did it. I escaped it.

Perhaps because long service had taught me a philosophy, I early adopted a mood of passivity.

It seemed to me useless to butt in when so many were making plans and giving orders, and I imagine that my quiescence had in it something parallel to the stoicism of Doris Lim, and that it served me in equal stead.

Then—and possibly this is the most important reason of all—I was determined not to die. It never crossed my mind that survival would come about because our boat drifted to land—but somehow I never had any doubt that we would be picked up. Only very rarely did utter hopelessness descend on me.

And I do believe that it was the little matters of procedure, the adherence to my self-made rules about gargling, cleaning my teeth, etc., which served to maintain my morale. Once and once only did I surrender to the contagion of the suicidal urge.

It was by day that one felt the dreadful need to end it all.

Most of our suicides happened in daylight—when the sea was calm and warm, and one felt how easy it would be just to swim away into oblivion.

By night we cowered into the protection of the thwarts, afraid of the darkness and afraid of the sea.

One day, soon after the fracas with the murder gang, a youngster of the Loyal Regiment asked me if I thought there was a chance of any of us getting through.

We debated the possibility of something turning up. Then suddenly he said, "I've had enough. I'm going to finish it. Will you come too?"

It was at a moment when I was feeling down. "All right," I said.

We decided that we would drink as much salt water as we could, to make ourselves weak and ill, and then we would go over the side.

I drank until sheer sickness forced me to stop. Then we stood up, joined hands, took a deep breath and jumped together into the sea. We seemed to go down a fair way before I expelled the air from my lungs.

No sooner had I done so, and felt myself taking in sea water, than I was overcome by a desperate desire to go to the surface. I mustn't drown—I mustn't drown was the only thought in my mind as I tore my hand free from my companion's and kicked out.

When I came to the surface, the boat had drifted only three or four yards and I struck out madly to catch up with it. I pulled myself on board, and lay there panting and sick. The boy from the Loyals did not, as far as I know, come to the surface again.

No one had paid the slightest attention to the incident. We were so far gone by then—no one interfered with his fellow in any way. Perhaps by this stage there would be a score of us left. I cannot really say.

It was now just a case of another man fading out, and then the struggle, more and more difficult, to heave his body overboard. We had lost identity. Sun and salt water had rotted our remaining rags till all were naked.

Great ulcerated sores, where the flesh just seemed to rot away and leave a hole big enough to take a man's fist, formed on all of us, particularly round the small of the back where we rubbed against the thwarts.

We had lost count of time, and the order in which incidents happened after the clash with the murder gang is hazy to me. But I remember the day the rain came, and the day, too, that we caught the gulls.

Many a time we had seen the rain afar off. It would happen in the cold of the evening—we would see the rain moving across the horizon like a screen or curtain.

Tense and excited, we waited. "It's coming, the rain's coming," we said. Our mouths were open and our tongues out. And then we would see it move right away from us—once or twice, indeed, pass right over our heads.

Our rain, when it reached us, was a cloudburst—a three- or four-minute affair of huge, cold battering drops which were nearly enough to make us forget our thirst and cower away from them into the shelter of the boat.

Now in charge, as I was, I had asked every man to control everything until we had filled the four empty Bols gin bottles which remained.

Everyone helped. No man tried to drink until, scooping with our hands, we had filled the bottles. The rain water which collected in the bottom of the boat was, of course, mixed with the salt water already lapping there—but who cared about that? The bottles filled, we flung ourselves on hands and knees and lapped our fill while the rain lasted.

The gulls numbered about twelve. They were bigger than those you see around the British coast.

They arrived out of the blue, flew around the boat for some minutes, and then settled, very tamely and seemingly with no fear at all of humans, on parts of the boat and on men's heads and shoulders.

We had gone tense and rigid. No man dared move. Then, with one accord, we pounced. We got seven of them!

Minutes later, there was nothing left but feathers settling around the boat. We tore the gulls to pieces and gulped the raw flesh.

So . . . on, hour after hour, day after day.

Drifting, in a silence broken only by the creak of the timbers and the wash of the water. No man speaking, rarely moving. The Chinese girl and I clasped sometimes to each other for the comfort of animal warmth.

Once, once only, throughout our whole time in the boat—and that towards the end—did I think of Doris Lin with thoughts other than neuter.

Then, strangely in a man emaciated and spent as I was, I was seized with a male urge towards the girl as she lay in my arms. I began to fondle her.

She stared back at me with blank, lacklustre eyes. "Please let me die in peace," was all she said.

There was never such another moment between us.

There came a day, most horrible of all in that odyssey of horror, when a big gunner (whose name I never knew) and I gazed at each other and realized that we were the only two white men left aboard.

Wasted and skeleton though he was, he remained a man of fine physique. He was, I recall, very tall and very dark. A fine, wide-shouldered fellow. Without doubt he would have survived, because a day later, God help us, we were to sight land.

But up in the bows sat the four Javanese who were still alive. The old serang was one of them. The girl and I were near the stern. The gunner lay on the starboard side, up nearer the bows. Suddenly, I heard his voice, "Jock, Jock . . . help me, Jock."

We looked up, and there were two of the Javanese pounding at the gunner's head with rowlocks. He had ceased to struggle. Blood was running from his head, down his shoulders and body.

As we watched, a third Javanese, with a tin which he had pressed to form a blade, started tearing at the body of the gunner. I can still hear the grating of the tin against the bone and flesh as we heard it then.

The lascar plunged his hand into the wound, like someone groping in a handbag, and pulled out something, dripping with blood, into which he dug his teeth like a dog snatching at a bone. The other two ceased to hammer the gunner's head, and grabbed greedily at the wound.

They were unquestionably mad. Blood dripped from their faces as, still chewing, they grinned horribly at us. One of them shouted to us and proffered something he held in his hands.

All we could do was shake our heads. This one vile meal seemed to be enough to satisfy them. Immediately it was over they and the serang pushed the body overboard.

The serang died that night. We heard the other three chanting some kind of service in the dark, and while they were about it I crawled along the bottom of the boat and one by one found the rowlocks and threw them overboard. If we were to be the next to go, they must find some other weapon.

When daylight came, one of the Javanese made signs to indicate that they knew I had slipped the rowlocks into the water.

The girl and I dared not take our eyes off the three in the bow. We were determined that at the slightest movement towards us we would slip overboard together.

But at night we could not keep our eyes open. I woke with a jerk as I felt a movement near my elbow. It was one of the Javanese. He grinned his wolfish grin as he repeated a word over and over again. I did not understand—but it was the Javanese word for "land".

He was pointing as he spoke, and looking over the side I saw a shadow darker than the darkness. We clung, all five of us, to the edge of the boat, trying to drag ourselves up and peer into the night.

We had so often seen the mirage that we were afraid to let ourselves believe that this was land. So often what had looked like land had just dissolved into cloud. But this looked too big, too near, to be any cloud. Then—and I think all five of us, lascars, girl, myself, heard it at the same time—came an unmistakable sound.

It was the sound of surf breaking against coral.

CHAPTER SIX

WE were in tears, all five of us, even the Javanese, as the noise of the surf grew louder and louder, the shadow of the land larger and larger.

The speed of the boat's drift increased as we neared the shore. There was a jerk, and a grating sound, as she grounded. Then she swung round broadside, and the waves tilted her over.

We scrambled out, and fell into the surf. The boat was aground on coral, and the waves came crashing in, skittling us over as we tried to gain our feet.

I grabbed the girl's hand, and together we crawled, staggered, fell towards the beach.

We could not speak, but we made breathless, inarticulate, grunting noises as we urged each other on.

Uppermost in my mind, as in hers, she told me afterward, was the prayer, Don't let us drown now, so close to safety.

The coral tore our feet and knees and hands, but we were insensible to pain. The Javanese we did not see from the moment the boat grounded. Afterwards we found that one of the three was drowned in the surf as he tried to reach the beach.

On hands and knees we crawled over the last yards to dry land. Together we lay there, gasping and exhausted. I tried to stand up, but the whole place seemed to be swaying about with the same motion as the boat. My first coherent thought was, Oh, God, we've landed on a floating island. We're no better off—we shall just float here as we floated on the boat.

We mumbled unintelligible nothings to each other. Hysterically we mouthed thanks for our deliverance. We kept trying to rise to our feet and collapsing again by the edge of the water. At last we managed to crawl to a safe distance from the water and fell, clasped in each other's arms, into an exhausted sleep.

The island on which we landed was Sipora, one of the Mentawai group, which runs down a line sixty miles west of the coast

of Sumatra. We had drifted over a thousand miles, and we must
have been just a month in the boat.

The girl woke me. Something had disturbed her. All around
us, the beach was lit by glowing lights which advanced and
receded every few minutes. The air was filled with an incessant
rustling noise, like the crumpling of paper.

As we lay still, the lights came nearer, and the noise increased.
It was an uncanny sensation. Then, as the light of dawn spread
over the beach, we saw the explanation.

We were surrounded by huge crabs, hundreds of them, the size
of dinner plates. The beach was literally covered with them. The
glowing lights came from their eyes, the rustling noise was caused
by their movement.

Above the beach lay a mangrove swamp. Beyond that the jungle.
We crawled to the swamp. We were so weak now that we could
not even get to our hands and knees, but we pulled ourselves along
on our bellies, dragging ourselves forward by roots and bushes.

We lay in the swamp as the sun rose. The depression our bodies
made in the mud quickly filled with black oily-looking water,
which we lapped down in huge gulps.

It was the first brine-free water, in quantity, we had tasted
since the *Rooseboom* was sunk.

A great peace, a peace of utter exhaustion, fell on us, and I
think we might have lain there and died had we not been spurred
to further movement, first by leeches from the swamp, and then by
the flies, twice as large as British horse flies, which arrived to
attack us. They drove us back to the beach.

Before we made the move, I should certainly have died but for
Doris Lim.

I had fallen asleep again, and woke to find myself immersed in
the swamp, with only my head above the mud. The girl was supporting my shoulders, and urging me frantically to shake myself
free.

Oddly, from the time we reached land, it was she who seemed
to take the initiative—she, who from the first day to the last day
in the boat, had been completely passive.

Back on the beach, we looked out to where the lifeboat lay
grounded on the coral. There was no sign anywhere of the
Javanese. We must have lain on the beach for hours. Strange
hallucinations seized me.

On the edge of the swamp there grew dead-looking leafless trees, and in their branches I could see the faces of person after person who had been in the boat. The wolflike features of the Javanese were there, and Mrs. Nunn, and Corrie, and the brigadier.

All the faces were immobile and stonelike. They have all got here, I thought. They have petrified. That is what will happen to us.

Around me, on the rocks and stones on the beach, I saw other faces, and suddenly I saw a figure skip down the beach into the sea and make towards the lifeboat. It was the figure of Piper McFadyen, who had been in the band in the Argylls in Secunderabad when I was a piper too. He had been no particular friend of mine, and I had not thought of him for years.

But there he was, dancing down the beach and striking out towards the lifeboat. I was seized by a choking dreadful realization that the lifeboat was evil. I wanted to warn McFadyen. I tried to shout to him, but no sound came at all.

I can still remember clearly the effort I made to call, McFadyen, keep away from that boat. I watched him go right up to the boat and clamber in. Then the vision faded.

In moments of consciousness we could hear the birds whistling in the jungle behind us. We knew we should try to reach further inland and look for water, but we just had no strength left.

It must have been about midday that we saw, a hundred yards or so out to sea, a figure in a sampan. At first I thought it merely further hallucination, till I realized that Doris Lim had seen it, too.

We watched as the sampan moved past the lifeboat and turned up the beach—which signified to me that over there must lie a creek of some kind.

We started to crawl towards it. It cannot have been more than a thousand to fifteen hundred yards away, but it took us the whole of the afternoon and far into the night to cover the distance. We would advance a yard or two and then stop, exhausted.

At last, in the moonlight, there before us were a sandbank and a wide stream. The beach sloped down to the water, and together we slithered down the decline.

We lay and gulped water. It was fresh. It seemed as if we would never stop drinking. We were too far gone to remember all the old precepts about sipping small quantities, but it seemed to do us no harm.

As fast as we drank the water came through us—just as if we had been pouring it in at one end of a funnel for it to run out of the other.

Replete, all our energies spent again, we scrambled from the creek, and fell asleep, huddled together behind a tree trunk on the beach.

We woke to find ourselves surrounded by a group of islanders.

They were fearsome enough figures. All were naked except for a G-string, all were tattooed in blue from the navel to the lower lip. They had no eyelashes and no eyebrows, and their teeth were filed to a point. They carried spears and bows and machetes. They were Mentawais, a Polynesian tribe.

It sounds amusing enough now, but it was deadly serious then, as thoughts flashed through my mind of Robinson Crusoe and cannibalism and cartoons of native stewpots.

We pointed to our stomachs and to our mouths, but they just ignored us, and chattered among themselves, obviously discussing what they could do about us.

Then they turned and walked away from us, up the creek towards the jungle. We could hear the thump of their drums, and the sky was lit red by their fire.

About an hour or two later, a canoe appeared in the creek, paddled by two boys about twelve or thirteen years old, carrying machetes.

They leaped ashore and came running towards us. Again we pointed to our mouths and stomachs.

They chattered, and grinned understanding. One of them ran to a coconut tree and brought two green coconuts which they opened with their machetes. They watched us as we drank the juice and ate the pulp. Then they fetched others, cut them open, and laid them beside us, returned to their canoe and paddled away.

At dawn there arrived another canoe with two men in it. They picked us up, placed us in their boat, and paddled off into the open sea.

We must have travelled along the coast of the island for three or fours hours before they turned into a beach, lifted us from the canoe and unceremoniously dumped us down.

They had placed us, we found later, where we would be found by members of a Malay village which was close by.

The island was used by the Dutch as a penal settlement—as the

Andaman Islands were used by India. The Malays were trans-
portees, who had formed a settlement close to the shore.

That evening, two Malays carried us, wrapped in sarongs, to
their huts.

There, on a verandah, skeletonlike but alive, lay the two
Javanese from the boat. They stared stonily at us, giving no greeting or sign of recognition.

We ate ravenously of the fish and rice the Malays brought as
our first meal. We were to stay in that village for six weeks before
the Japanese arrived and carted us off to prison camp and a new
chapter. There we were to regain our flesh and our strength.

But one memory of the islands stands out above all others.

It is of the day, just after we landed, when the Malays brought
me a mirror.

I had grown used to the sight of the Chinese girl, her once
pretty features now the face of an old, old woman, framed in hair
which was lank and matted. Her once shapely body gaunt and
emaciated, and red-raw where the boat had rubbed. Her ribs
standing out and her dark, expressive eyes dull with suffering.

They brought me a mirror, and I looked into it. A wild, black,
high-cheekboned face, like the face of an Indian fakir, the hair
and beard long and matted, gazed back at me. It was perched on
a body completely without flesh, the skin stretched black and
burned over the ribs, the buttocks completely gone, so that all one
could see was the framework of the pelvis.

It was for all the world like looking at a charred piece of furni-
ture, some twisted frame salvaged from a fire. But as I laid down
the mirror, Doris Lim and I looked at each other, and suddenly,
for the first time since the torpedo struck, a smile crossed her face.

We were alive.

CHAPTER SEVEN

WE spent six weeks on this island of Sipora, only a hundred miles
from the port of Padang from which we had sailed in the *Rooseboom*—and at least half of the six weeks was over before we could
feel that we had even regained our strength. The Malays put us,
first of all, into a hut in which was stored fishing gear, old baskets,
and dried fish—a hut in which was brought home to us the full

significance of that phrase, "an ancient and a fish-like smell," which Shakespeare used!

We told the Malays we were husband and wife, and must be left together. We seemed suddenly to hate the thought of being parted.

The sores caused by the salt water took a long time to go, but the island women did their best for us with herbs and ointments.

As the black sunburn began to peel off in patches, leaving us piebald, we presented an odd sight.

Gradually, as her strength came back, Doris Lim became more talkative, and I heard the whole story of the events which had caused her to be a passenger in the *Rooseboom*.

She was born in Shanghai. But her parents were dead, and, brought up as she had been in the American convent, she spoke only a little Chinese.

As far back as 1933, in the early days of Japanese aggression in China, she had been engaged in work for Chinese and British Intelligence.

Just prior to the Japanese occupation at Tientsin, she was working there and had got out just by the skin of her teeth.

Again in Shanghai she fled just as the Japs came in, and made her way to Singapore, where she worked for some time as assistant to a Chinese news cameraman, the Far East representative of Metro-Goldwyn-Mayer.

As the Japanese siege of Singapore grew more intense, the film man tried to obtain a passage for her to Batavia.

But difficulties of nationality held her up, and she became the responsibility of the British Press Relations Office.

When Singapore fell, five newspapermen who were escaping in the steamer *Kung Wo* took her with them.

The *Kung Wo*, Doris told me, set off from Singapore on Friday, February the thirteenth.

"That was surely asking too much of the fates," she said. "We were immediately bombed by a Jap plane, and lay helpless, just like so many other ships around us, in the midst of the islands."

They had no lifebelts and no raft, but the whole ship's company, over a hundred of them, made shuttle trips in their one lifeboat to one of the islands.

A destroyer took them to Java. Her companions elected to go on to Australia, but Doris—she never told me why—preferred to join a ship bound for India.

Thus it was that she joined the *Rooseboom* in Batavia, and was aboard her when the ship called at Padang to pick up the rest of us.

Among people who got in touch with me after my story first appeared in the newspapers was Athole Stewart, an Australian war correspondent who was one of Doris's five companions on the *Kung Wo*.

"What a charming little girl she was," he said. "We used to remark on how pretty she was.

"When we said goodbye to her in Batavia, we all thought that she was off to safety, and that Australia was going to be the danger place.

"Doris had seemed like our mascot during the bad days in Singapore and while we were escaping. She was the kind of girl who makes you marvel at the courage of women."

One day I put it to Doris that, rather than wait for the Japs to come to the island and find us (as we both knew they must one day), it would be better to push off into the jungle, and try to establish ourselves with some natives bent on keeping out of Japanese reach.

She shrugged her shoulders and said: "What good would it do? How would we live? The natives are all anti-white. None of them could be trusted."

What will you do, I would ask, when the Japs come.

"I?" she answered. "I will be killed. You will be all right. You will be a prisoner of war."

Two races form the population of Sipora—the native Mentawais and the transported Malays.

Most of the land had been parcelled out by the Dutch to the Mentawais, for the Malays were too lazy to be good husbandmen.

The Mentawais did all the cultivation, raising rice, tapioca, peanuts, and fruit. They did considerable trade with the Malays on a barter system, bringing along their crops and exchanging them for other necessities.

The average Malay contented himself with a little fishing, and as soon as I felt fit enough, I went on one or two of those fishing trips.

The Malay method was to go out in a small boat, drop one end of a net, then sail round and drop the other end some distance away.

All the inhabitants of the village would then join in pulling the net to shore, where the catch was shared by everyone.

Later on I took part in many fishing expeditions with the Mentawais on another part of the island. They were colourful affairs.

The natives paraded through the village late at night with blazing torches, then sailed out into the bay in their sampans, with the torches still ablaze. The light attracted the fish to the surface, where they were adroitly speared.

The Mentawais were wonderful marksmen with bow and arrow. Their bows were massive weapons, six feet in length, and so powerful that, experimenting with them, I could hardly draw them back. With them the natives would hunt monkey, iguana, and small bears in the jungle.

The arrows were tipped with a swift-acting poison prepared by the womenfolk, so that after an animal had been killed the flesh had to be cut out where the arrow had impaled it.

One day I saw a Mentawai pick off a monkey at what seemed extraordinary range. So I paced it. It was 112 yards!

The native cooking was done in hollow bamboo shoots. The Mentawais packed the bamboo containers with food, sealed them and threw them on the fire.

Then the bamboo was pulled out, the outer covering stripped off by a smart blow with a machete—and there was the food ready for eating.

Many of the Mentawais were Christians—you could recognize them because they cut their hair in European fashion, and wore trousers and vest instead of the loincloths and nose ornaments of the others.

Doris and I spent the latter part of our stay on Sipora in the chief Mentawai village, which was graced by a pier built by the Dutch and also by a main street, Juliana Street, which led from the pier to a medical post the Germans had built before the war.

Right up to the end I remained an object of tremendous curiosity. My meals were always a public occasion. Groups of boys and girls came down to watch me eat, amidst much talking, chuckling and sly commentary.

In the end I began to take my audience as much for granted as if they had been an orchestra playing for me in some restaurant!

The Mentawais lived in communities, in huge huts built off the ground on piles twelve feet high.

Some of the huts were over a hundred feet long, housing a

number of families in separate cubicles. The council of elders would meet to discuss the affairs of the community in a space in the centre of the hut.

Mentawai boys and girls usually marry at about eleven or twelve, and there is a custom of trial marriage by which, after informing the elders of their intention, a couple of youngsters live together experimentally for a fortnight.

If, at the end of that time, they still want to marry, they do so. If not, the whole affair is off.

Every Mentawai smokes—from the very earliest age. I sat fascinated one evening, in the midst of a chat with two elders of the tribe, when a tiny naked child, who could not have been more than two or three years old, came toddling across to us smoking a huge cigarette rolled from a palm leaf.

One of the elders was sucking an unlit pipe, and the child solemnly approached and offered him a light.

Another peculiarity I found it hard to get used to was the deep tones of the womenfolk and the high-pitched falsetto voices of the men. It was odd to hear a deep guffaw from a woman and then a high-pitched, adolescent titter from a man.

I became particularly friendly with the schoolteacher and medical orderly who ran the hospital post.

They were both Bataks, and like all members of that Sumatran race, were gentle-natured and tremendously intelligent.

They treated Doris for malaria, which she had now developed, and they treated the wound in my leg where a piece of metal had remained lodged from the time of the torpedoing until they probed it out.

The broken shoulder had hardly bothered me at all after Mrs. Nunn made her makeshift sling. Even in the clash with the murder gang I had been hardly conscious of it.

Both the guru (schoolteacher) and the mantray (orderly) were Christians, and both, to my delight, knew a fair smattering of English.

Their post was furnished with a church, a medical hut, and a stone building used as a hospital.

Daily treatment at the hospital and the generous meals of rice, fish, fried bananas, and potatoes which we were given soon began to show results in our general fitness.

But one day I had a shock. A Mentawai—one of the few who ever evinced any hostility towards us—stepped in front of me on a footpath and exclaimed: "Balanda, sudamati" (white man, you will die).

They always addressed me by the term they use for the Dutch —"Balanda", meaning, literally, "Redneck", much like "Rooi-neck" of South Africa. No matter how many times I explained, "I am not a Dutchman," the description persisted.

Now this Mentawai pointed towards my body and said—"beri-beri" and again "Sudamati".

I hardly realized what he meant, but the two Bataks brought it home to me.

We had been accustomed to receiving huge helpings of rice at their house, but now, suddenly, they announced that they had stopped eating rice, and we sat down instead to fried bananas, tapioca, and baked sago.

The procedure continued for several days, and I was puzzled, for I could see signs about the house that rice was being eaten when I was not there.

Then I realized that I was suffering from beri-beri, caused by eating polished rice, with consequent lack of vitamin. What I had begun to imagine was a pleasing stoutness about my body was the dropsical symptom associated with the disease.

The Bataks, noticing the symptoms, and knowing that continued rice-eating would be fatal to me, had removed rice from their own menu as well as mine, rather than tell me that I was ill.

A lassitude began to creep over me about this time—another symptom of the beri-beri. I became affected by little things—such as one day, when making a listless way along the beach, I kicked against a thread bobbin, and saw the words, "Anchor Mills, Paisley" inscribed upon it.

I rushed to the village headman, and told him excitedly that this was from my country, from Scotland.

"No, no—London," he replied.

Then he told me that the thread was used for repairing their nets. The Dutch imported it to Sumatra, and the natives bought it when they traded on the mainland.

It was good thread, he told me. The Japanese thread "was not good thread".

(Nowadays I live only ten minutes walk away from the Anchor Mills. I got in contact with them soon after my return to Scotland, and told them of this incident of the bobbin, and was shown round the mills.)

I decided that if I was to die of beri-beri it would be as well to leave some record of what had happened to the company of the *Rooseboom*.

So I composed a letter, and left it with the Batak, addressed to the commander of whatever British force might someday come to the island.

I told the story of the lifeboat, giving all the names with which I was familiar, and recounting the incidents in brief.

I enclosed the names and addresses of relatives, and wrote "Please notify them and please notify my regiment."

A few days later the Japs arrived on Sipora.

Later, years later, I could afford to laugh at the comic figures that the Japanese would have cut to any disinterested spectator as they staged their arrival.

They went through all the motions of an invasion exercise as they landed in the face of nothing more intimidating than a bunch of terrified villagers whose armoury contained only bows and arrows.

The Japs were patrolling the islands. They arrived in one of the Dutch military steam launches to which they had fallen heir.

As they disembarked, they mounted machine guns on the little pier, and trained them on deserted Juliana Street.

Most of the villagers had fled into the jungle but the Japs were determined to impress with a show of might, and a motorcycle patrol raced noisily down the roadway. Behind came two or three dozen soldiers mounted on bicycles, and all heavily armed.

The first question the Japanese sergeant in charge of the patrol put to the headman was "Where are the white man and his Chinese girl?"

The story of our arrival was already fully known, it appeared, at Japanese headquarters in Padang—and they suspected that we had been placed there deliberately to stir up anti-Japanese feeling.

We were marched down the street to the launch, where a Japanese officer in green uniform, with top boots and sword, sat at a table on the deck.

The headman explained, through an interpreter, how we had arrived. He assured the Japs that he had given us just enough sustenance to keep us alive until the patrol appeared.

I heard the interpreter say, in Malay, to the headman: "There are other islands to be visited. The prisoners cannot travel in the launch. You will take them to the mainland when the prau which carries the mail makes its next trip. You will be held responsible for their safe delivery."

Then we had a glimpse of the Japanese occupation machine in action.

The attendant elders were handed parcels of supplies which consisted of one tin of condensed milk for each member of the island's population, three or four Japanese flags for each hut, and a massive assortment of propaganda leaflets.

The Japanese officer barked a few farewell sentences which the interpreter translated as a review of the many kindnesses which the islanders had had at Japanese hands.

It concluded with a further reassurance—that any who did not co-operate would have their heads cut off.

Then the motorcycle patrol came racing up the road, their foolish exhausts making a noise like a speedway meeting, the launch put out to sea again, and the main body of villagers emerged from their hiding places in the jungle.

When we boarded the prau for Padang, there were many tearful farewells from the islanders—and a few gestures from some whose sense of humour caused them to point towards the mainland and then significantly draw their fingers across their throats.

On May 18, just seventy-nine days after we had left it in the *Rooseboom*, we arrived back in Padang, and as we approached the harbour, I saw with astonishment two white men, in white shirts and drill shorts, walking briskly along the sea front.

I had not set eyes on a white face since the Javanese butchered the big gunner, and I cried out and hailed them excitedly. They were Germans, who were, of course, allowed the run of the island.

For four days the Japanese subjected me to prolonged interrogation—and soon made it evident that the person about whom they most wanted to know was Doris Lim.

Again and again—first in an interview with an English-speaking Malay, then with a stout elderly Jap in a shirt with a sarong, then with a tall Japanese with a bloodstained bandage about his head, and finally with a shaven-headed officer of the Japanese secret police—the same questions were fired at me.

How long had I known Doris Lim?

What was she doing on the *Rooseboom*?

What did I know about her job?

What had she told me on the island?

Was it not strange that she should be the only Chinese national allowed aboard a ship evacuating British soldiers from Malaya? Finally—fantastically—were we lovers?

All these recurring questions were interspersed with others in which they sought to identify villages which had been helpful to the fleeing Argylls in Malaya.

Doris Lim, said the police interrogator, had confessed that she had been working against Nippon. I might as well "come clean", and admit that we were working together—that the British had placed us on the island to foment trouble.

To all these questions I answered, as well I might, in all truth, that I knew nothing about Doris beyond the barest details of towns in which she had lived.

I had never seen or heard of her in my life before she appeared on the *Rooseboom*. I had no idea why she should be aboard.

The Japanese varied their "softening up" methods in their usual way.

I was left without food for the last three days of the interrogation. I spent most of my time in a cell where there was only a floor to lie on, and where a shadeless electric light glared down throughout the night.

There was a periodic punching and pummelling by the soldiers who escorted me to the interrogation rooms. The officer with the bandaged head twice flung his chair in my face.

But the most painful of all the "exercises in tongue-loosening" was when they perched me, kneeling, on a block of wood about three feet long, four feet wide, and two feet thick.

I knelt there for what seemed hours, my hands behind my back and the pain of my uncomfortable position growing more and more excruciating. Each time I moved in attempt to ease my muscles, one of the guard would strike me in the face. Each time I keeled over, dizzy with pain and exhaustion, I was brought round and the question was repeated: "What do you know of Doris Lim?"

Eventually it must have dawned on the Japs that I really did not know more than I had said. I was passed on to the prisoner-of-war authorities who were to be my hosts for the three years that followed.

Only once, in all this time in Padang, was I close to Doris Lim, and that was when at the end of the first day's interrogation we were brought together and given a meal of rice and vegetables in a kitchen.

A Japanese soldier tossed us a packet of cigarettes and, quite expressionless and without interrupting his conversation with his companion, leaned across and lit them for us.

Immediately we had finished our smokes, we were marched to separate cells—and I never saw Doris again.

About a week later, as I lay in hospital, one of the medical officers said to me: "I have a message for you. Someone called Doris Lim. She says to tell you that she is in hospital, still in Padang. She hopes you are well."

But a month later, after I had been passed as fit and was awaiting transfer to a prison camp, another officer came to me and said: "I'm afraid there's bad news about that Chinese girl you talk about, Gibson. They tell me she's been shot."

And every inquiry I have made since then, in Singapore at the end of the war, among various authorities since I came home, and among the people who knew her before she joined the *Rooseboom*, has elicited no further clue to her fate than that.

CHAPTER EIGHT

AFTER three years of observing that strangest of human characters —the Japanese—not always, perhaps, being his prisoner, from a quite objective viewpoint—I was no nearer understanding him that I was at the first encounter.

No standards of Western logic could be applied to his conduct. One moment after giving you cause to reflect that he was perhaps, after all, just an ordinary not-quite-so-bad-as-painted human being, he would become a raging, demoniac ape.

From my cell in the interrogation offices I was taken to the prisoner-of-war encampment in Padang. I arrived there barefooted and holding up my native trousers with one hand.

A month later the whole camp, consisting of some sixteen hundred British, Dutch, and Eurasians, was shifted by lorry to Medan, in Northern Sumatra, a nine hundred mile journey which took five days.

On the way, we came to a point on the road, indicated by marks on the cliffs which rose on either side of us, which had special significance.

It was the Equator, and the Japanese guards immediately

ordered us to descend from the lorries, walk across the Equator and then em-bus again.

One of the lorries skidded over at a precipitous part of the road, and all the prisoners in it were injured.

In the hospital they were visited by a Japanese general, complete with retinue, and two A.D.C.s carrying fruit and flowers! The general solemnly addressed the injured, offering apologies in the name of the Imperial and Invincible Nipponese Army, and assuring them that the driver would be severely punished for the carelessness that had endangered their lives.

Prisoners from the Argylls were at this time located in two main groups, those captured before the fall of Singapore being held at Kuala Lumpur and those taken at Singapore being kept at Changi, on the island. But there were also hundreds of us in Sumatra or Java, having escaped to these islands or been captured at sea.

The Japs' lack of shipping prevented us being moved, as they would have wished, to work on the infamous Bangkok-Moulmein railway in Thailand, and I was in the Medan camp for two years.

For the first six months the camp was under the command of an odd character, a major, past middle age, who spent most of his time in a drunken haze.

Each morning at seven he would take roll call, wearing pyjamas, a military cap, and his sword.

He was, like so many of the Japanese, a homosexual, and a number of prisoners were beaten up for resisting his advances.

On his more maudlin days he would tell us, sadly and to all intents and purposes benevolently, how unhappy our misdemeanours had made him.

Then he would make a prisoner stand at attention in front of him, while he swung his big two-handed sword above his victim's head, stopping the blade within what literally *was* a hairsbreadth.

To all who flinched—and I saw only one who did not—the major delivered a lecture on timidity.

The one who stood perfectly still while the sword whirled above him was a Dutchman. Our bibulous major shook him by the hand, slapped him on the back, and presented him with a prize of fruit and cigarettes.

From the beginning the major insisted that the roll call numbering-off be in Japanese, and one would hear "itchi . . . ni . . .

san . . ." (one, two, three) followed by the "four" of some forgetful or defiant individual.

Then the corporal would curse us as "bugaros" (fools), slap number four in the face, and make us start again. If he was lucky he got us up to seven, and then went through the same performance again.

Things on a whole were bearable under the rule of our first commandant, but he was replaced, and Koreans were substituted for Japs as guards.

The Koreans, themselves terrified of the Japanese, excelled their masters in brutality to the prisoners. Those of us who refused to sign non-escape forms were forced by starvation and thirst into submission—we were left for five days without food or water.

On our first Christmas, however, we were each issued with ten cigarettes, a glass of wine, and extra rations. And that is the odd thing, now that the years have passed—one remembers, because they were outstanding in the grimness of our existence, the pleasant moments, the amusing moments.

Sometimes nowadays I meet up with men I knew in Medan, and always our talk turns to the things about the Japs which made us laugh.

One whom we recall is Captain Pat Kirkwood, of the Indian Medical Service, a Highlander from Forres, whose tall and black-bearded figure came to be regarded by the Nips with positive awe.

He treated them with complete disdain, and even when the senior British officer—mistakenly, we felt—ordered him to shave off his beard, the Japs' respect was only slightly lessened.

Kirkwood was six feet three inches in height, and even the Japs seemed to find it funny as he and I, who had become very friendly, used to pace round the wire together, he exactly ten and a half inches taller than I was.

Let me describe an incident which was typical of Kirkwood.

He was shaving outside the hut when a small and self-important Japanese guard approached. Rules said that we must always bow to our guards, but Kirkwood, with the merest glance, continued his shaving.

The Jap cursed angrily, but Kirkwood just looked at him contemptuously, indicated by signs that he was shaving, and testily waved the Nip out of existence.

Positively screaming with rage, the guard brought his rifle and bayonet to on-guard position, and made a lunge at Kirkwood's stomach.

In a flash the doctor's long left arm shot out, his great sinewy hand grasped the collar of the Nip's tunic, and the guard was swung clean off his feet.

Then Kirkwood calmly relieved him of his rifle and bayonet, which he propped against the hut. Holding the small Jap out at arm's length, he proceeded to deliver a lecture in broadest Scots, culminating in a declaration that if the Jap annoyed him again he would skelp his bum very hard indeed.

The Jap, almost black in the face and frothing with rage, was then lowered to the ground and told to run along and behave himself.

The story swept round the camp like wildfire, and there was considerable perturbation as the sentry was observed to be making his way to the guardroom.

Sure enough, out came a squad of six, headed by an N.C.O. with drawn sword, who came marching towards our hut.

The little sentry pointed to Kirkwood, who was marched off under escort to the guardroom.

The rest of us spent a very unhappy hour, for we knew how summarily others had been decapitated for annoying the Japs. Then towards us came strolling the familiar figure of Kirkwood, alive and whole, in his white shirt with Red Cross armband and his Boy Scout type shorts.

"What happened?" we demanded. "Are you all right? What did they do to you?"

"Of course I'm all right," said Kirkwood. "They didn't do anything. They've just told me that it is a very serious offence to disarm a sentry. In fact, it appears that it is punishable by death. They have asked me not to do it again."

Several times we saw the Japs' predilection for making the punishment fit the crime.

They were tremendously scared of fire, and smoking was sternly restricted to certain times and certain places. When we smoked we must carry an ash tray.

One of the prisoners, a middle-aged Dutchman, was caught smoking out of regulation hours, and was straightway placed in front of the guardroom, pipe in mouth and a pile of black, strong tobacco at his feet, and ordered to start smoking, and not stop.

As soon as he finished one pipe, he was ordered to fill another,

and the process went on for hours, while the sun climbed high
and a guard of six stood impassively watching him.

The Dutchman turned a dirty green, was violently sick, and
passed out several times, only to be roused and ordered to continue smoking.

At last, out to the wide, exhausted by his retching, he lay unable to hold the pipe any more in his mouth, and the corporal
administered a final slap and warning not to smoke out of hours
again.

Then there was an occasion when a soldier was caught eating
fruit in the garden which we cultivated and which the Japs
harvested.

He was ordered to pick about a dozen papayas, fruit about the
size of melons, and we were paraded to be given an example of
what would happen to anyone who ate Nipponese-owned fruit.

"Start eating," he was told.

After he had finished four of the papayas, he indicated with a
wan smile that he could eat no more. He was immediately clouted
with a rifle butt and ordered "Eat on".

More and more fruit was stuffed into him, till we thought he
would burst. First he was sick, then he indicated to the guards
that he desired to evacuate.

He was told to do so on the spot, and then eat on.

Finally, as he lay half unconscious and deathly pale, the Japs
delivered their usual lecture to us and ordered him back to
quarters.

One of the most extraordinary incidents occurred when, as
the Medan camp began to run short of food, the Japs issued rifles
and five rounds of ammunition each to some fifty prisoners, and
ordered them to go out and hunt for wild pig!

At Christmas time they would become drunk and friendly.

A Dutch doctor asked me one Christmas morning to help him
collect some parcels of food which he had arranged to have
smuggled into camp from a Chinese outside (a Chinese who later,
we learned, was executed for his anti-Japanese activities).

The parcels were to be thrown over the wall at a certain time,
when there were usually no Nips near that part of the camp.

Unfortunately, on this morning of all mornings, a sentry elected
to come over and start pacing this stretch of wall a few minutes
before the appointed time.

The doctor engaged him in conversation while I stood discreetly in the background. The sentry answered sullenly and suspiciously.

I saw the doctor glance at his watch, and knew that any minute now the parcels were due to arrive.

The doctor tried, by walking slowly away from the wall, still talking to the Jap in Malay, to divert attention.

But it was no use. Bang on time, flung with all the aim and precision of an expert grenade thrower, a parcel came sailing over the wall and landed almost at the feet of the sentry. Then another, and another, and another—while time, as far as the doctor and I were concerned, seemed to stand still.

From over the wall came a voice which said, "Salaamat muchan, tuan" (Good eating, master).

Then silence. We gazed at the sentry and the sentry gazed at us. Our trepidation, I am certain, was only equalled by his astonishment.

"Ini apah?" he exclaimed at last—in a tone which I took to give his words the meaning "What the bloody hell is all this?"

"Sedikit sedikit muchan, ini hari Kerismas," answered the doctor—"Just a little food, as this is Christmas Day."

The Nip gazed at us blankly for a moment. Then slowly he drew in his breath and as slowly nodded. "Ah soka! Kerismas."

A wave of his hand. "Sahaya tao" (I understand).

He grinned, and indicated that we should pick up the parcels. "Sayah tedah mata," he said. "I don't see anything."

We uttered profound "Arigatos" (Thank you's) and accompanied our thanks with ceremonial bows. It seemed no time for dignity—or even for racial feeling!

For the rest, those days in Medan seem very far away now. Monotony, feuds, jealousies, antipathy between British and Dutch, British and Australians, Australians and Dutch . . . beatings up . . . beheadings . . . news from Europe on our secret radios which in the end found the Japs quite openly discussing the war situation with us because they knew we were more familiar with what was happening than they were. . . .

In June, 1944, I was embarked, along with 743 other P.O.W.s, in the cargo steamer *Van Wyck*, thirty-three years old and swarming with rats. What our destination was to be we did not know—we presumed Thailand.

But whatever it was to be did not matter, because forty-eight hours out from Sumatra I found myself, for the second time, treading water while a torpedoed ship went down!

We were in a convoy of eight, the others mainly tankers carrying high-octane spirit to Singapore, and we had an escort of three bombers and four river gunboats.

The Allied submarine commander, whoever he was, got five of the convoy. Glory be!

Our ship, struck by two torpedoes, literally fell to pieces; seventeen Japanese and one hundred and thirteen prisoners were killed or drowned.

Twelve Dutchmen brought off a feat which makes the performances of the Channel swimmers who spend weeks in training seem pretty poor stuff. Gaunt and only half fit after their years of captivity, they actually swam the twelve miles to the Sumatran mainland, making a concerted and deliberate attempt to reach freedom.

That a Jap patrol, warned by airspotters who had observed them, was waiting for them on the shore made their attempt none the less gallant.

Then a tanker from the convoy—the only tanker left—picked up survivors and took us, after a couple of days of grilling on its iron deck, to Singapore.

And in Singapore it was, in August, 1945, that the forces of freedom, storming back after three and a half years of absence, discovered us and brought us home.

THE CHASE

Richard Unekis

*"The Chase" is published by
Victor Gollancz Ltd.*

The Author

Richard Unekis was born in Westville, Illinois, the son of a coalminer; his father's family came from Lithuania, his mother from Ireland. He is married with three children, and now lives in Louisiana. *The Chase* is his first book.

The Mystery Writers of America chose *The Chase* as one of the three best first novels to be published in the United States during 1962, and gave it the Edgar Allan Poe Special Award.

CHAPTER ONE

LATE July, in the black, flat farming country south of Chicago, brings eight-foot corn standing in marching rows; mile after mile for almost two hundred miles, broken only by the gravel roads which run along each section line. These roads are a mile apart, running straight by the compass in all four directions. From the air, they make the countryside look like a giant checkerboard, running perfectly flat all the way to the horizon.

There are so many roads that, in any manhunt, it is impossible to block them all. The state police do not even try. They just block the major highways—and hope.

On this particular day, the sun broke swiftly across the flat, unbroken line of cornfields.

Blood-red, huge and bright, it had the sky all to itself; there wasn't a cloud in sight. It had the slightly hazy, brassy look that means another steaming, blistering prairie day—the hot, searing kind of day that brings out the animal in men—the kind of day that promises violence.

CHAPTER TWO

EVELYN FAIRMOUNT said into the phone: "Oh, there goes the doorbell, Madge. It's probably the men for the TV. Let me call you back."

She hung up and walked down the steps of the tri-level to the front door. As she opened it, a gust of 10 A.M. heat swept in.

Instead of the service driver she had been expecting, there stood a rather thin young man in a neat blue suit.

"Mrs. Fairmount?" he asked pleasantly. He was of medium height, with a hawkish nose and piercing gray eyes. Something about his eyes bothered her. They were veiled, somehow, and cold beneath the polite exterior. "Are you Mrs. Fairmount?" he said again, in the same pleasant voice.

She realized that she hadn't answered his question, and said, with a little embarrassment: "Yes."

He half-turned, casually, to the car in which he had arrived.

"Mrs. Fairmount, I'm with the customer relations department of the telephone company," he said. "We're conducting a customer survey of placement of phones in the home, to see whether people are satisfied with the arrangements they have——" He moved closer to her as he spoke, as if expecting her momentarily to invite him in. Finally, she yielded to the pressure and hesitantly moved half a step back.

Quickly he was inside, still talking without a pause. "Let's see, you have, uh, how many extensions?" He started toward the kitchen.

"Two," she said, following him, uneasy about having let him in, and now becoming suspicious. Surely he should *know* how many phones they had.

"What did you say your name was?" she said to his back. It was all she could think of to say.

He ducked into the kitchen, then back out again. Still without replying, he brushed past her, went rapidly up the two half-stairs to the upper part of the house, and disappeared down the hall.

Alarmed now, she followed, clutching her housecoat around her. She caught up to him as he finished looking into the bedrooms and then the den on what was obviously becoming an inspection trip. In the den was a little girl about four years old, playing with a doll.

"Hi," she said, looking up. "Are you going to fix our TV?"

He did not reply, but started to back out of the room as the aroused housewife accosted him in the hall.

"Now just a minute!" she said with all the indignation and force she could muster, hoping her voice did not tremble.

"Is there anybody else here?" His voice cracked like a whip. There was now not the slightest pretence of patience or deference in his tone. His eyes were hard as diamonds.

She gasped, putting one hand to her mouth. A wall of ice rose up in her, swept past her heart, finally settled in the pit of her stomach.

The emotionless, flat voice lashed out at her again. "Are you going to answer me?"

Unable to speak, she shook her head helplessly from side to side.

"You'd better be telling the truth." His eyes never left her face. They seemed to bore in relentlessly, pressing her, holding her prisoner. "Don't lie to me if you don't want the little girl to get hurt," he said slowly.

At the reference to the child, her face went white. Still not able to talk, she shook her head more vigorously. She swallowed hard and started to stammer, "Wha—wha——"

Ignoring her, he said, "Are you expecting anybody—any calls?"

"No," she managed to say in a small voice.

Deliberately he stepped closer and slapped her hard across the cheek, so that her head snapped back. She turned back to face him, her jaw slack in sheer amazement. No one had hit her in the face since she had been a child.

"Don't lie to me, and do just as I say." His voice was almost soft now. "Are you sure nobody's supposed to come, and you're not expecting any calls?"

"No, no," she stammered, then added, "Yes, somebody. Wait, oh yes, the TV repairman."

"Okay, get on the phone and tell him not to come, and make it good, 'cause if you don't, something might happen to——"

He flicked his eyes toward the little girl, who, unnoticed, had come out of the hallway, and now crouched in the doorway, crying. At the sight of her, the mother rushed over and gathered her up, crooning and smoothing her hair.

The blow on the cheek had done something for her; it had stopped the first dizzying rush of panic that had been threatening to paralyse her. It had restored her brain to functioning. She was just as frightened as before—maybe more so—but now she could think again. She had experienced the same sort of shock as if she had been in a bad accident, and was not quite certain what had happened. Now, her sense of reality was returning. She realized clearly that she and the child were in mortal peril.

She determined to do anything in her power to avert the danger that threatened them both. She put the little girl down, but kept hold of her hand, then turned to face the stranger.

"What is it you want me to do?" she said calmly.

His head came up slightly at the calmness in her voice, and she saw relief in his eyes. It made her realize that he had been worried that she might panic, and now was glad she was in control.

"Call 'em," he said.

She sat down at the desk in the den and in full self-posses-sion called the repair shop and told them she did not want them to send a man out to fix the TV. She used just the right tone of voice so that they did not question her. She hung up. His glance told her that she had done it right.

"If you do as I say, nobody'll get hurt. Now get the little girl and take her over to that chair." He motioned to a leather armchair. "Both of you sit there and keep quiet." His voice was still harsh, but without the hard, almost metallic quality it had had earlier, which had made her flesh creep. His voice was so totally unlike George's. George! Oh, dear God, did George really exist? Where was her big, friendly husband, who seemed suddenly so remote, almost a part of a different life?

She felt a sudden intense yearning, almost a physical ache, for a return to the warm security she had enjoyed only a few hours ago, when her husband had left for work at the supermarket.

CHAPTER THREE

EARLIER that morning, as George Fairmount had backed down his drive, two cars, each with a single driver, had entered town on the blacktop highway from Chicago. One of the drivers had on a business suit, the other a brown uniform such as plant guards wear. Under the uniform he wore casual slacks and a sport shirt. He did not wear the uniform cap. It was on the seat beside him.

The uniformed man owned the car he was driving. The other car had been stolen the night before in a Chicago suburb. The license plates on the two cars had cost fifty dollars each, the price paid to the auto wrecker for "forgetting" to take them from demolished autos.

The man in the stolen car was thin, with brown, crew-cut hair and a hawklike nose. He was in his middle twenties and might have passed for a college boy, except for his eyes. There was no innocence in them, or immaturity. They were gray and cold, and constantly alert.

He had a slight pallor, too, as if he had been ill, or confined away from the sun.

His name was Floyd Rayder, but no one had called him Floyd for years. He did not travel in circles where men were called by their first names.

It was beginning to get hot now, a heavy, muggy heat that promised thundershowers. Rayder stuck his hand out the open window and pointed his finger toward the side, then swung swiftly in onto the broad asphalt apron of a drive-in restaurant. The place was not open yet.

He walked back to the other car, and said, "How's it running?"

"Like a doll," said the round-faced man in uniform. "Like a little doll. No cruiser in the country could touch her."

"Let's just hope none of 'em get a chance to try," replied the hawk-nosed man. He walked around to the other side, opened the door and slid into the back seat.

"Let's try the set," he said, turning to a large, professional-looking radio in a metal cabinet resting on the back seat. He turned it on and began to adjust the knobs.

A voice came in: ". . . you have a fare at Chestnut and Main, Number Seventeen, a fare at Chestnut and Main. . . ."

He switched to the local police frequency: ". . . a complaint about a barking dog. . . ." There were a couple of squawks, then very loudly: "Okay, give me that address again."

The transmitter came in: "Okay. It's a woman in an apartment."

"That patrol car's close around here somewhere," Rayder said, turning down the volume and glancing around. There was no one in sight. He dialed to the frequency of the nearest State Police transmitter.

". . . red over black, 1959 Edsel hardtop, two-door, license number five-eight-six-two-three-two-seven, Chicago; dark-green 1956 Hudson four-door, license number six-two-four-two-nine-four-six, Chicago; black 1957 Packard, two-door. . . ."

Rayder, with a practiced hand, switched the dial again, this time to the other State Police station, farther downstate. The same voice was droning out car descriptions and license numbers.

"The morning line!" The young man in the front seat swung around sardonically. "Must have been a busy night." He was swarthy, with gleaming, even teeth and carefully groomed straight black hair. He looked like the ladies' man he was.

Rayder glanced up. He rarely exchanged banter. Switching back to the local police wave-length, he listened for a while longer. Finally he said, "They don't sound very sharp. That dispatcher sounds like a nitwit to me."

The dark-haired man, sitting sideways with one arm on the back of the seat, said nothing.

Abruptly switching off the set, Rayder turned and said, "Grozzo, are you sure you didn't bring a piece?"

The other man slumped, then gestured expressively. "Look, like I told you before, no. It's agreed. I'm going along with what you said. No guns. It makes sense. If we fall, it's only for burglary. Fine, okay."

The thinner man did not smile, but his eyes lit up just a little. "Okay, forget it," he said.

He reached into a map case on the seat, thumbed for a minute, then pulled out a map about a foot square. "Tell me how to get from the caper to Bucola," he said.

Without hesitation, the other replied, "The highway running in front of the store goes straight on down. Off the highway, the section line roads are a mile apart. Bucola is twenty-five miles south and three miles east. All you have to do is count the intersections—twenty-five down and three east."

He paused a minute, then continued, "Rayder, why did you pick Bucola to leave this car in? It's out of our way."

Rayder looked at him with flat eyes. "Because I want it to be out of our way, just in case they connect the job with the Olds when they find it." He jerked his thumb at the car he had driven. "They'll think we're headed for St. Louis. Also, the town's too small to have a cop." He thought for a minute, then added in the same tone: "Did you check the Olds over?"

Grozzo nodded without looking. He slid out. "Let's get on down there. You follow me."

He led the way out of town, past the shopping center with the big supermarket which ironically displayed the huge sign: "Help Yourself to Our Bargains."

A mile south of town, he turned on to the county road, then right at the next one. About twenty miles down he pulled into the shade of the only clump of trees they had seen.

Rayder did not see, until too late, the remains of a barbed-wire cattle gate across the entrance to the little grove. As he went through it, the rusty wire and old lumber crumbled with a crash. Cursing, he hopped out to inspect the damage as Grozzo drove up.

"You just wrapped a few strands around this wheel," said Grozzo, inspecting it. He walked back to his car and came back with a large pair of pliers. "No sweat," he said with a grin to the tense-looking Rayder.

He squatted by the wheel and in a few minutes had worked

the strands loose. "Okay," he said as he arose, dusting his clothes.

"We're late, let's get on it," Rayder said tersely while opening the door of Grozzo's car and taking out the radio. He started to the other car with it, then wheeled quickly in mid-stride and returned. From the glove compartment he took a small box on which was mounted a little roll of magnetic tape. Putting both items in his car, he said, "Let's go!" He jumped into the blue and white Olds, backed out of the grove, and the two cars headed for the small town of Bucola, a few miles farther south.

CHAPTER FOUR

BACK in the town through which the two men had driven, Sergeant Tilton of the State Highway Patrol stood in front of the headquarters radio building. He looked at the scattered clouds, then at his wrist watch. It was 8:33.

"I hope to God it rains soon," he muttered to himself, shaking his head.

His Post was due for an inspection that morning at eleven by no less a personage than the governor's hand-picked appointee, Lieutenant Preen.

Preen was a retired army colonel, who traveled by helicopter and lived by the book. Tilton knew that the helicopter would descend in back of the transmitter at precisely 11 A.M., barring only an act of God.

The entire force in Sergeant Tilton's command had spent almost the whole previous week cleaning and tidying up the Post, and primping their bright blue cars.

Now the last of the cars was coming in for its final cleaning; a total of twelve would be in. Only one was left out on patrol. This was an irreducible minimum for their seventeen-county area.

The Sergeant stuck his head into the radio shack and told the operator to let him know when he was notified by downstate that the inspector had taken off. Then he turned his mind to the innumerable last-minute jobs remaining.

As he stepped out of the shack, he looked at the sky and muttered, "Please, just enough of a shower to throw that damned schedule of his off."

CHAPTER FIVE

HE made a noise. She shook her head and looked up. He was looking at her as he said, "If anybody calls here, put 'em off. Use your
head. That is, unless it's your husband. If he calls, I want to talk
to him."

"What are you going to do to us?" she insisted.

"We came here to do a job," he said, standing with one leg
cocked on the chair by the desk, and his eyes cold on her. "It
involves your husband. If he doesn't do anything stupid—and if
you don't—then everybody will be all right. We won't hurt anybody unless we have to." He paused a minute, then said slowly:
"So don't make us have to."

Her eyes on him were a study of emotion: fear, outrage, bewilderment. Nothing remotely like this had ever happened to her
before. She didn't know how much of what he said was true, but
as time wore on and it became apparent that he planned no
immediate harm to them, she relaxed, just a little.

Cindy, too, quieted down, but it was obvious she was still very
much afraid of the intruder. She clung to her mother's skirts and
stared at the man. He seemed almost unaware of the child, as if
she were only some remote distraction.

Presently, the woman laid the little girl down on the lounge at
the side of the room, and said, "It's about time for her nap.
She——"

"No nap," snapped Rayder. "Keep her awake."

Again the feeling of fear flowed through the woman—fear
mixed with resentment at this stranger who had invaded her
home.

Rayder sat backwards on the desk chair, facing them. He
loosened his tie, then glanced at his watch. He looked at it again
after a few minutes, then held it out, as if intent on timing something to the second.

Abruptly, he stood, picked up the phone and dialed a number.
After a few seconds pause while the number rang, he said, "Is this
you?" Then, after listening for a few seconds, he said, "Yes, okay,
let me know." He hung up, sat down in the chair, and faced her.

"Sometime in the next two hours, a man is going to call here
and ask for the 'man of the house'. Let me talk to him. I also want

to talk to your husband if he calls. As I said, if anybody else calls, or if anybody comes to the door, put 'em off. Make it natural and don't try anything. This isn't TV. This is for real."

CHAPTER SIX

FARTHER downstate, in the state capital, a grim, almost austere brick building fronted on a small lake. It was the headquarters building of the State Police Force.

An atmosphere of quiet discipline pervaded the place. Even as the day shift trickled in, and the baggy-eyed night force drifted out in ones and twos, it was apparent that this was a force with pride in itself. It was most noticeable in the younger men. They walked with the clear-eyed look of men who feel they are a part of a going concern.

A trim man in civilian clothes with red, crew-cut hair walked briskly in the front door.

"Hi, Bill," he said to a uniformed man sitting at a communications desk. "Busy night?" he asked, sitting with one leg halfway across a desk and starting to thumb through a sheaf of reports on a clipboard.

"Quite a few car thefts, Chief," the other man said casually. "Hot weather seems to stir the kids up, or something."

"Yeah, I can remember," the red-haired man said with a half-grin, putting down the reports and walking down the hall. He went in a door that said "Superintendent, State Police."

Closing the door behind him, he took off his jacket and turned the shirt cuffs, flipped on his automatic coffee pot and sat down to work.

The intercom sounded. He said "Uh-huh."

"Mr. Franklin," a girl's voice replied, "two more books on mathematics came in while you were out yesterday. One's the *Calculus of Probabilities*. I can't read the other title."

"Oh, fine," he said, cutting her off. "Put them on my bookshelf, will you, Carolyn?"

He had dismissed it and was turning to his phone when she said hesitantly, "Uh."

"Yes," he replied, "something wrong?"

"Well, uh, it was C.O.D."

"Huh, oh yes, well, uh, take it out of petty cash and put an

I.O.U. in for me, will you? Oh, yes," he continued, "call the airport and see if the Bonanza is ready, will you? I want to leave in about an hour."

"Okay," she said.

He had decided to fly upstate this morning to watch an inspection at Post Seven. He did not like military-type inspections, and considered them a waste of time. He had been thinking of abolishing them entirely, but hesitated to do so because of the ritual-like importance attached to them by some of his older officers. To be fair, he had decided to go and see one before making his final decision.

The electric pot made a gurgling sound, and the aroma of strong coffee filled the room. He walked over and poured a cup.

A roaring noise went overhead, and a helicopter passed his field of vision out the window. That would be Lieutenant Preen, off to make the inspection. He remembered he had not told his new officer that he would be coming along to watch the inspection. "Oh, well, no matter," he thought.

As he sat down again, the early sun, refracting in the window, broke into a thousand highlights, turning the glass into an opaque screen.

Just as a scene from an old movie, or a bar from a song, instantaneously transports one back in time, the opaque window suddenly reminded him of the plastic lucite plotting board which had dominated the end of the darkened room in Combat Information Center, aboard his old attack carrier in the South Pacific.

He slid down in his chair, giving himself further to his memories. The cup of coffee in his hand helped. In those days it had always been there. He felt again the constant humid heat, the wilted khakis, the muffled background rumble and motion of a carrier, the tension. Then the background impressions faded, as they always did when he began to think about the work he had done in that dark room.

How he had loved that job. The sudden thought of it startled him, but it was true. He had functioned there at a higher peak of intelligence and efficiency than he had ever thought possible. The weight of responsibility—assessing a fast-breaking, constantly shifting situation of complex variables, doing it fast and doing it right, with the lives of hundreds and sometimes thousands of men constantly at stake—had goaded him into feats of inductive reasoning that he could never rival in calmer moments.

Just as a good poker player, when the stakes are high, will rise far above his usual ability, so he, too, as information of bogeys and subs wove up and down that luminous screen, had risen above himself to master a game of probabilities that could make poker look like musical chairs.

A whole new science of applied mathematics had sprung up, almost overnight, in the effort to analyse and manipulate these complex fluid situations, plastic in both space and time, to predict possibilities and probabilities, to reduce to some rational control the wild games of three-dimensional chess played by ship and plane and submarine. And the men behind the scenes, struggling desperately to interpret and therefore to control events, had been the players.

"The theory of games," he said half-aloud. How, mathematically, to maximize or minimize the chances for interception. He had begun, recently, to try to incorporate some of these ideas for use in the department's problems.

There had been a little success with the younger men, but in the seasoned veterans he had met solid resistance.

People, he thought ruefully. In the last analysis they were the real problem.

CHAPTER SEVEN

An hour and a half later, Grozzo wheeled the Olds into the big parking area in front of the shopping center. The supermarket was at one end of a tasteful semi-circular row of stores. He parked at the end opposite the big grocery store, near an outdoor glass telephone booth. The area was slightly uphill from the store. He had a clear view.

He lit a cigarette and stepped out of the car, then walked around it and gave it a casual inspection. Satisfied, he paused, looked at his watch, and walked to the phone booth.

He remained standing up in the booth, pushing the little stool over to the wall. Taking the phone from the hook, he held it in his right hand as if listening to someone talk, then with his left reached and pulled down the receiver hook, leaving the phone free to ring if the number was called. While waiting, he twisted around for a view of the pale-yellow brick, modernistic store, which dominated the entire far end of the pavilion.

Presently, the phone started to ring. He immediately released the hook and said "Yeah?" Then the tone of his voice changed, and he said, "Uh-huh, it's me. I'm parked at the far end, right by the phone. I'll call you." Then, after a short pause, he said "Okay," and hung up.

He walked back to the car and glanced around. Apparently feeling that it was not in just the right place, he got in and moved it a few rows down, among some more densely parked autos.

Pulling in at an angle such that he could see the store without turning his head, he slouched back in the seat, picked up a newspaper and pretended to read. To any casual observer, he would have been just a bored husband waiting for a shopping wife.

He adjusted the paper carefully so that between its edge and the car's windshield post his field of vision covered the store and the approach to it through the parking lot.

With gradually increasing excitement, he maintained his vigil.

CHAPTER EIGHT

AT the airport on the edge of town, a blue airplane with a peculiar Vee tail slipped nimbly to the runway, then taxied slowly toward the control tower and stopped.

Superintendent Franklin climbed down, kicked his legs, then looked around in apparent mild surprise that no car was waiting. Then he remembered he had not told anyone he was coming.

He walked over to a cab parked at the stand and said to the driver, "Take me out to the State Police post."

The man grunted and, flipping the flag, set the car in motion. After a short ride across town they were there. As the cab pulled off the road onto the paved area in front of the Post, it became necessary for the driver to pull clear over and drive partly on the grass.

For the entire paved ramp was covered by a precise double row of spotless blue cruisers, gleaming in the sun. Standing at rigid attention in front of each machine was a smartly dressed officer. Facing the double row, also at attention, was the Sergeant in command of the Post. Catlin was his name.

"A good man," the Superintendent mused. "Much too good to be standing out here in the hot sun in a dress uniform waiting for a military inspection."

As he climbed from the cab, Franklin looked at his watch. Ten past eleven. He was a little late. The fact that the Sergeant was still standing at attention with his men meant that the inspection had not started yet. He was surprised. Preen had a reputation for rigid punctuality. He walked around back of the Post to the helicopter landing pad, then scanned the sky. There was no sign.

Walking inside, he gave the radio operator—the building's lone occupant—a chance to get over his surprise, then said, "Any word from the helicopter?"

"Yes, sir," the man replied. "Fifteen minutes ago they said they had to detour around a thunderstorm and would be five minutes late, but they're overdue about, uh, seven minutes now even by that estimate."

"Thanks," Franklin replied. He walked over to the window to look at the men and cars.

Each of the men out there, he reflected, had now been put through a special high-speed driving course, pioneered in California. They had been taught to maneuver their machines at speed. They could drift and corner the heavy cruisers using the same techniques as racing drivers. They had had a chance to thoroughly assimilate the trick techniques of drivers with years of experience. They were thoroughly skilled, and more confident because of their skills.

Programs such as this, he thought, contribute a lot more to public highway safety than seeing who can get the brightest polish on his car. He sat down to await the arrival of the helicopter carrying his Lieutenant.

CHAPTER NINE

THE store that George Fairmount managed was the pride of the chain—the newest and biggest.

Set in a row, looking almost like sixteen bowling alleys, were the checkout counters. At the end of the row near the door, and raised four feet from the floor, was the manager's office. It was in the shape of a square. The lower three feet of the walls were pine paneling, the rest was glass. The office dominated the store, and was designed so that all parts of the store were visible from it.

On the side nearest the front door were two check-cashing

windows. Each was equipped with a camera for photographing check-cashers.

Inside the "goldfish bowl", as he called it, George spent most of his time during the hours the store was open. He shared the space with two cashiers and a large gray fireproof safe.

There was a system of elaborate precautions guarding against a holdup. The safe was wired into a system which rang an alarm at police headquarters in case of tampering. In addition, there were foot pedals—which could set off the alarm—by the manager's desk, by the two cashiers, and by all sixteen of the checkout counters.

George sat in his chair looking absently at the twin lines of people waiting to cash checks. He had always been mildly apprehensive about a robbery, but nothing had ever happened in the time he had been at the store.

He was worried because his store had become popular. "Well, not exactly worried," he had said to himself. It was silly to be worried when the store's gross kept going up and he kept getting bonuses, but nonetheless he was uneasy. It was the pay checks.

The town's one big industry paid on Thursday. Every Friday more and more women queued up before the two windows to cash their husband's pay checks. Last week he had gotten a delivery of sixty-five thousand dollars, then had run out and had had to send to the bank for ten thousand more.

He shifted around, looking for something to lift his mind out of the little worry. Really, there was nothing he could do about it, anyway.

His eye lit on Mollie. In the third lane, the "hot spot", the most popular checkout lane for some reason, stood Mollie, his best and most accurate checker.

She caught his eye and winked. She flirted with him openly, much to his embarrassment. He realized it was most likely only a form of kidding, and that she probably did not mean anything serious, but this did not stop him from reacting. He reddened.

He turned around again and glanced up at the clock on the far wall. It was 10:05. About time for the delivery.

Then he turned to face the front window. In a few minutes a heavy steel truck, painted gray and shaped like a square box, stopped in front of the store. Nothing happened for a minute, then a back door opened and a uniformed guard jumped out with a revolver in his hand. The revolver was pointing at the ground.

He looked in all four directions, then nodded into the truck. Two more uniformed men climbed out, carrying a large canvas bag between them. In their free hands, they each carried revolvers.

They carried the heavy sack in through the automatic doors. The first man remained by the truck, gun still out. The other two brought the money sack back toward the manager's office. He pressed a button and the door to the office swung open. They carried the bag into the office and, at George's wave, pushed it on inside the waiting safe.

George swung the door to the safe closed, against the stops, heard the lock catch, then turned around and, with a relieved grin, signed the receipt one of them presented.

They left.

His mood relaxed and his step cheerful once more, George headed back to the meat cooler for a Coke.

CHAPTER TEN

THE car was hot. Slouched behind his paper, Grozzo felt the sweat gather on his collarbones, then trickle down his ribs. Out of the corner of his eye, he saw a dark cloud on the horizon and wished for rain.

He tensed into alertness as the armored truck drove up to the store. In spite of himself, his pulse and breathing quickened.

Without changing position, he watched the guards go deliberately through their routine and finish the job. Then he watched the truck finally pull out, head past the row of stores, hit the highway and disappear. It drove right by him on the way out. When it had pulled out onto the main street and accelerated away, he slid out of the car and walked rapidly back to the phone booth.

His call was answered immediately, as if the other party had been waiting, receiver in hand.

"They just pulled away," he said. He talked fast, but in a low voice, as if afraid someone would overhear him, although there was no one around. The other man's voice sounded calm.

"Okay," he began. "Now, hold down the booth till I call."

Grozzo nodded his head yes, then repeated his previous performance of holding down the receiver hook with his left hand while holding the phone to his ear with the right.

CHAPTER ELEVEN

RAYDER turned from the phone to the woman.

"Come here," he said. "Now listen. This is the part that counts. I want you to call your husband at the store. When he answers, don't answer him. Just hand the phone to me. Understand?"

She nodded and reached for the phone. He waved her back.

"In a minute I may do something that'll scare you. Don't panic. Nothing's going to happen."

She nodded dumbly, and he handed her the phone. She dialed, waited a minute, then said, "May I speak to Mr. Fairmount, please. It's important. This is Mrs. Fairmount."

This time there was a pause of several moments. The man slowly began to stiffen in his chair, like a snake starting to coil, as the wait continued.

Abruptly, she handed him the phone.

In the store, one of the two cashiers had taken the call, and had sent a clerk to the cooler to get the manager.

"Mr. Fairmount, your wife's on the phone. She says it's important," the boy said.

"Um, okay," he replied.

He was puzzled. His wife rarely called him at the store. He walked back up to the office and picked up the phone on his desk.

"Hi, hon," he said, settling comfortably into the padded swivel chair. "What's up?"

"Mr. Fairmount," came a crisp, business-like male voice, "your wife can't talk for just a minute. Will you ask the girl to hang up the other receiver, please?"

Looking startled, the chunky man waved almost automatically to the cashier to cradle the other phone, then said, "What's the matter? Is something wrong with my wife? Who are you?"

"Listen closely," the voice replied. "I have something very important to say to you." He slowed down. "It's a matter of life and death for your family."

Fairmount squirmed as a wave of apprehension hit him. He leaned forward in his seat. His first instinct was to bluster. "Who is this?"—his tone was indignant—"Where is my wife? She's supposed to be call——"

"Shut up," snapped the voice. "Shut up and listen to me, and don't interrupt again if you value your kid's life."

At the mention of Cindy, the big man sat bolt upright in his chair, and his face paled. However, he said nothing, but sat very quietly.

"I am in your home," the voice announced, speaking deliberately, "in your den. I have your wife and child here. They are my prisoners. If you make any move toward calling the police, I'll kill them." He paused. "Do you understand what I'm saying?"

The enormity of what was happening pressed in on Fairmount, but this was outside the realm of any previous experience. He had always been a warm man, averse to violence. He couldn't accept it. His mind revolted. He heard his own voice say weakly, "Is—is this some kind of joke?" His voice was almost pleading for the other to say yes.

In the house, Rayder whirled on his wife.

"Tell him," he said.

She was frightened again, after Rayder's threat to kill them, and came falteringly to the phone. She clutched it as if it were her only means of salvation. Suddenly she blurted, "It's true, it's true, George. Oh, please do whatever he says, honey, please! He'll kill us!"

At the other end, Fairmount sagged, his eyes glazed over. All his resistance ended; all thoughts faded from his mind. He waited numbly for what was next.

Rayder, unable to see him, was taking no chances. He wanted the man softened up enough so there would be absolutely no chance for him to regain his nerve. In a stride, he crossed the room and pulled Cindy over to the phone.

"Daddy, daddy," she sobbed, "a mean man has got me. I don't want him to have me. Please make him go away. Please, daddy."

At that instant Rayder grabbed the child's forearm with both hands, and rotated his hands in opposite directions. The wringing action produced violent pain. She screamed and dropped the phone.

Instantly, Rayder picked it up and growled, "Now do you believe me?"

The man at the desk was unable to answer. His child's pleas and then the scream had reduced him to jelly. Something deep inside him drained away until he felt empty, and lost, and confused. His stomach boiled with a violent nausea, and he was momentarily grateful. Grateful because it gave him something to focus on, to think about, to hold on to; to let him avoid having to hear Cindy's scream ringing in his ears.

The echoes of the scream died away. His raw reaction subsided. He became aware that he was still sitting at his desk in the hub-bub of the busy store, and that the man on the phone might demand something to save his child's life.

The two cashiers, blissfully unaware, were still busily cashing checks, tending the two lines of women.

Again there was the insistent voice coming from the phone: "By God, answer me or you'll be sorry. Do you hear me, Fair-mount?"

He fought down his nausea enough to croak: "Yes, yes, I'll do anything you say. Please don't hurt her any more. Please!"

"Keep your voice down, you fool," was the reply. "Remember, I told you if you sick the cops on me, it's the end. That goes for their coming out here by accident, too, so be careful." He paused, then continued, "Listen good, now. First, I want you to sit right where you are and count to twenty-five—to yourself—then tell me if you've got yourself under control enough to do what I say with-out giving yourself away."

After a pause of perhaps a minute, the pale-looking man said into the phone: "Okay."

"All right, where's the money?"

"In the safe."

"Can you get it? Is there a time lock?"

"No, no time lock, just a combination."

"Open it, and tell me when it's done."

Rising, he noted the back of his trousers was stuck to the chair. He wondered dimly if he had urinated. It was funny, but it seemed absolutely unimportant at the moment. The only important thing seemed to be Cindy.

He kelt and fumbled at the safe. His fingers trembled. Finally, on the third try, it came open.

He went back to his desk. On the way he glanced up at the row of checkers to see Mollie looking at him peculiarly. He looked quickly away. "Oh, God, don't let her interfere," he prayed des-perately.

"It's okay," he said into the receiver.

"Is it still in the bag they brought it in?"

"Yes."

"Now get this. In a couple of minutes a man wearing the same uniform as those guards is going to come in. He will stand at the door to your office, the one between the cashiers' windows. You will take the sack from the safe and hand it out to him, in view of everybody. Do you understand?"

"Yes."

"If any employee questions you, say, 'I'm the manager here. What do you mean?' Say it indignantly. Can you do that?"

"I—yes, yes, if I have to."

"You have to. Do you know what will happen to your little girl if you fail?" The voice took on its cutting edge again.

"Please, please don't."

"Shut up! After he leaves, I want you to go into the toilet. Stay there for exactly ten minutes. Then come out and sit at your desk. Act busy and talk to no one. I will call you and tell you when I leave. Don't call at all back here. If the cops come out here before I call you and tell you that it's all right, you know what's going to happen to your family."

The line went dead.

CHAPTER TWELVE

GROZZO's left arm was beginning to get cramped, holding down the receiver hook, but he was too tense to be very aware of it. For some crazy reason he began to feel almost as if he were hanging from a cliff as he stood there waiting, waiting, waiting for the phone to ring.

At last it did ring, jarring away his feelings, snapping him to alertness. He released the hook, and said "Yeah?"

"It's all set—go—don't waste any time." Rayder's voice was tense.

Without replying, the swarthy man cradled the receiver and walked rapidly to the car. He drove it to a point near the store's door, but off to one side, out of the line of vision of the office and checkout counters. Leaving the engine running, he put on the uniform cap and started walking toward the door. After a few steps he realized he was going too fast, and checked himself to a deliberate stride.

He was nervous now, in spite of himself. His palms were wet. As he stepped on the rubber mat before the door, there was a loud hiss. He jumped in wild alarm. It was only the automatic door opener.

He stepped into the air-conditioned interior, somehow expecting all hell to break loose as he did so, or at least to find everyone staring at him. He was surprised when no one even looked up. The busy clatter of the checkout counters continued without pause.

As he stepped over near the office door, the manager looked at him through the glass partition with glassy eyes and a pale face. He felt a little reassured. From the look on the manager's face, Rayder had softened him up good. He gave a small nod, and the man stood up and went to the safe.

He took a quick look around. The two cashiers on either side of him were curious at his standing there between the lines of waiting women. One of the checkers was really curious, glancing rapidly around between stabs at her cash register.

The clock on the wall read 10:35.

Suddenly, the other man was handing him the heavy sack. He nodded quickly, then turned to walk the twenty steps to the door.

It was the longest walk he had ever taken.

With every step he expected to hear a scream, a gun, an alarm —or to feel something hit him.

Nothing happened.

Nothing at all.

As the automatic door swung shut behind him, he could hear the uninterrupted rhythm of the store, until the heavy glass shut it off, and he was alone again in the heat.

Alone with the heavy sack.

He wrestled down a tearing urge to run. It seemed like a mile to the car. His nerves, his every instinct, screamed at him to get away, GET AWAY, FAST, FAST, FAST! He had a wild impulse to pound the throttle and send the car screaming across the lot and down the highway.

Grinding his teeth until he felt a filling break, he smothered the impulse and smoothly feathered the car out of the lot and down the lane toward Fairmount's house.

CHAPTER THIRTEEN

As the hawk-nosed man put down the phone again, he whirled, pointing at Mrs. Fairmount. "All right, there's not much time. Get on that couch." Her eyes opened wide in fear. Immediately sensing the cause, he said, "No, not that, damn it, I'm not going to hurt you."

He produced a roll of wide adhesive tape, and after making her lie on her stomach with her hands behind her back, he taped her wrists together, then her ankles. Next, he put a broad strip across her mouth.

Looking down at her, he said, "You'll be all right till somebody comes. Just don't struggle around and make yourself sick so that you vomit, or you'll choke to death."

He did the same thing to the sobbing, hiccuping little girl, first laying her on the floor.

Next he took from his pocket the small metal box he had brought from the car, on which was mounted a little spool of plastic tape. From one end of the box, he pulled two wires out to about an eighteenth-inch length. A metal clip was attached to each one. Taking a penknife, he cut back some of the covering on the telephone line which coiled from that instrument down to the wall, then snapped one clip to each of the exposed strands. He set the box on the desk.

After this he took out his handkerchief and went rapidly around the room, and then back over the route he had taken into the house, wiping every hard surface he had touched. He seemed to have made a mental note of them.

Finally, he returned to the den and looked in, as if surveying his work. The little girl was hiccuping quite badly between her sobs. He listened and looked at her for a few minutes as if weighing something. Then he went over to her and stripped the tape from her mouth.

Half defensively, he said to the prostrate woman, "Don't want her to choke if she vomits."

It was the only time he had come close to exposing any emotion other than constant icy composure.

He walked down the half-stairs, and down the hall, then stood by the front door and waited until the blue and white car appeared. He walked briskly down the sidewalk to it and climbed in. The car turned the corner down the subdivision's access road, and then moved off into the network of county roads. It proceeded east until it came to the road the men had reconnoitered in the morning. Then it turned south toward Bucola, accelerating rapidly.

With the speedometer needle quickly climbing to 70 on the

gravel road, loose rocks thrown up by the wheels began to drum a steady tattoo against the floorboard of the car.

Rayder quickly jumped into the back seat to tune in the local police frequency on the short-wave.

Grozzo began to count the crossroads as they came up, an even mile apart.

He had got up to five when he noticed a fluttering object cross the field of vision high and to the west of them. He had just turned around to tell Rayder there was a blue helicopter in the sky off to their right when, with a crack like a rifle, the left front tire blew.

CHAPTER FOURTEEN

As the stocky man in the guard's uniform went out the pneumatic door, George Fairmount walked, rather unsteadily and with his head down, back to the men's room.

The two cashiers paused to exchange wondering, curious glances, then turned to continue their work. The dawn of suspicion pressed upward in their minds, but they would not let it come through—not yet. Something more would have to happen before they would be able to admit to themselves that something threatening might have happened. Something definite. Something so real and immediate that they could not possibly refuse to see it.

Not so with Mollie. She was beside herself trying—unsuccessfully—to get a look at George's face as he slouched past.

Her curiosity infected one or two of the other checkers momentarily, a few feet away from the scene of action, but they had all been too intent on their work to have caught the little byplay at the office. The lines of shoppers moved steadily through to the continuing staccato of the registers.

George did not stay in the toilet ten minutes. He tried, but he could not force himself to stay more than a couple of minutes. When he came back and sat at his desk, his head was still down.

Shifting in his chair so that he could see the clock on the wall, he stared at it. He put one hand on the phone and left his back turned to the row of checkers, waiting for the promised call.

The clock went around to 10:45. It was ten minutes. The phone did not ring. His face showed more strain.

Mollie could stand looking at the back of his neck no longer. She said "Excuse me" to an indignant fat lady as she stopped counting in the middle of an order and walked around to the office.

"Is something wrong, boss?" she started, then stopped. One close-up look at his pasty, scared face, as he turned toward her, told her plenty was wrong.

He said, "No, nothing's wrong, go back," and waved vaguely toward the row of checkers. He went back to staring at the clock.

Mollie walked back toward the rows of shoppers, hesitated only a second, then walked rapidly on around them and out the front door.

CHAPTER FIFTEEN

SUPERINTENDENT FRANKLIN stood looking out the front door at the men standing at attention in the hot sun, awaiting the helicopter.

He had just put out his hand to open the door and go out and put a stop to the foolishness when the phone rang. Pausing with his hand on the knob, he waited while the operator answered. As the man listened, his face paled. He looked up quickly. "Robbery in progress, Riteway Supermarket at Dale Shopping Center."

"Robbery in progress" is as much an automatic alarm signal to a policeman as the gong for General Quarters is to a sailor. Franklin yanked open the door and took the steps at a jump, yelling "Inspection is off, robbery in progress."

"Sergeant," he said to the astounded man, "in there, on that radio." He sprinted down the row of cars and men until he came to the last four. "You men come with me," he shouted.

He jumped into the last car, told the driver where to go, and pulled the mike from the dash. "Sergeant Catlin," he said. There was a short pause, and the reply, "Yes, sir."

"We have a 'robbery in progress' at Riteway Supermarket, Dale Shopping Center. I have four men with me. Contact the local force and the Sheriff's office."

"Yes, sir."

"Also, you'd better move your force off the lot there. Get them out and moving so we don't get jammed up."

"Yes, sir."

"Okay, and stay close to your transmitter." He hung up the mike.

CHAPTER SIXTEEN

AT 10:48 George Fairmount was unable to stand the strain any longer. He dialed his home.

He did not even hear the phone ring, before it was answered. He started to say, "Honey, are you all——"

The man's voice came on, even more harsh than before, cutting through his own. "Damn you, I told you not to call back here, that I'd call you. This is your last warning. Don't try it again."

With trembling hand, George hung up the phone, then buried his face in his hands and sobbed uncontrollably.

He did not see a State Police car come to a fast, bouncing stop in front of the store, closely followed by three more. The officers leaped out and walked rapidly toward Mollie, who went up to meet them. They stood in front with her for a few minutes, talking rapidly. Then they came into the store.

The officer in charge walked up to the office. The other four stayed back in a half crouch, near the door. Their right hands were atop their holsters. Their glances walked rapidly over the store, looking for trouble.

The first man, in plain clothes, stepped through the still-open office door. George looked up, his eyes red.

"Sir, I'm Superintendent Franklin, State Police. What's wrong here?"

George paled.

"Nothing," he said. "Nothing's wrong, go away."

"Have you been robbed?" Franklin persisted.

The two cashiers gasped.

One by one, as they became aware something was going on, the checkers stopped working. The steady medley of the cash registers dwindled and stopped. Checkers and customers stood gaping.

George writhed under the Superintendent's firm gaze.

"Just go away, please. It's all right. There's nothing wrong." His voice was pleading.

Franklin was obviously convinced otherwise. He beckoned one of his men.

Before the man could get there, the phone rang. Putting his hand over the manager's phone, Franklin said, "I'm taking all calls."

"No. Please! Please let me take it," George almost shouted, then finished lamely, "I—I'm expecting an important long-distance call."

Franklin said, "Wait." He stepped over to the cashier's window and put his hand on the phone, then said, "Are these phones on the same line?" One of the cashiers nodded meekly and said "Yes."

Franklin nodded to the other man, and picked up his phone at almost the same instant as George did.

An excited woman's voice came on: ". . . George? George, this is Madge, George, I think there's something wrong at your house. A man was there a long time, but he left. Then, when I tried to call, a terrible man answered and cursed and said that he told me not to call back, and I thought I had the wrong number, so I called back, and he told me exactly the same thing again. I'm scared. I——"

Franklin broke in. "Lady, this is the police. Let me have your name and address, please." He scribbled it down as she talked, then turned to George. "How much did they get?"

George floundered for a minute, then collapsed. "All of it," he faltered. "Eighty-five thousand, but don't do anything, please. They're at my house. They've got my family out there. He told me he'd call and tell me when they were leaving. Please wait. Please!" Tears stained his puffy cheeks. His eyes were red and swollen.

Franklin dropped his gaze, then turned to the officer nearest him. "Get on the radio and tell Sergeant Catlin we have a confirmed eighty-five-thousand-dollar robbery here, tell him to put an alert on the state wire, and tell him we'll try to get a description."

He turned back to the distraught man. "What's your home phone number?" Then he said, "No, wait, you call so they won't get suspicious if they're still there." He motioned to the phone.

George dialed, with the officer listening. The same voice came on and repeated the previous warning. Halfway through, the manager suddenly hung up and cried hysterically, "That's the same one. He said just exactly the same thing as the other time I called."

"*Exactly* the same thing?"

"Yes."

"Dial it again."

"No, no, no!" George ran from the office, toward the back of the store.

The officer turned to one of the petrified cashiers. "Dial his number."

She complied.

The voice came on again. Before it had said ten words, Franklin hung up.

"That's a tape!" he shouted. Turning to two city policemen who had come in, he said, "You two get out there fast. Find out what you can."

Another local car came screaming on to the apron and screeched to a stop. Two officers bolted in. Franklin intercepted them, and gave them a piece of paper.

"Find out who or what this woman saw going into or out of George Fairmount's house this morning. Radio in any descriptions you can get."

He turned back to the cashier who had placed the call for him. "You were right here. What did you see? What did they look like?"

She dissolved into tears.

Grimacing his impatience, he looked around.

Mollie came up and said, "I saw him. There was just one. He had on a guard's uniform like the guards who deliver the money. He was kinda short and heavy and dark. He had black hair."

"Only one?"

"Only one," she repeated.

"What did the car look like?"

"I didn't see any car. He walked around the corner after he left the building."

Franklin's face was grim. "Okay," he said. "Stick around."

He phoned his information in, then went toward the back of the store for George. Bringing the almost incoherent man back to his office, he tried, unsuccessfully, to question him.

After a couple minutes of this, he picked up the phone and called a number. Then, after listening a minute, he turned back to the heavy man and said, "Your family is all right." He then continued talking rapidly, as if trying to get his point across before the other reacted. "Do you know anybody who might have been at your house this morning—two men in a blue and white car?"

George shook his head, and Franklin said into the phone: "They must be the ones. At least, they're all we've got. Put the description you got from that woman on the wire. Two men in a blue and white car, make and model unknown, license unknown, one man short, heavy and dark, with black hair, wearing a guard's uniform."

He glanced at the clock. It was 11:05. He headed back out to the car for the ride back to the Post.

CHAPTER SEVENTEEN

As soon as Franklin had stopped talking, the Sergeant at Post Seven had leaped to the door and bellowed at the waiting troopers: "Into your cars and head for your duty areas; we'll dispatch you on the way."

Sensing a chase, and glad of a chance for action after the morning's tension, the men piled into their cars. The precise geometry of the parked formation dissolved into the milling bedlam of a Le Mans start as the cars jockeyed for position, engines roaring, then poured out on to the highway to the accompaniment of a steady screech of rubber and pounding exhausts.

When the last one had screamed off, the Sergeant said dryly into the transmitter, "Very cute. The next time that happens we're going to have some suspensions. Now slow those cars down and stay within the city limits for the time being."

The command channel from downstate opened up, and the heavy voice he recognized as Captain Prescott's filled the room. "Sergeant, what's going on?"

Quickly the Sergeant explained that they had had a "Robbery in Progress" and that the men had been dispatched out but only within the city limits. Before he could mention the Superintendent's name, the Captain cut him off. "Get those men out and set up highway blockades; you know the standard procedure. Don't dally around."

The Sergeant was trapped. He couldn't interject the Superintendent's name without appearing to be defying a direct order. Besides, Franklin had not in fact given him any orders *not* to set up a blockade.

He hesitated a minute, then said, "Yes, sir."

"Any word from Lieutenant Preen in the helicopter?" said the voice.

"No, sir," he replied.

"All right, get on with it."

"Yes, sir."

He spun to the other transmitter and said, "All Post Seven Cars, this is Sergeant Catlin. Proceed to your duty areas and set up standard highway blockades. We will have descriptions for you by the time you can get in position. Acknowledge this message as soon as you are in position."

CHAPTER EIGHTEEN

LIEUTENANT PREEN squirmed in the bucket seat of the helicopter. With his swagger stick, he flicked a piece of dirt from one of the highly polished paratrooper boots into which his uniform trousers were bloused.

He was annoyed. Very annoyed. Through absolutely no fault of his own he was—he glanced at his watch again—already fourteen minutes late, and they were only now approaching the subdivisions at the south edge of town.

Drat helicopters, anyway. Imagine having to go an extra fifty miles to avoid a rainstorm! Why couldn't they have let him use a decent, heavy aircraft that could go from one place to another in a straight line? These slow, noisy contraptions . . .

His reverie was interrupted by the pilot, who took off his earphones and handed them to him. The pilot annoyed Preen. Still, he reflected, the man did seem competent enough. Only, what was he handing him these headphones for? Communications was not his job.

With a sigh, he carefully removed his faultless uniform hat and slipped on the phones. The pilot pointed to the radio, to indicate that he had tuned in the frequency of the regular State Police communications net, rather than the command frequency they normally used.

The voice of the local dispatcher came in loud: ". . . consider them to be armed. Repeat. All points alert. Be on lookout for two men in blue and white car, make and model and license unknown. One man short, squat, with dark hair, in guard's uniform. Wanted in connection with robbery of supermarket this city. Consider them to be armed. Repeat, all points alert. . . ." The crisp voice droned on.

Preen looked in some surprise at the pilot. But what had this to do with them? He had an inspection to make. The pilot caught his eye and, with a questioning look, glanced up, and made an upward motion with his thumb.

"Oh," grumbled Preen. "You want to go up and make a search. But we don't have any authorization, the inspec——"

It dawned on him that it just might be prudent if they did make a search. While in service, he had observed that sometimes it paid to follow the leads of these reckless types, like his pilot. They sometimes seemed to have almost a sixth sense about what their superiors wanted. Well, there weren't any flies on him; the inspection would just have to wait.

He motioned thumbs up, took off the phones and hung them from a peg. They hurt his ears.

The pilot opened the throttle and the flop!—flop!—flop! of the big blades speeded up. The craft rose swiftly, straight up, giving the occupants the same sensation as going up in an express elevator.

As they approached 5,000 feet, the machine rocked in the drafts of the thunderstorm they had just skirted. It was still approaching. Preen took the binoculars from their rack and began trying to scan the checkerboard of roads beneath them.

In a minute they were through the turbulence, and he adjusted the glasses and began to scan in earnest; one north-south road, then one east and west, another one north and south, then another east and west. He could see nothing, except an occasional farm truck.

Shifting, he tried another north-south road. Out near the limit of the glasses' effectiveness, he caught a glimpse of blue. There! He adjusted the lens. It was a blue and white car. Stopped! There were two figures near its front on one side. He hesitated. Should they check it, or keep sweeping? It was a slim chance, and a nuisance, to boot.

"Oh, well," he sighed, "better check it."

He pointed. The pilot tilted the ship at an awkward angle, and they slid down a long curtain of air toward the car.

CHAPTER NINETEEN

For a split second after the explosion of the tire, nothing happened. Then, the steering wheel gave a great tug in Grozzo's hands. He was an expert driver, and at the sound of the blowout he had instinctively gripped the wheel with his whole strength. This was all that kept it from turning and pulling into a high-speed skid on the loose rock.

The flat tire immediately began to disintegrate and pull away from the rim, causing the car to jump up and down with great sharp bounds and, at the same time, increasing the forces acting on the steering wheel. Grozzo rose to his feet, hunched over the wheel, his face contorted and arms knotted, fighting. The car slowed somewhat. Then something jammed. In spite of all he could do the steering wheel began to turn, to drag them into the skid.

Finally, as a last resort, he jammed on the brakes, locking the wheels and sending the machine into a long slide. It went around, end for end, and finally stopped in a great cloud of dust, crosswise in the road.

They sat for a minute, shaken. Then Grozzo climbed out. Looking at the ribboned tire, he said in a rising voice: "You goddam, dirty, lousy, sonofabitching bastard. Sonofabitch! Sonofabitch! Sonofabitch!" His curse ended in a scream. He picked up a rock and threw it against the side of the car.

Rayder started toward him. But Grozzo had got it out of his system and was already running around to the back, throwing open the trunk lid and frantically pulling out the jack and spare tire. In a few minutes, working with sure hands, he had the car jacked up, the shredded tire removed and the spare mounted.

Motioning Rayder into the car, he jumped in himself. The engine started readily, apparently unaffected by the wild slide. He started to turn the wheel, to get them out of their sidewise position in the road. The wheel wouldn't move. He pulled harder; no result. He tried turning it the other way, and then from side to side. It was locked.

Cursing furiously, he jumped from the car and ran around, wiggling under the front end, with the other man following and looking down at him.

His somewhat muffled voice came out: "The sonofabitching Pitman arm is jammed by that sonofabitching wire out of that gate. That's what ruined the tire, too." He paused, then continued, "Look in the trunk and see if there's a pair of pliers."

Rayder ran to the back and looked, then reported that there was not.

"Jack it up. I need more room."

Rayder complied, then peered under. Flat on his back, Grozzo was tearing desperately with his bare hands at a tangle of barbed wire, snarled around a juncture of two metal bars. Blood streamed from his hands.

"Hand me that lug wrench," he said.

Rayder crawled in himself, on hands and knees, pushing forward the wrench he had just used to lever the jack.

"Here," said Grozzo, pointing to a loop. Rayder began to yank, as Grozzo slid back, sopping his flowing hands against his trousers.

"No, no," Grozzo almost screamed. "You'll tighten it up again. Work it easy, easy. Here!"

He came back and started gently, but firmly, to work the wire loose, ignoring his torn hands. Blood streamed down his arms and onto the uniform shirt, already dark with perspiration.

"Go up and move the steering wheel back and forth. Easy, like I tell you," he said, all in a rush.

Wordlessly the man who was usually the leader complied. He was out of his element in mechanical things. He got back in and moved the steering wheel slightly back and forth in response to the shouted instructions from below, meanwhile keeping a worried eye on the road, which they were blocking. So far, no traffic had come.

Gradually, the wheel began to turn more freely, but unnoticed by the preoccupied men, the agitation of the front wheels was causing the car to travel on the jack. As the car slowly moved, a fraction of an inch at a time, the jack began to lean. Finally, with a soft *thunk*, the car rode off the jack and fell.

Horrified, Rayder leaped from the car and peered underneath. To his amazement, Grozzo wiggled out untouched and unworried.

"Sonofabitchin' good thing we put that wheel back on," Grozzo said.

As he bent down to pick up the jack, a shadow passed over them, and a roaring, flapping sound grew rapidly louder. Looking up, they saw a bright, blue helicopter gliding down toward them from a few hundred yards away. As they stared, stupefied for a second, a figure in the cabin, peering at them with field glasses, became visible. Also the legend "STATE POLICE" as the machine turned broadside to them.

Rayder recovered first. "Get in," he yelled and dove for the car. He started the engine and gave a tremendous yank on the steering wheel. It moved. As the other man hit the seat, he floored the gas pedal. The car swirled in a great spout of gravel. It fishtailed somewhat as it headed down the road under full acceleration, then straightened on its course.

In the helicopter, the Lieutenant's pulse had quickened. "Follow him," he yelled at the pilot. "Try to get his number." The pilot nodded, and again opening the throttle and raising the tail to its peculiar slant, sent the bird bowling down the country road in hot pursuit.

CHAPTER TWENTY

As his first panic subsided, Rayder got hold of himself and rapidly took stock of the situation. The car was wide open, the needle on the speedometer hovering around 105. He looked around. The helicopter was about a half-mile behind and did not appear to be gaining. Maybe they could outrun it! He stood on the accelerator.

Without taking his eyes off the road, he yelled to the man beside him, "Get on the radio and see what he's saying."

Grozzo had stripped off the bloody uniform shirt and was trying to tear it with his hands. At the other's words, he stopped and crawled into the back seat.

He turned on the radio. While waiting for it to warm up, he sat back trying to think of some way to slow the flow of blood from his hands. He stripped off the uniform trousers and wrapped them around one hand. He reached back to the front seat for the shirt, which he wrapped around the other. He looked vaguely like some awkward boxer with huge gloves.

Working the end of a finger and thumb loose, he twirled the radio dial to the State Police communication frequency, and turned the volume on full force so that the driver could hear over the road noise.

Incredibly, there was only some chatter about a stolen car.

Instinctively, unbelievingly, both men looked back for the helicopter. It was still there, about a half-mile in back of them. It was only visible part of the time above the eight-foot-high corn which grew to the edge on both sides of the road.

"Spin the dial," yelled Rayder. "They must be on a different frequency."

The stocky man nodded. He turned the knob slowly around to

the stop, then back again; no result, except the static from the thunderstorm moving in from the east. He tapped the other on the shoulder and yelled, "Nothing!"

It was incredible, and yet——

An idea began to form in Rayder's mind. Even though the helicopter was not transmitting, there was no guarantee that its radio was out. It might start at any minute. And they were leading it straight toward Bucola and the other car which they planned to use to get back to Chicago.

The fact that the car they were in might be known to the police wasn't too important, provided they could get to the other car unnoticed. Then they would have a fresh start. They would be unidentified once more. One of hundreds of thousands of cars on the roads.

If only there were some way to get that damn machine off their backs. A flash of lightning startled him, and made him think of something.

As they approached the next east-west road, exactly a mile from the last one, he eased on the brakes. He would have liked to have waited until they were right on top of the intersection, then braked heavily and taken the corner at high speed. But this was impossible on the loose gravel. He would have to accept the helicopter's gaining on them. It wouldn't make much difference anyway, if his plan worked.

Tenderly, he negotiated the curve, then floored the throttle again. The car shot forward, straight east, straight toward the heavy, black clouds of the approaching thunderstorm.

After a few minutes, rain began to spatter the windshield. Then, abruptly, they were in the dark, lightning-streaked maw of the summer thundershower. A deluge of water cascaded on them.

Rayder slowed the car. No helicopter could live in a boiling rainstorm like this. The only trouble was, they were heading the wrong way. He slowed and stopped.

Grozzo said, "What was that for?"

"He can't follow us in here," was the reply. "We'll sit here a few minutes, then turn around and come out the same road we went in. That's the last thing they'll expect."

He let the car sit absolutely still for several minutes in the drumming rain. After their chase, their pulses seemed to match the rhythm of the raindrops.

"That oughta be long enough," Rayder said abruptly.

He turned the machine around and drove back the way they'd come.

In the helicopter, the Lieutenant had been wildly excited by the chase. He had never been a man who remained cool in a pinch. As it had become apparent that they couldn't catch the fleeing car, Preen had become almost frenzied.

"They're getting away. Go faster, faster! Don't let them get away!" he shouted at the pilot, jumping up and down in the seat as far as the safety belt would let him.

The pilot hadn't replied. He had had his hands full, maneuvering the machine at full speed, following a car down a county road. He had been only seventy-five feet off the ground, and buffeted by the advance drafts of a rainstorm that was blowing up.

To top it off, the car was out of sight part of the time behind the growing corn. But just when it began to look as if the car might be creeping away from them and the Lieutenant's face had begun to take on a greenish hue, the car inexplicably slowed, and then turned left.

The pilot immediately set his skittish craft into a left turn, and since he did not have to follow a road as the car did, it was not necessary for them to reduce speed to make the turn.

The helicopter went around in a wide arc, cutting away some of the distance between itself and the car. The Lieutenant babbled with joy. He did not look at the pilot's darkening face.

The pilot's look became more and more strained as they came closer to the squall line. His trained eye detected in advance the ominous gusts, approaching in the van of the storm, as they shook trees and caused ripples, like waves, to march across the fields of corn.

Abruptly, at the moment the car disappeared behind the curtain of rain, the pilot changed the controls. The forward rush stopped, and the steep angle at which the machine was going changed to an even keel. They hovered motionlessly.

The Lieutenant's jaw dropped in surprise and consternation. He glared at the pilot. "What do you mean?"

The other man only shook his head and pointed at the line of menacing clouds. He thought it should be obvious even to the Lieutenant that they couldn't go in there. As if for emphasis, the helicopter bobbed up and down in a downdraft.

The Lieutenant looked around, wildly frustrated. Suddenly,

his expression changed. He motioned the pilot to set the machine down in a cleared area next to the road.

The pilot was surprised, but did as he was told. The Lieutenant's reason for wanting to set down at this time became obscured in his own mind. Within a few days after the event, when it became necessary for him to write his report on the chase, his official story, and the one that he himself eventually came to believe, was that he had acted on a hunch, that he had "had a feeling" that the car might turn around. The simple fact was that he had had to answer a call of nature. Excitement always affected him that way.

When the machine landed, it remained poised for flight, its rotors still spinning, the pilot at the controls. The Lieutenant walked toward the road, to accomplish his mission. The rain into which they had almost flown swept through the fields toward him. He watched apathetically as it advanced down the road. His mind was on other things.

Suddenly, from the dark background, emerged a blurred shape, which rapidly took on substance as a car. In the instant it took the Lieutenant to identify the car, its occupants, emerging into the clearing air, beheld their uniformed pursuer by the roadside in a timeless posture, his machine patiently standing nearby like a grazing charger waiting for a knight.

Three pairs of eyes met in mutual astonishment. The confrontation lasted only a second. Then the car was past, roaring down the road.

The Lieutenant squawked and jumped upright. He tried to run, and tripped on his trousers. Hopping, waddling and jumping, he somehow made his way to the aircraft.

He pointed down the road and started to stammer. The pilot, who had seen it all and was waiting only until Preen got back in, ignored him. He reached over to latch the door, then gunned the engine to full power. The Lieutenant was thrown to the floor, still desperately grasping his pants.

CHAPTER TWENTY-ONE

As they emerged from the store, Franklin waved at the men who had accompanied him. "You men are turned back over to your local dispatch control." He got into his car for the ride back to the Post, and said to the driver, "Hit it."

As soon as the police car pulled away from the store, Franklin reached for the mike and said, "Sergeant Catlin? Franklin. Did your men get off the lot?"

"Yes, sir, and while you were conducting the investigation, Captain Prescott called from downstate and ordered blockades——"

"What?" Franklin interrupted, sitting upright. "The orders you received from him are countermanded. Now, listen. If the men who pulled this have a thirty-five minute start and your men just left the Post a few minutes ago, it's probably hopeless to send them out a few miles from here and set up roadblocks." He paused just a second, then continued, "We'll do the sweep search instead. We may have a chance to overtake them. Do you remember the technique from your last staff school? Have your men had a skull session on it?"

He didn't wait for a reply, but continued in a rapid voice: "All right, this is how we'll do it. Pair your men, two cars to each highway in your service area, in each direction. Have them proceed as fast as possible, overtaking all traffic, out to the limit of the area.

"If a suspect is sighted, the lead car will flag it down and make an examination, while the second continues the sweep." Without pause the voice continued, "All right, Sergeant, dispatch them. Do not acknowledge this message. Get to it."

The Sergeant leaped to the other transmitter and pressed the switch. He thanked the Lord he had thoroughly briefed the men on this.

"Post Seven to all cars. Sweep search. Sweep search. Pair as follows:—he glanced up at the big wall map showing the city and the five arterial routes leading out of it, then down again as he dispatched from memory—"Cars Ten and Eight, Route Ten, west. Cars Eighteen and Four, Route Forty-five, north. Cars Two and Nine, Route Ten, east. Cars Five and Seven, Route Forty-five, south. Cars Six and Twelve, Route Sixty-two, northwest. Car Twenty, return to Post. Suspects are two men, white, in blue and white car, make and model unknown. License unknown. One is short, heavy and dark, and dressed in a guard's uniform. Suspects are wanted in connection with eighty-five-thousand-dollar supermarket robbery this city at approximately 10:40 A.M. That's it! You know what to do. Acknowledge and question."

The receiver squawked.

"Car Two, okay."

"Car Four, okay."

"Car Five, on the way."

"Car Six, roger."

"Car Eight, me, too."

"Car Nine, okay."

"Car Ten, okay."

"Car Twelve, okay."

"Car Twenty, on the way in."

The Sergeant waited a few seconds, then said, "Car Seven, acknowledge."

There was no reply.

"Car Seven, if your receiver is working, but transmitter is out, stop and call in by telephone. Car Twenty."

"Car Twenty."

"Where are you now?"

"About eight miles north on Forty-five, headed back in."

"Go on through town and take Car Seven's place, sweep south on Forty-five with Car Five. Car Five, where are you?"

"Car Five. I'm about twelve miles south, almost halfway to Bucola."

"Okay, keep going, don't wait for Car Twenty. He has to cross town."

"Okay."

Franklin came in just as the Sergeant was finishing the dispatch. To the Sergeant he said, "I want to stay abreast of this. Where's a map?" The Sergeant pulled one from a drawer.

"I didn't hear all the dispatch," Franklin said. "Will you scribble the car numbers on some pieces of paper and let me have them? Also some thumb tacks."

The other nodded and complied.

Franklin cleared the top of a desk and set up his map. Once it was set up, he sat back and relaxed. There was nothing to do now but wait for something to break. Captain Prescott's attempt to set up a blockade came into his mind.

A crisis had been building in the high levels of the department for several months, ever since the Governor had broken with tradition to go outside the department to secure a new Superintendent. The young Superintendent's ideas and methods—based on his naval experience—were a little bit hard for the seasoned veterans to take.

The "sweep search" idea was one. To the older officers, the idea of stationary roadblocks to seal off an area was as natural and normal as putting on shoes in the morning. Now, they were told by this young scientist that there was a better way, that a wall chart of an area was no longer enough, that they had to calculate; to use time as a factor, to be familiar with the theory of games and such expressions at "least possible chance" and "minimum probability," and to use, or at least understand, the algebraic terms in which these concepts were expressed.

Some of the younger officers had responded enthusiastically to this new application of symbolic logic to the search problems of their police department. After all, the state covered almost sixty thousand square miles, and was covered by a tremendous network of roads. But a large percentage of the executive force—the arm which ran the department from day to day—responded with frustration and resentment to this imposition of new ways.

Until today, this conflict over tactics had remained under wraps. There had been no occasion calling for a choice between the old and new methods. Now Franklin had a feeling that this would be the day. He would either have to force the adoption of the new tactics, or retreat and forget the whole business.

This was a situation made to order for a sweep search or perhaps it was better to say that a sweep search was the only thing that might have a ghost of a chance. Unless, that is, the fugitives had obligingly doodled along at thirty-five miles an hour while the cruisers passed them to get out to the place where the roadblock was to be set!

He hated publicly to countermand the Captain's order, but it was the man's own fault. There had been specific instructions issued to cover situations exactly like this one. And those instructions called for use of the sweep.

He shifted around in his chair to watch the chattering teletype, then glanced at his watch. It was 11:35, too early for any possible results yet. Actually, he didn't hold very high hopes for the sweep. But he was convinced it was the only method offering even a chance, and that made him determined to see that it was used, if only for the purpose of enforcing discipline in the organization.

CHAPTER TWENTY-TWO

THE Sergeant brought over the map and spread it on a desk, and Franklin began to pore over it. As to the superiority of the sweep over the blockade, Franklin had no reservations at all. Mathematically, the sweep represented a way to go back in time, a time-recovery system.

A blockade, he thought, was like a dam. It was essentially a static, passive thing, and it affected only the cars that came to it in any given period of time.

A group of cars leaving a city at any specific time interval, say fifteen minutes, would travel more or less as a coherent, fifteen-minute-long "block" in the traffic stream—like a log in a river.

Since the blockade was passive, it could only sit and wait until the "block" or log got to it. And most important, it had to be set up *before* the wanted block arrived.

The sweep, on the other hand, was an active, offensive method. Since it moved outward from the city itself, faster than the traffic flow, it was in effect like a speedboat in the stream. It could not only overtake and examine the "log," the block of fifteen-minute-long traffic, but *it could pass them and examine cars which had left even before the sweep car.* In terms of effect, then, the sweep went back in time, recovering that portion of time represented by travel that had taken place before the sweep car had left town.

The limit to this time recovery effect was governed only by the speed of the sweeping car, and the distance it was prepared to go.

The application of this principle here, he thought, was obvious. It was to recover, if possible, the thirty-odd-minute lead that the fugitive car enjoyed.

He settled down to compute the optimum distances and times the cars on sweep might have to go before making contact. A doubt of some kind kept bobbing around in the back of his mind, but he wasn't able to put his finger on it.

CHAPTER TWENTY-THREE

"That's him. That's the sonofabitch," Grozzo shouted as the car accelerated past the Lieutenant and his idling helicopter. "What we gonna do?"

He sounded a little hysterical, as if his nerves were on edge. Rayder turned and froze him with a hard look.

"We're gonna outrun him," Rayder said at last. "We'll go on

down to Bucola and get the other car. It'll run faster than this one. We'll beat him down there in this one and get the other one before he gets there to see us switch." He was not as confident as he sounded. He turned again and said, "Keep on that radio. If he starts to broadcast, yell."

Grozzo nodded.

The car had made two miles back toward the west before the helicopter rose to take up the chase. Soon they approached the road down which they had been traveling toward Bucola, before they had turned off into the rainstorm.

"At least we know this road," the driver mumbled.

He pumped the brakes, then took the corner as fast as he dared. He wished Grozzo were driving. The chunky man could handle a car as if he had been born to it.

He glanced back again. The other man was in turn giving his attention to the radio and to the helicopter, which had followed them around the turn like a kite on a long string. Both machines were wide open, and appeared to be about evenly matched. The car might have just a slight edge. It appeared to be gaining a little, but not enough to make much difference in the ten miles left to Bucola.

"Anything on that radio?" Rayder yelled.

The other man turned the dial, then said, "The Post back in the city is on to the caper. They're dispatching cars down all the highways."

"That means the helicopter radio must be out, or he would have told 'em about us," Rayder replied.

Grozzo leaned forward on the back of the front seat. He seemed to be calmer now, but still worried. He talked loudly, over the noise.

"If he tails us down there and sees us get in the other car, all he's gotta do is set down some place and call in on a phone, and we've had it."

"I know. Any ideas?"

"We could go back into the rain."

He gestured at the line of clouds parallel to them and now only about a mile away.

"This storm can't be more than ten miles across. With that helicopter and a few cars, they could sew us up like we were in a net."

There was a moment's silence, then Grozzo said, "Well, if we went in, we'd have a few minutes to think. Christ, they're gonna pick us off the way it is."

Ahead a couple of miles a blob of green stood along the highway, higher than the corn. It was the grove into which they had driven in the morning, running over the barbed wire gate. Rayder began to think rapidly.

"That grove!" He pointed. "Wasn't it at the corner of a road going east and west?"

"Not quite at the corner. That gate was a couple of hundred feet south down this road from the corner."

Rayder glanced back at the helicopter, which was being bounced around some by the winds of the storm. It was far enough behind so that it dropped out of sight behind the corn whenever a gust of wind blew the craft from one side of the road to the other.

He said to the other man: "If we turned down one of these crossroads, he wouldn't be able to see us till he was almost over head. Right?"

"Yes."

"Will this car run through that corn?"

"Yeah, but don't go in there over twenty miles an hour unless you want to wreck it."

"I don't mean speed. Will it keep going through a cornfield?"

"I think so."

They were approaching the grove.

"Hold on," Rayder yelled.

He slammed on the brakes and let the car skid, raising a large cloud of dust from the gravel as he killed speed. At the crossroads he spun the car left, turning toward the rain clouds.

To the men in the helicopter, the car was lost behind the corn. The pilot immediately began a left turn.

Rayder, however, instead of accelerating toward the east again, went only a hundred yards, then abruptly turned off the road to the right straight into the cornfield. The car sagged and almost stopped as it rammed the wall of tough corn stalks.

"More gas," yelled Grozzo. "Don't let it stall."

Rayder nodded, flooring the gas. The engine roared. The automatic transmission screamed at the unaccustomed stress between the increased engine torque and the resistance the car was meeting from the thick green plants. They held their breaths, but the car continued to move.

The stalks swished, scraped and rasped against the front and sides. Small, immature ears of corn thumped and splattered against the windshield and top, leaving milky streaks. The windshield wipers and antenna were carried away. The headlights were smashed.

The engine rapidly heated under the load, and the smell of hot oil filled the car. They could see nothing except a wall of the green stalks advancing on them.

Grozzo, who had had the presence of mind to orient himself to the direction of the rows of corn, reached over and twisted the wheel to correct their direction. The car had begun to veer, and with nothing on which to guide, they might have missed the grove they were aiming for, and circled aimlessly in the field.

Abruptly, as if driving out of a tunnel, they were in the grove. The car shot forward as the resistance to it ceased. Rayder clapped on the brakes barely in time to miss a tree.

They hopped out, and between rolls of thunder, could barely hear the flop!—flop!—flop! of the helicopter rapidly diminishing toward the east—and the storm.

Exchanging a grin of mixed relief and triumph, they jumped back into the car, then steered it out of the grove and south again toward Bucola at ninety miles an hour.

As the blue and white car slowed and made its second turn east, apparently headed for the storm again, the Lieutenant unbuckled his seat belt. Jumping to the front like a child pushing his nose against a window, he pressed against the plexiglass bubble, striving for a view of the car.

The pilot immediately set the craft into its peculiar tilting turn toward the curtain of rain, now about a mile to their left. They came out of their turn directly above the road, going east. The car was not in sight.

Just for a second, the pilot had the crazy idea that the Lieutenant was going to cry.

"Land there," Preen shouted, pointing to a barn lot alongside the road. "We'll wait for them to come out again." He began to tug at the riot gun clipped to the roof.

The pilot had just begun to wonder how the car could have made it into the rain without their seeing it—it hadn't seemed that far ahead—but he was jolted from his train of thought by this latest madness.

"Wait! Wait till I set it down!" he shouted to Preen, who was wrestling at the gun, unaware that he was jostling the controls and bouncing the machine in the air.

Preen turned around and shouted at the pilot: "Hurry up! I want to be waiting for them this time."

He seemed obsessed by the idea that it was all going to happen again.

The pilot took advantage of the respite to land the helicopter quickly and turn off the engine. He leaned over the yoke with a long "Whew!" then, noting his superior again working frantically at the simple catches securing the gun, he quietly slid his catch, opened the port and stepped out.

He walked around to the blind side of the machine, lit a cigarette and leaned against the side, listening to the commotion, shuffling and muttered curses as the other man continued his furious struggle with the gun.

Finally, there was a triumphant cry as the Lieutenant got the gun loose, and then a thump as he opened his hatch and leaped to the ground. He ran around to the other side, swinging the gun wildly, and yelled, "Come on, come on!" He took off for the road a few yards away.

"Good God!" said the pilot softly, then thinking fast, he yelled, "The rain's moving in. We can't leave her here. I'll fly cover for you."

Without waiting for a reply, the pilot leaped in and started the motor. Immediately, since the engine was warm, he lifted off and moved out to the road, directly over the Lieutenant, who was apparently too intent on his job to notice. Peering down, the pilot thought, "Well, even if he didn't hear me, he couldn't do anything about it now, except shoot me down." He smiled. Abruptly, the smile faded, and he sent the craft up another two hundred feet before leveling off.

Below, crouched in the road with riot gun cocked, like a big-game hunter awaiting a charging rhino, the Lieutenant waited for his foe to emerge from the rain-curtain, a hundred yards away.

Luckily, no farm trucks appeared.

As he hovered, watching the Lieutenant stalk his prey, the pilot wondered what would happen next. Vaguely he sensed something missing, but he couldn't put his fingers on it. Slowly, he raised a hand to his ear. Then it dawned on him. He didn't have any earphones on. What with the excitement, the Lieutenant, the car and the chopper to watch simultaneously, he hadn't been aware up till now that they were off.

"Jesus," he thought, reaching for them. "This all should have been reported when we started."

He consoled himself by thinking that, as busy as he had been, he couldn't really have been expected to pay attention to the radio. But a doubt immediately set in as to whether his superiors would see it that way.

He had an inspiration.

Hanging his earphones back where they had been, he guided the helicopter close behind the officer—making plenty of noise—and set it down. Then he yelled, over the rush of the blades, "Sir, that rain's getting too close again. We'll have to move back. Let me ferry you a couple of hundred yards back up the road!"

He watched closely for the reaction. Yes, it penetrated. The Lieutenant jumped in, but didn't take his eyes off the road.

"Hurry," the Lieutenant insisted.

As the pilot set the craft in motion once more, he gestured toward the hanging phones.

"Sir, do you think we should call in and tell them what's up? Maybe they'd send reinforcements."

The smartly uniformed man had begun to look annoyed, but at the mention of the word "reinforcements" his face cleared.

"Yes, yes, yes," he said.

He managed somehow to continue gripping the gun in one hand, and to get the earphones on with the other. He reached for the microphone and gestured for the set to be turned on. The pilot reached over and set it for the command channel.

"Hello! Hello! This is Lieutenant Preen," Preen shouted. "We need reinforcements. They're liable to come back out of the rain any minute. Hello! Hello! Do you hear me?"

At the Post Seven radio room, Sergeant Catlin had just been wondering whether to suggest to Superintendent Franklin that the Civil Air Patrol be notified of the missing helicopter, then had decided against saying anything. It would be just a little beyond the scope of his job to make the suggestion.

As the Lieutenant's voice came in over the radio, Sergeant Catlin looked questioningly up at the Superintendent. The other man nodded, and the Sergeant said into the mike, "Lieutenant Preen? This is Post Seven, Sergeant Catlin. We thought you were down somewhere." He looked at his watch. "You are almost forty-five minutes overdue. Are you in trouble?"

The agitated voice came in again. "Sergeant, send some men, send some cars. We chased them inside this rainstorm and they're going to come out again. We need help, we——"

His thin voice was brusquely interrupted by the heavier one of Captain Prescott at headquarters. The voice had a nasty ring to it, the sound of a man who is mad at somebody, who has something to get off his chest.

"Lieutenant Preen, this is Captain Prescott. Now stop that damn chattering and answer my questions."

Catlin could sense a sudden change in the atmosphere. This kind of talk wasn't used over the air.

The deep voice continued. "Where are you?"

There was a sound like a mike being covered, and a muffled conversation.

"About twenty miles south of Post Seven." There was fear in the answering voice.

The grilling went on. "About twenty miles south of Post Seven. About! What do you mean, about? Don't you know? Are you down?"

"No, we're in the air."

"Then why didn't you call in?" The voice took on a sharper edge. "Don't you know we were about to notify the Civil Air Patrol to make a search for you?"

Catlin felt sure this was an exaggeration, but said nothing. He glanced across the room. The radio operator sat silent at the teletype, pretending to be reading, but actually listening. Catlin noticed that the teletype itself was strangely silent. Probably every communications man in the state was listening to this.

Franklin, a glint in his eye, and jaw set, got up and walked over toward the transmitting console.

"Why didn't you call in? Was your radio out?" The Captain's voice continued. The tone had become deceptively soft.

There was just a slight pause as if Preen were going to grasp at the bait, but he apparently saw the trap.

"No, sir, the radio wasn't out."

"Well, then?" Softer yet.

"Well, you see, we were chasing this car, and——"

"Chasing—a—car—with—your—helicopter? You know, here at

headquarters we thought you were making an inspection at Post
Seven at eleven A.M. Why are you chasing cars?"

The reply was faint, almost pleading, all in one breath. "We
were almost to Post Seven when we heard their alarm on the
supermarket robbery and the description. Then we saw this blue
and white car sideways in the road and when we went down to
look, they left as fast as the car would go and we chased them."

At the mention of the "blue and white car," the Sergeant's head
went up. This could be something real.

The Superintendent reached over to take the mike from the
Sergeant and said, "This is Superintendent Franklin. Lieutenant,
tell your pilot to figure your position as nearly as he can. Don't
wait for him to do it; get back to the mike."

"Yes, sir," was the reply.

There was a short pause, then the slight pop of the switch as
the mike button was pushed again. Without waiting for the Lieutenant to speak, the Superintendent continued rapidly: "Did
you say you pursued a blue and white car with two men in it?"

"Yes, sir."

"Do you have it in sight now?"

"No, sir. They drove into a rainstorm, and we had to stop."

"Are you at the point now where they entered the storm?"

"Yes."

"How long ago?"

"Uh, about five minutes."

"What kind of car was it?"

"I don't know."

"All right, give me your pilot."

After a bare moment's pause, Franklin's voice, tense but controlled, went on: "Is this the pilot?"

"Yes, sir."

"Where are you?"

"A half mile east, and either four or five miles north of Bucola.
I'm not sure which."

"Fine! Now stay where you are, keep your receiver open, but
don't transmit."

Franklin covered the mike with his hand and turned to the
Sergeant, saying, "Call off your sweep on Highway 45, south, and
Highway 10, east. Have those four cars converge on the helicopter.
While you are dispatching them, have your radio operator contact
the Weather Bureau—or the Air Force, if necessary—to get a

radar fix on that storm. Find out how big it is and approximately where it lies. We may be able to surround it. Understand?"

"Yes, sir," said Catlin. He pointed his finger at the radio operator, who nodded his head in silent agreement and turned to the telephone.

Franklin turned the set back to the Sergeant, making a mental note to have a conference with Captain Prescott in the morning.

Catlin switched his set to the communications channel. "All units," he said, "this is Post Seven. We have a possible sighting of suspects near Bucola. Cars Two, Nine, Twenty and Five, discontinue your sweep. Converge on the intersection of the two section-line roads five miles straight north of Bucola. Car Five, where are you now?"

The answer was immediate. "About a mile south of Bucola."

"Did you read the dispatch?"

"Yes, I'm turning around now. I'll be there in a few minutes."

"Okay. Call in as soon as you spot a helicopter or the search area."

"Right!"

"Cars Two, Nine and Twenty, acknowledge."

Amid some static developing from the slowly drifting storm, they replied.

"Okay," said the Sergeant. "All other units continue your sweep search. Do not acknowledge."

He flicked the switch, then turned to the radio man, who was still on the phone, calling the Air Force.

CHAPTER TWENTY-FOUR

THE blue and white Olds, at ninety, drew a long plume of dust behind it. Ninety was all it would do. The overheated engine was running rough. As they approached Bucola, Rayder slowed somewhat and glanced at his partner.

"How're those hands? You gonna be able to drive?"

"I think so." The other had managed to tear some strips from the discarded uniform which he had made into crude bandages. "It's better if I drive," he said simply.

"Yeah, I know, but don't do it unless you're gonna be able to stick with it all the way. We may not get a chance to change."

"I'll stick," the dark man said quietly.

"Everything set?"

They were almost to the town. Grozzo looked hurriedly around the back seat.

"Okay," he said.

"Give the hardware a quick wipe," Rayder said.

"Yeah," replied the other, vaulting into the back seat with a piece of the torn uniform. He quickly wiped all the exposed metal surfaces. Sliding back into the front, he repeated the process, then paused. "Say," he said, "how about underneath?"

"Nah, nobody'll think of looking there. Besides, there's too much loose dirt on the parts down there for 'em to carry prints."

They were by now going slowly down the main street, just as they had earlier in the morning. The town was drowsing in the summer heat. Only a few cars, and fewer pedestrians, were about. In between the times when cars went by, it was so quiet that the automatic timer on the town's lone traffic light at the highway intersection could be heard clicking.

Rayder turned in and pulled up next to the green car, which sat as it had been left, undisturbed, in the lot a half-block from the intersecting north-south highway.

Deliberately, trying to seem unhurried, but desperately anxious to rush, they started the transfer. Rayder walked over to the green car and opened the trunk, then walked back for the money bag. Grozzo, working gingerly with his damaged hands, reached into the Olds to get the heavy radio, and the tatters of the uniform.

Just as each had got his burden clear of the car, they heard the sudden sound of a car approaching the town at extremely high speed. Almost simultaneously came the high-pitched squall of tires, protracted as the driver fought to brake off his excess speed for the turn. Then, mingling at first with the tire squall, but rapidly mounting to a scream, came a police siren.

It happened before they could have taken a half-dozen steps. Neither moved. They froze as the high-powered cruiser came into the turn, still at speed, and in a partial skid, came around in an expertly executed racing drift.

They watched with frozen hearts as the trooper's glance flicked over them for the barest instant, then flicked back to the road to the east as he accelerated heavily through the little town, siren screaming.

Their poise completely routed, the two men dumped their gear into the green car, then, with Grozzo at the wheel, backed violently into the street which the trooper had traversed. With a great screech of tires, ignoring the stop light in their near panic, they crossed the highway and headed in the opposite direction from that taken by the trooper.

Several people who had been aroused by the police car watched them go, including a small boy whose bicycle they had very nearly backed over.

As they cleared the town, Grozzo floored the accelerator, and the large V-8 special, finely tuned, lurched against its mounts as it delivered a flood of power to the rear wheels. The speedometer spun past the 100 marker, and continued climbing rapidly.

Rayder, as usual, recovered his wits first. Tapping his partner on the shoulder, he said, "Better back it off to about seventy. We'll call attention to ourselves going too fast."

Reluctantly, Grozzo eased the throttle.

Rayder leaped into the back and picked the radio from the floor where they had unceremoniously dumped it.

"I'm going to try to see what that cop was up to—if he's transmitting. Maybe he was after somebody else," he said half-heartedly.

He extended the fishpole antenna and set the receiver at the State Police communications wave-length.

CHAPTER TWENTY-FIVE

THE radio operator turned from his phone to face the Sergeant and Franklin. "The Air Force says their radar shows the storm has two cells. The first one is about five miles across—east and west—and ten miles long. It's slowly moving west, and its center is about five miles to the north-east of Bucola. The second one is bigger, about fifteen by fifteen miles. It's directly south of the first one."

Franklin pondered for just a minute, then beckoned the regular radio operator. "Switch this equipment to the communications channel so the patrol cars can get the benefit of this directly," he said. The man complied, and the Superintendent picked up the mike.

"Lieutenant Preen," he said.

In a second there was a reply. "Yes, sir."

Again just a slight pause. Then the Superintendent said, "Um, better let me talk to your pilot."

The pilot came on. "Yes, sir."

"Any sign of anything?"

"No, sir."

"Are you still at the same place where you saw the car go into the storm?"

"Almost, I think it was back toward the east a few hundred yards from here."

The Superintendent's inflection became sharper. "Did you say *think*? Didn't you *see* the car?"

"Well, not exactly. You see, when we first chased the car, it drove into the storm and stayed a few minutes, then came back out again. We chased it again, straight south for a couple of miles, then it turned back east toward the storm again, but they were about a half-mile ahead of us. When they turned east, we couldn't see the car on account of the tall corn. By the time we got up to the road, we couldn't see them, so we just figured they'd gone back into the storm." His voice weakened. "We didn't see anywhere else for them to go."

The sharp voice said, "Did you look?"

"No, well, I guess we just figured they had gone back in, since we didn't see anything of them."

"You're still in the same area, aren't you? Suppose you have a look now."

"Yes, sir," the weak voice said. Then, after a pause, he added, "Well, there's a grove of trees down here almost under us now, and——" The voice got weaker.

"And what?"

"And it looks like some tracks, by a tractor or something, leading into it from the road. The corn's mashed down."

"Tractor or something!" The voice was sarcastic now. The usually mild-mannered man had lost his temper. "It looks like you two got sucked in. Okay, get some altitude in that thing and see what you can see. Tractor!"

The Superintendent realized it was bad for discipline and morale for him to lose his temper in public, but he hated this incompetence and shoddy work. As he sat struggling to regain his composure, the voice came back on.

"Sir?"

"Yes!"

"Sir, we're almost out of gas. Can I have permission to go on to Post Seven?"

The Superintendent fought down a terrible urge to say, "No, by God, stay there till you fall." He still hadn't gotten himself cooled off. With an effort, he said, "Yes, come on in to refuel."

To the practised ears of those listening, it was obvious that the Superintendent still had his finger on the mike button; the faint sound of the open mike persisted for almost a minute. It was becoming obvious that he didn't know what to do next. Finally, without saying anything, he let go the button. The mike noise stopped. No one else spoke; the air was dead for a minute, then another mike opened up.

It was immediately apparent to Catlin that it was one of his cars, because the transmitter carried part of the sound of the engine, turning at high speed.

"Post Seven, this is Car Five."

The trooper's voice sounded a little hesitant. He had undoubtedly overheard the conversation, and now felt himself to be in an awkward situation, like a little boy accidentally happening on to an adult quarrel. The Sergeant immediately sensed that the man must have something to report, or he would presumably have remained quiet. He reached for the mike and said, "This is Post Seven, go ahead," keeping his voice to a matter-of-fact one.

"Uh, I came a mile east and I'm almost five miles north of Bucola now, at the dispatch point. Uh, shall I remain here?"

Catlin, pursuing his hunch that the man had called in for more than this, but was hesitating for some reason, said, "For the time being. Have you seen anything that might be worthwhile?"

The trooper said "Uh" again, hesitated a moment, then decided to plunge. "When I came through Bucola just now I caught a glance at a blue and white Olds, about a '58. Two men looked like they were unloading it. They both had things in their hands. I don't know what. I just got a quick look."

The Sergeant opened his mouth to speak, but the Superintendent cut him off.

"Get back there fast and see if that car's still there. Report in on it. Check around town and see if anybody has anything to say."

"Yes, sir."

"Sergeant Catlin!" Franklin turned to the other man. "Where is the car that was paired with the one we just talked to?"

"I had to pull him in across the territory; they didn't connect," was the reply. "Let me call him," he continued. "Car Twenty, acknowledge."

"Car Twenty."

"Where are you?"

"I'm just clearing town, now, south. Got caught in traffic."

"Did you hear these last transmissions?"

"Yes, sir."

"Okay, proceed to Bucola and help Car Five. Hit it!"

"Yes, sir."

The siren sounded faintly in the speaker as it was turned on.

The Sergeant was aware that the Superintendent's presence in the dispatch office was unusual, and it might make the men more cautious about reporting anything except solid information, especially after hearing the chewing out the Lieutenant and his pilot had got.

He said, "This is Post Seven to all cars. Have any of you boys anything suspicious to report? If negative, you do not need to reply."

He waited; there was no answer.

The Superintendent turned to Catlin. "Sergeant, how many cars did you pull off the sweep?"

"Four, including the two to Bucola."

"Then these four should be converging on the area north of Bucola from which the helicopter reported."

"Yes, sir."

"Okay. At this point I think it would be useless to send them back out to finish their sweep. We've lost too much time. Have them search the area of the storm from the plot the Weather Bureau gave you. It is just possible that they did go back into it."

Franklin walked back over to his desk, feeling somewhat contrite for having temporarily taken over the dispatch from the Sergeant. Catlin was a capable man, and his men were used to him. There was a danger here that Franklin might muddy the waters by too much intervention.

He busied himself at the map again, trying hard to force himself back into the frame of mind he'd had when he had functioned with such precision on the aircraft carrier.

But he realized it was something you could not force. It had to come with practice. He felt desperately that he should be making better use of the units he had in hand. But he was rusty.

He stared intensely at the map, trying to make the insights come.

CHAPTER TWENTY-SIX

THE trooper in Car Five wheeled around and sent his car once more screaming toward Bucola. In just over three minutes, he had covered the five miles to the little town.

He wheeled in toward the place he had seen the two men unloading the Olds. It was still there.

Parking his car so as to block the other, he looked carefully around. His scalp tingled. Seeing no one, he called in. "Post Seven, this is Car Five."

"Go ahead."

"The Olds is still where I saw it. I've got it blocked."

"Any sign of them?"

"No, I'm going to check now."

"Okay, don't take any chances. Oh, give me the plate number, if you can see it."

"Just a minute." The trooper read off the number of the rear license plate.

The voice on the radio repeated, "Don't take any chances. Do you want to wait till Twenty gets to you?"

"No, I don't think so. It looks quiet."

"Okay, leave your door open and the transmitter on, just in case."

"Okay."

The trooper was being made a little edgy by the dispatcher's caution. He glanced up at the riot gun clipped to the ceiling, then down again; it would get the people in town in an uproar if he came out carrying it. He didn't really think the robbers were here, anyway.

Just as a precaution, he loosened the strap tying his revolver to the holster. Turning the transmitter clear up, he slid out of the car, leaving the door open. Glancing around, he walked over to the other car and opened the door. Then he walked around the back and opened the trunk. Sniffing something, he walked back to the front, raised the hood and peered in at the engine. He walked back to his own car, then glanced around again before he slid in.

"Car Five to Post Seven."

"Yes, come in."

"Car is not locked. Some pieces of a torn-up uniform in the back seat. Nothing in the trunk. The motor is still hot, and it has been driven hard; oil was splashed back up out of the filler tube."

"Okay, check that license number again."

The trooper complied.

"That number was issued in Chicago to a 1953 Chevrolet," the dispatcher's voice said.

"Well, it's on this '58 Olds now."

"Get the serial number from the fire wall."

The officer did so and called it in, then added, "By the way, the car's all streaked up with something, and there's some corn stalks stuck in the grill and fender wells. The headlights are knocked out. Looks like it was run into a field of corn."

There was minute's pause, then the dispatcher's voice came back on, more excited. "That car was stolen last night in Chicago. They must have used it for a switch car. Have you had a chance to talk to anybody yet?"

"No."

"Okay, go ahead, and call in if you get anything at all."

"Yes, sir."

He slid out of the car once again, and walked to a small store, diagonally across the street. The proprietor was standing in the doorway watching him.

"Hello," he said, then pointed back toward the blue and white car. "Did you happen to see who pulled up in that car?" he asked.

The shopkeeper shook his head. "No, I sure didn't, but I'll tell you something. About ten minutes ago a State Police car came through here goin' like hell. Was that you?"

The trooper nodded.

"You was goin' pretty fast. As soon as you cleared town, a car backed out of the lot there and took off, just a-hellin'."

Urgently the trooper pressed him. "Which way? What kind of a car? How many were there?"

"Wait a minute, now," the older man said, rocking back on his heels. "It was a green car. It had two men in it. I don't know what kind it was, because I don't know one from the other. It wasn't none of the local bucks, though, 'cause I know all of their cars."

"Which way did they go? Did you get a look at the license?"

"They went right straight west down Main Street, just as fast as ever the car would go. Didn't even stop for the stop light at the highway."

The trooper was halfway out the door. "Thanks," he said over his shoulder.

On the sidewalk, he hesitated a second. Should he call in with what he had, or try to get more information? Better call in. As he started to jog-trot across the street, a boy of about ten, holding up a bicycle, yelled at him from in front of the store he had just left.

"Hey, Mr. Policeman."

He turned and started to say "Just a minute, son," but the boy had screwed up his courage and was unable to stop. The words bubbled out. "I heard you ask Mr. Peters about that car." The trooper quickly jogged back to the side of the boy, as he continued talking rapidly. "Those men in the car almost ran over my bike. I had it parked right over there." He gestured. "It wasn't even on the road, and they backed out clear across and almost hit it. Ain't it agin the law, goin' so fast?"

The policeman stooped and took him gently by the shoulders and looked into his eyes. "Son, this could be very important. Do you know what kind of a car it was?"

"Yes, it was a 1961 Chevy four-door, with twin pipes."

The officer's face showed his gratitude. "What color?"

"Green."

"How many men in it?"

"Two."

"Now, just for luck, you didn't happen to get the license number, did you?"

The boy, who had begun to expand in the glow of the officer's approval, was crestfallen.

"No, sir, I didn't," he admitted.

"Well, that's okay," the trooper said, patting him on the shoulder. "You've done a real first-class observing job, seeing as much as you did. Now I've got to run over and radio it in." He gave the proud boy a farewell pat on the shoulder, and this time ran for his machine.

He radioed the information in as fast as he could, and ended his report without a pause.

"Shall I go after them?" he asked.

"Yes, yes," came the excited reply. "It hasn't been more than fifteen minutes. They can't be far."

CHAPTER TWENTY-SEVEN

SUPERINTENDENT FRANKLIN sat in the radio room at Post Seven. He listened as the trooper at Bucola radioed in his findings, and as the Sergeant told him to take up the chase.

He did not interfere. He wanted to think. He waited to be sure the Sergeant got Car Twenty, which had been headed south toward Bucola on Route 45, turned and headed west on a route parallel and ten miles north of Car Five.

Deliberately he blanked his mind out, and walked down the hall to the pop machine and quietly drank a bottle, while leaning with one hand against the wall. In this manner, he tried to shake, or rather control, the tensions that had been building in him. He didn't want to be tense. He needed to be completely clear in order to think. During the war he had discovered that he was not one of those men who can perform well under stress; who can continue to think clearly even in battle.

He was different. He had to get out of it for a few seconds, to be alone every so often—just for awhile—to clear his brain and start his thinking afresh.

As the tension began to drain out of him, he suddenly realized what he had been doing wrong. He had organized the sweep search! The reasoning and mathematical logic behind the sweep were fine—but only if applied in a situation where the quarry's freedom of action was limited to the area to be swept! In other words, the fugitives had to be confined to the highways. But in fact there was nothing to confine them to the highways. They had complete freedom to use the many secondary roads, and they had done so!

His logic had been confined to too narrow a set of assumptions. He had made a rigid, formal application of mathematical reasoning, and then stopped without covering the full range of possibilities. The chase situation here called above all for an empiric, not a formal, approach.

He began to recapitulate. About an hour and a half ago, two men had engineered a slick supermarket holdup—without guns. It had the appearance of a professional job. Unless they were now chasing phantoms, the holdup men were from Chicago, or at least had a getaway car stolen from there. They were now somewhere west of Bucola, with a fifteen-minute start on a single trooper who had taken up the chase at that point. In addition, there was one other trooper going west parallel to the first, about ten miles to the north. No one else was near them.

The Superintendent lit a cigarette.

Fifteen minutes start. It might as well be fifteen hours.

He built a mental picture. West and north of Bucola, for over a hundred and fifty miles, extended the great prairie plain, so level that it took drainage ditches to get the water off. Along each section line, exactly one mile apart and running true to the compass, were the county roads, gravel or crushed limestone, graded, smooth and maintained. Flat and level, they were the best network of secondary roads in the country. Any fool could run sixty-five on them. A reasonably good driver could maintain seventy-five, and a really skilled man would be fairly safe at ninety. Except for one thing: the intersections!

Since there was a road every mile—east, west, north and south —there was also an intersection every single mile in every road. At this time of year, the corn was high enough so that all intersections were blind for oncoming drivers. A car at speed was risking collision once in a mile. This risk might just slow the men down, he reflected. Unless they were scared. More likely, they were just willing to take the risk.

Assuming that they could average no more than sixty miles an hour, they were still traveling a mile in each minute. In fifteen minutes, they would have passed fifteen intersections, each one an opportunity to turn off.

Not only that, but on any of the roads on to which they might have turned, they would have again passed an intersection each mile, and each of these also presented an opportunity to turn off. And then (he followed it through in his mind) it followed that any road they might enter would present the same opportunity to leave it again each mile. He pondered.

It was a maze problem.

The math formula occurred to him. It was to square the number of roads they had passed. Fifteen. It seemed hard to believe, but there it was. In fifteen minutes, they'd had an opportunity to make any of two hundred twenty-five turns.

And it would get worse as they went further.

The troopers were looking for a needle in a rapidly expanding haystack. Unless they had a real piece of luck, or sprouted wings —Wings!

In his concentration, he had forgotten about the helicopter. He strode to a back window to look at the landing pad. It sat there all right—soaking in the driving rainstorm that had moved up, unnoticed by him. There was no sign of the Lieutenant and the pilot.

No helicopter. That meant a fundamental change in the way they must plan. Instead of a chase operation with his own forces holding the initiative and tracking down the quarry like dogs after game, they would have to switch tactics.

His mind slipped back briefly to his Operations Research training days. There the men in training had been immersed in the theory of games and its application to the classic positions in which the hunter and the hunted find themselves in a chase situation.

In application, it was used most frequently in the case of an airplane trying to find a submarine which it knew only to be somewhere in a certain large area.

From the point of view of the pilot, the question was: what move, or combination of moves, would give the best chance of the plane's intercepting the submarine, under the laws of probability? The converse was the sub skipper's problem: what series of moves would give the best chance of evading detection?

The whole problem assumed that the plane could see the sub only if their paths crossed. There were no trick solutions.

He walked back to his desk and lit another cigarette.

Basically, they had here a similar situation. The robbers' car, because of the numberless roads, had almost unlimited freedom of maneuver. There was only one pursuing car within even fifteen miles, and the mathematical chances of successful pursuit were almost nil.

What to do, then? With the area involved as large as it was, he knew they could put several hundred cars into the search, and the fugitives would still have a fair chance of slipping through. They didn't have several hundred cars, or anything like it.

But there was always chance, and he knew that the laws of chance had confounded mathematicians through the ages.

If probability theory ruled out the chances for a successful intercept and dictated a change in strategy, what strategy was possible?

He stood up and walked around his desk to a map rack. Thumbing the maps, he pulled one down, a big one. It showed the entire state and every road in it. A glance at the large number of fine lines representing the county roads—it looked like a wire screen—convinced him that he was right. Barring a lucky break, an active pursuit was out of the question.

Since offensive searching was out, the alternative then was some plan of defense. He backed a few feet away from the map to get perspective, and squatted on his haunches. First of all, it was necessary to make some assumptions, and base the strategy on them. If the assumptions were wrong, the strategy would fail. But that chance of failure was inherent in the nature of the situation.

All right, then, what assumptions?

The first one had to be that the men were professionals, for the job had been too well planned and executed to be the work of amateurs, especially the business of using a stolen car to leave town, then switching to another car in another town.

This led to another conclusion. Since the men weren't amateurs, they probably did not live in some small town downstate, toward which they might now be heading. Professional criminals did not live in small towns, or even middle-sized ones. Probably this was because of the anonymity offered by big cities. Men who lived by their wits and who pitted themselves against society wanted all the privacy they could get, plus the company of their own kind, so they congregated in cities.

So, being professionals, very likely they would be heading back to the city.

But which one?

Illinois had a metropolitan complex at each end: Chicago and St. Louis, just across the Missouri line. It could be either one. Chicago was probably the best bet, because the Olds had been stolen in Chicago, and had plates issued in Chicago to another car.

He knew this was far from conclusive. Professionals often left false trails. But it was all they had. He'd have to base his assumption on it. He stood up and exercised his legs.

The first two premises, then, were that these men were pros, and that they were headed back to Chicago. They seemed to be intelligent and resourceful. They would undoubtedly avoid the cities on their way back. In all probability, they had planned to use the network of secondary roads, and would most likely stick to the network as much as possible, avoiding both cities and highways if they could.

How could he form a defense? He went over and pulled at the rack of maps until he found what he wanted. It was a detailed map of Chicago and its surrounding areas.

How could they go about getting back into the city? Go around to the west, or even to the north, and enter? Not likely. Either approach would prolong their passage through rural areas, where they faced the greatest danger of discovery and capture.

Their greatest chance of escaping capture lay in getting into the city again as quickly as possible. He was sure they knew this. There were almost a million cars within the metropolitan area. Once they gained the city, they were, for all immediate, practical purposes, safe. They would almost undoubtedly try to get back by the shortest possible route.

The *fastest* way, ordinarily, would be to get over to Route 66, a divided four-lane highway running up through the middle of the state, and drive straight in. But it would be relatively easy to intercept them on this road. He gave them credit for being aware of this, and decided that they would probably stick to the back roads, even if they were slower, rather than risk the highways or superhighways leading into Chicago.

He looked closely at the map. How could they be stopped from taking the back roads up to the edge of the city, then just driving in on one of the city streets? How? He peered at the map.

Then something caught his eye. A ribbon-tracing in bright green ink running snakelike almost from the Indiana line around and up, west of the city and then north off the map toward Milwaukee. It was lettered periodically: TRI-STATE TOLL-WAY. It reminded him of maps he'd seen of the Chinese Wall. *Of course.* Maybe he could use it as a Chinese Wall—for defense! As a toll road, it had only limited access. Only major arteries passed over or under it by means of interchanges. All others, including all secondary roads, simply stopped dead when they got to it. To get into Chicago, they would have to go through one of the interchanges of this tollway system!

Excited now, in spite of himself, he took out a pencil and began making a small circle around each interchange shown on the map, counting as he went. He counted from the Indiana line west and north.

When he got to Roosevelt Road, running straight west from Chicago's Loop, he stopped. Forty-one. That was quite a few. He felt a little less elated.

Could they round up forty-one units and get them in place in time? He pondered the situation.

The two upstate posts near enough to get men there in time had a total of forty-seven cars. With the inevitable subtractions, equipment off for repair, and so forth, it would be touch and go whether they could muster that many machines.

Another thing was that, even if they could get forty-one units in place, this was no guarantee they would catch the suspects. It took three units to man an effective roadblock. That would mean one hundred and twenty-three would be needed to set up roadblocks on all forty-one intersections. This was out of the question. It would take most of the cars in the state.

The only thing they could do would be to assign one car to sit alongside the inbound lane, waiting, ready to give chase as soon as their quarry was sighted. Of course, they would all be in touch by two-way radio, and the one making first contact would immediately call in the cars on either side of him.

He leaned back a minute, then forward. "Okay," he said softly, and turned to the next problem. How much time did he have?

He looked at his watch: 12:05.

The men had left Bucola about twenty-five minutes ago. They had over two hundred miles to go, probably a good bit more than that on the graded roads; they couldn't make it in less than three hours.

Three hours!

He hesitated. As always, in moments like this, he felt a nagging self-doubt. The safest course for him would be simply to follow the book. Have each upstate Post man a roadblock on each of its major highways, and hope the fugitives decided to use the highways. That was the way it had always been done in the past.

If they got through, the papers would report only that they had "evaded a police dragnet." He wouldn't be blamed.

But he was a man of conviction. He was positive that this method offered their best chance of capturing the pair, and was determined to see it through.

He paused a few minutes to make a brief analytical recap. In terms of force available to him and his opponents, his advantage seemed almost overwhelming. Yet the advantage was more apparent than real, because he had to dilute and disperse his forces for the search. The laws of probability, operating strongly against an intercept, were forcing him to retreat from an offensive search and to man, instead, a static defense line.

In the myriad downstate roads the almost infinite number of choices open to his quarry made the chances of capture one in thousands. At the Tollway, the range of choices open to the men narrowed to forty-one, the number of intersections. Under probability theory his best chance was at the place where the opponent's range of choices was smallest. Actually, the range at the Tollway was smaller by a ratio of several hundreds to one.

They had a definite chance to catch them there!

He got up and started for the radio, when suddenly another thought occurred to him. How secure were his communications?

The analysis he had made would hold water only in a situation where each opponent operated in the dark, without knowledge of the other's intentions.

What if they had a radio!

He turned and walked down the hall to the teletype room.

CHAPTER TWENTY-EIGHT

THE green car headed straight west at an even seventy. Flying gravel roared against the floor board and fender wells in a steady drumming monotone.

Rayder was trying not to hear it. He was hunched over the receiver in the back seat, a finger over one ear, and the other pressed against the speaker.

When he heard the officer in Car Five transmit the description given him by the boy, he abruptly straightened and leaned forward to shout into the driver's ear: "They're on to us. Somebody in that hick town saw us. They just put our description out. Let's get off this road. Turn north at the next one, and let it out."

The driver nodded. As the turn approached, he braked the car smoothly so as not to break traction. Once around the turn, he accelerated rapidly.

The car they were using had not been selected by accident. Rayder had had Grozzo, with his knowledge of machines, pick it out with the idea that they might be chased.

Of course, they had not wanted a chase, and still did not. They were not thrill-seeking adolescents out to bait the cops. Their strategy had been to avoid detection, once the caper was completed. The use of the other car, and their decision to use the secondary roads, were part of that strategy.

However, being professionals, they had prepared for any eventuality, including being chased. This car was to be their insurance.

Grozzo had considered a sports car, since some of the competition models could do up to a hundred sixty miles an hour, and corner better than any ordinary car. But the drawback here was that sports cars were conspicuous, and if they were ever identified and chased, they would be too easy to spot anywhere farther on, even if they were able to outrun the first car to pursue them.

He had decided, instead, on a Chevrolet. A popular car that wouldn't stand out, it was in some ways a very capable machine. This model had one of the most powerful V8 engines made for American cars. In addition, it was equipped with a four-speed "floor-box" transmission, which provided for maximum acceleration and the use of the big engine's potential, at any speed.

With special wheels and tires and heavy-duty shocks for cornering, it was a "beast," capable of shrugging off the competition of almost any other machine, except some of the specially equipped interceptors which a few police departments were now being forced to buy in self-defense.

As Grozzo had swung the corner, he had dropped the gear shift into second, then delicately feathered the throttle for maximum acceleration. Had he pushed the gas pedal to the floor, the power available from the engine would have spun the back wheels impotently. There was enough power to do this even on dry concrete, which offered maximum friction.

Holding the engine just below the point at which the back wheels would break loose, he watched the speedometer needle climb. It swung as if tied to a string. When it touched the number 7 on the dial, he gently and quickly shifted to third. The needle continued its swing almost without pause. As it nudged 11, he brought the stick back into fourth gear, and again the needle mounted rapidly. The numbers on the dial stopped at 12, but the pointer kept going on into the unmarked quadrant. It went the equivalent of two more spaces before it stopped, wavering gently back and forth.

The driver looked up; they were less than halfway to the next

intersection. Less than half a mile! He grinned his confidence
in the machine. Then he stopped grinning to pay full attention
to driving.

He was a highly competent driver. That was one of the reasons
Rayder had chosen him. He was competent and experienced
enough to know that a car—any car—at speeds approaching one
hundred forty on gravel, was in a very precarious state.

At their speed, the gravel offered next to no resistance to the
tires; no friction. In some ways, the car was as unstable as if it
were being driven on glare ice. Actually, an abrupt movement
of the steering wheel in any direction could have upset the car's
delicate equilibrium as it sat poised on its needle point of high
velocity.

Braking was, for practical purposes, impossible. Even a slight
attempt to brake could cause a skid, from which there could be
no recovery. Deceleration, too, was tricky. At speed, it was necessary to let up on the gas gradually—to avoid a skid—just to slow
down. A fair-sized bump or dip in the road could accomplish the
same result, to say nothing of a blowout.

In driving this fast, they had taken their lives in their hands.
They were well aware of this. But, to them, it was necessary.
They had known they might have to take this chance. It was only
one of many risks that had to be taken in a caper such as this.

Perhaps if they had shared the Superintendent's mastery of
maths, they would have been aware of the slight chance of their
being intercepted, and would not have been taking such risks.
But they did not share his knowledge. To them, the broadcast
of their description by a trooper only fifteen miles away meant
that they were in imminent danger of capture. Their only safety
lay in flight—high-speed flight! They had both lived in danger,
complete with various risks, before. It was not a strange sensation
to either of them.

As the car hit its maximum speed, the roar of gravel stopped.
Conversation and the radio became audible, although there was
still a whistling wind-noise.

Like a jet leaving behind its own sound because of its speed,
the car moved out of the path of the spray of gravel it threw up
before the rocks could hit it.

The men sat tensely. Rayder was perched on the edge of the
seat, perhaps more nervous than his partner, because he had
nothing to do. Grozzo sat awkwardly stiff, with his back braced

against the seat, but with a feather-light touch on the wheel. There was no need for him to grip it tightly; a one-finger nudge could send them to death.

An odd, rhythmic sequence of tension began. They were covering a mile every twenty-five seconds. And at the end of every mile they traveled, there was an intersection—the inevitable intersection—almost always blind, with corn growing solidly into the corners, completely obscuring the view.

They would pass an intersection and unconsciously exhale their relief. Within the space of three breaths, they were almost halfway to the next, and, as they whistled down to it, the tension would come upon them again. With tightening chests and shallower breath they approached. Then they would explode past, safe again but with another intersection approaching in the same inevitable swift sequence.

As they became accustomed to the rhythm, it seemed that the time of each cycle narrowed, the rushes through the suddenly empty crossings came more often, and their breathing became even faster and shallower.

Rayder suddenly became aware of perspiration running down his tensed neck muscles.

Then he noticed a strange, sleepy sensation. The tight, emotional rhythm of tension, ebbing and flowing, was beginning to hypnotize him. He turned around and forced his attention to the radio again, turning the volume up and straining to bring his mind back into focus on the steady chatter of transmissions. When he took his eyes off the road for a few seconds, the spell was broken. His mind came sharply back into focus. The radio gabble made sense again. His curious panic subsided.

He shot a worried glance at the driver, to see if he was having the same trouble. If so, he gave no sign. The dark eyes wandered ceaselessly with small, alert motions. Rayder followed his eyes down to the road again, then quickly away. They were almost to another road.

As they passed it there was a soft *thmmm* and a sharp, small pitch as the car hit a small bump, and rocked slowly and lazily for a few seconds, like a boat in a very gentle swell. Finally, it lost its mushy feeling and settled into solid contact again.

Without looking around, but with his face screwed sideways, and with a tickled-kid grin, Grozzo said, "Airborne."

He wasn't suffering.

CHAPTER TWENTY-NINE

THE transmissions tapered and stopped for a few minutes. The Sergeant took the opportunity to walk over to bring the map pins on the Superintendent's block up to date. Franklin himself was in the teletype room.

He put number Five a few miles west of Bucola, and number Twenty ten miles to the north of Five and also to the west.

After looking at the map for a minute, the Sergeant walked in and asked the other man to come back with him. Franklin typed MIN on the keyboard and complied.

"We still have six cars on the sweep," the Sergeant said, pointing. Franklin nodded. He was aware of this, but had delayed doing anything until at least establishing the machinery for setting up the Tollway blockade.

Now he sat down to review his immediate tactical situation. Ten cars had been dispatched on the sweep. Two down each of the five major roads out of town. Two had gone straight north and two northwest. That was all right; he could simply turn those four toward Chicago and use them there.

Two had been dispatched straight east. They had been told to discontinue the sweep and head for the area near Bucola where the helicopter sighting had taken place. That meant they had had to drive through the rainstorm. Since they had not reported in and were too far south now to use at Chicago, he dismissed them from his calculations.

Two cars, Five and Twenty, had gone straight south toward Bucola and were now headed west on the chase. Five was directly behind the robbers, and Twenty ten miles north of him.

That left two cars headed straight west on Route 10. He looked at their numbers on the map. Ten and Eight. He pondered a moment what to do with them. They were probably about thirty-five miles straight west by now. Should he pull them in towards Chicago?

Suddenly a thought occurred to him. Was he on the verge of applying too narrow a range of possibilities to the situation again? By concentrating exclusively on Chicago, he risked putting all his eggs in one basket.

If the shower lifted, he would have the use of the helicopter again! In that case he would need more than Cars Five and Twenty to deal with the fugitives. Even if the helicopter could find them, it couldn't stop them. And it was too risky having only those two cars available. He would have to use Eight and Ten as a contingency reserve, stop their westerly track and turn them south, so that they could be somewhere near the scene if the helicopter became useful again.

His mind went through a quick review as he turned to give the Sergeant instructions to turn Eight and Ten south, to fill them in on the situation, and to turn the four other cars now north toward Post Two outside Chicago.

Statistically speaking, he was desperately on the defensive. For all of their bustling activity, the odds were plainly against him and in favour of the men slipping through undetected.

"'Analysis is intrinsically negative,'" he quoted to himself. "'It must lead to positive action or it fails its function.'"

Were there any possible areas of positive functioning he had omitted? Hell, yes! Walking rapidly over to the Sergeant, he said, "Put out a blanket message to all Sheriff's offices and local police departments with radio equipment. Give them a rundown of what we have so far, and the car description."

CHAPTER THIRTY

THE green car rushed on, the tweed ribbon of gravel flashing beneath it in a constant blur. A cascade of rocks thrown up by the flying wheels rippled behind like a small wake in a calm sea.

Rayder, with his usual presence of mind, had managed to count the crossroads they had passed. Now, he reached over to the front and took a map from the glove compartment. It was almost a duplicate of the one that hung in the Post Seven office. Laying it out on the back seat, he began to pore over it, mentally plotting their position and simultaneously trying to keep his ear tuned to the radio. He had heard nothing since Car Five had been given the okay to go after them and number Twenty had been sent on its route paralleling Five.

At intervals of a few seconds, he popped his head up to make sure no road went by uncounted. By the time he had counted twenty-five, he was reasonably sure they were past the point, on their way north, where Car Twenty, going west, would have crossed their path. Since he had no reason to believe Five had turned north to follow them, he began to breathe a little more easily.

He was about to look up and suggest to his partner that it might be safe now to spill a little of their blistering speed, when he felt the sudden lurch of the car decelerating.

Grozzo was even more tensely alert, poised at the wheel, his right foot slowly coming up from the gas. In front of them a black speck on the horizon grew rapidly into focus as a wagon-load of hay being towed down the middle of the road, probably by a tractor. All that could be seen was the back end of the wagon.

On both sides, the road at this point sloped down to a ditch. There was no room to pass on either side.

The driver put his hand on the horn button and held it down. At the same time, as the indicator came down near one hundred, he began to work the brakes. Gently, almost with the tenderness of a caress, he pressed the pedal, and quickly let off as he felt the wheels begin to slide. He did it again, then again, and yet again, each time with more urgency, pressing, repeating the cycle, bringing them nearer and nearer to that fatal skid, as they bore down on the lumbering wagon at far too great a speed.

Time lost meaning. Things seemed to be happening in slow motion although only fractions of a second were passing.

At last the blasting horn began slowly to pry the great vehicle to one side. As if in slow motion, a back wheel of the tractor became visible ahead of the wagon as the driver turned toward the side of the road; the ponderous load began gradually to edge sideways.

But it was not going fast enough; they were now within a hundred yards, and still at seventy. There still wasn't room between the slowly opening side and the ditch.

Grozzo had gripped the wheel for a desperation heave to turn aside and try to override the ditch into the cornfield, when slightly ahead of the wagon, and on the opening side, he saw a patch of white leading from the road to the field. He instantly perceived it to be one of the little built-up areas which bridged ditches so that farmers could get their machinery into the fields. But, as he looked, it became apparent that the little culvert was nearly a foot high.

His hesitation made the choice for him. By the time he was through analysing, it was too late to turn, too late even to yell to the other man to hold on. Just time to grip the wheel and point it at the small rise.

As the wagon came abreast of the hill, they slammed into the side of the little culvert, still at sixty, missing the wagon by inches.

The front wheels, then the back, in rapid succession hit the one-foot lift. Even though the lift was graded, their speed made it feel like hitting a railroad tie.

The car sailed into the air and as it came back down, it was askew, the two wheels on the right side hitting first. This caused the car to slew to the right. It bounced again as it did so, depriving the driver of the ability to steer. As it came down again, it was in a full right broadside skid out of control. Then the back came around and it traded end for end.

As it spun past the still-moving tractor, the front bumper hit the tractor's front wheel. It was just a passing swipe, but it had results: it stopped the car's end-for-end slide, and left it, with its momentum finally running out, going straight backwards.

Also as a result of the hit, the tractor's front wheel was slapped sideways. The machine's forward motion tipped it over on its side. The cumbersome hay wagon rumbled straight into it, was in turn deflected sideways and tipped, dumping its load of hay squarely on the unsuspecting farmer who was just trying to scramble to his feet.

The car continued its backward slide through the gravel for perhaps a hundred and fifty feet, and came peacefully to rest in the middle of the road.

For a minute, nothing was visible in the dust cloud raised by all this, and the only sound in the sudden stillness was the radio, incongruously droning out police calls through the swirling dust.

Grozzo, still frozen to the steering wheel, let out a long breath. "Sonofabitch!" was all he could muster. Rayder, caught unprepared, had had a rough time of it. He was on the floor with the radio atop him. His eyes, for a second, blazed the kind of heat seen in an animal's eyes when it is attacked. Then, as realization flooded his face, they resumed their normal look. His face, however, remained white and tense.

Pushing the radio aside, he struggled up and climbed out over it. He walked to the driver's window and looked hard at Grozzo, who was staring ahead and still clutching the wheel. He reached in and gripped the other man's sleeve, giving him a shake.

"Snap out of it," he barked. "Try the motor and see if it'll run."
The dark man's eyes came alive.

Not waiting, Rayder took a quick turn around the car. As he did so, and unnoticed by him as the dust cloud drifted off, one end of the large pile of hay down the road began to shift and heave. Presently a mound appeared. It opened, and there emerged a purple face, covered with chaff and ringed with hay. This was followed by a muscular neck and torso, and finally the whole man. The enraged farmer glared around, then saw the green car and the figure going around it. Glancing wildly about for a weapon of some kind, he saw the pitchfork which had been atop the load, lying now in the middle of the road.

With an inarticulate roar that brought Rayder's head snapping up, the farmer pounced on the weapon. Scooping it up on the run, he came charging head down, roaring at the car like a maddened bull.

Mouth agape, Rayder opened a back door and dove into the car. "Move," he yelled.

Grozzo ground the starter frantically. Just as the man was bounding the last few feet to the car, the engine caught. Instantly, the shaken driver floored the gas and let out on the clutch. The car roared backwards down the road. For a time, it seemed that the farmer, like a jousting knight chasing a fleeing green dragon, would catch and spit the wildly backing, swaying automobile.

Finally, Grozzo brought it under control and was able to get it backing in a straight line without whipping from side to side. Then he was able to add speed, and the race was over.

In a last futile attempt at revenge, the thick-muscled farmer, from a dead run, gave his pitchfork a mighty heave. It hummed quivering through the air, then fell, its energy spent, harmlessly scraping the rocks in a place left vacant by the accelerating car.

The farmer, his rage subsiding, turned aside across the field toward the nearest phone.

The green car, far down the road, came to a cautious stop, made a quick turn and headed rapidly north again.

CHAPTER THIRTY-ONE

As if to prove that he wasn't shaken by their experience, Grozzo defiantly ran the car back up to top speed.

Rayder, basically more sure of himself and feeling no need to prove or demonstrate his courage, let his stocky friend run on for a couple of miles, then quietly suggested they slow down "to save the tires."

This face-saving device served its purpose. Grozzo backed off the throttle, and the car slowed to ninety.

Their speed was deceptive. Ninety was a very high speed for the road, but after the extreme speeds at which they had been going, it felt as if they had slowed almost to a crawl.

Now a peculiar mental state began to develop. Somehow it seemed to them that after coming through their narrow escape they had in some way "had their share" and that nothing more would happen to them. They felt that they had had their moment of danger and survived it; they were immune. It was irrational, but they both sensed it, and it was fully shared, although neither spoke of it.

Rayder, his hard eyes relaxed somewhat by this confidence, turned to the radio, which a few minutes before he had pushed away. Although it had come through the skid unharmed, he had, in throwing it off, pushed something that had made it stop playing.

He tugged it back onto the seat and began adjusting its knobs. In a few seconds, it came back on, clear and strong. He got it on just in time to hear the Post Seven dispatcher tell cars Ten and Eight, the two which had been going straight west of the city on Route 10, to turn south. Nothing in the dispatch or the conversation which followed gave him an inkling as to how far west of Post Seven the two cars were.

He did some rapid thinking.

They had gone straight west of Bucola for fifteen miles and turned north. At this time—he had managed to keep his count of intersections—they should be about twenty-six miles north of where they had turned. This would put them, then, about fifteen miles west of where they had pulled the caper, and four miles to the south. He absently watched the road ahead as he made his calculations.

They would, therefore, be four miles south of East-West Highway 10, the one cars Ten and Eight were on, and from which the dispatcher had turned them south.

As far as he knew, Car Five, the one which had picked up their trail at Bucola, and Car Twenty, which had been dispatched west, paralleling Car Five, had both been left behind.

He pursed his lips in a concentrated mental effort, and then started upright. Out of what looked like a solid wall of corn, about two hundred yards ahead of them, on the right, popped a small, bright-red farm pickup truck. He could see plainly as the driver, just a boy, turned to his right, away from them, and playfully gunned the engine, sending the truck around in a small skid, and raising a cloud of dust which promptly enveloped it and closed it off from view.

Grozzo, the instant he had seen it, had stomped the brake pedal. Wheels locked, the car slid on almost without slowing, the tires boiling and plowing a path futilely through the loose gravel. Almost as a reflex, he had hit the horn, as well as the brakes.

With nothing to turn it, this time the car tracked true. In a storm of flying rocks and with the horn blowing full blast, it slid straight as an arrow into the yellow dust cloud raised by the little truck.

Into it—and out again—the car skimmed past by inches. The driver of the pickup only then became aware of his peril—as the green car scrubbed wailing past him and on down the road, nose down and tail high, throwing a hail of pebbles against the little machine.

The boy's jaw dropped open and his eyes bugged wide as he realized how closely death had brushed him. He turned the little truck into the ditch and sat, shivering, white-faced and scared.

It was now apparent that if they continued down these blind roads at high speeds, they were sooner or later going to be wrecked.

Grozzo, who was at bottom weak, tried to conceal his weakness with bluster and defiance. As soon as they were clear again, with a snarl he slapped the car into second, then third, rapidly running it back up to a hundred.

Rayder, who had been born with a touch of ice in his soul, had never in his life given way to panic. Even at times when sweat involuntarily stood out on his forehead, he managed to grip some corner of an inner reserve. At this moment, he was not even badly threatened, but was concerned about Grozzo. He waited a few seconds, watching from the corner of his eye to see if this was just a sudden surge of nerves which would pass.

It wasn't.

As he watched, the driver's brown eyes danced around the road ahead. Two big muscles in his neck stood out, one against each side of his shirt. His chest heaved with quick short breaths.

When the needle on the dial had climbed to 12, Rayder said evenly, "Pull it down a little, Groz."

The other reacted as if his courage, or even his very manhood, had been questioned. He turned hot eyes on his accuser.

"Whattya mean, pull it down. I ain't bugged by that little slide." He was defiant. "I ain't slowin' down."

Until this moment, Rayder had been the unquestioned leader of their expedition. The stocky, bushy-haired man had followed his quiet leadership without hesitation. He had never until now asserted himself, or shown defiance. Something kindled deep in Rayder's eyes at this challenge. He hissed, "Cool it! Now!"

Grozzo wilted. The threat suddenly confronting him now became bigger than the one which had shaken him in the first place.

His muscles relaxed. The tenseness went out of his neck. Cowed, but clear-headed again, he turned his attention to the business of getting the car back down from speed.

The thin man turned to the radio.

"Whattya think?" came the voice of the man in front.

"What?" He looked up.

"I mean, how fast?"

"Oh, sixty ought to do it."

He turned back to the set. The dark-haired man nodded as he gently braked down.

CHAPTER THIRTY-TWO

THE teletype in front of Superintendent Franklin was going *clackety-clack-clack-clack*, jumping in its mounts like an awkward, loose-jointed typewriter. He stood watching it, puffing hard on his pipe—too hard. He was sending small, fiery coals hopping up out of the bowl with each back-puff.

As he was not paying attention to the pipe, he was reacting to the information coming in: not enough cars. The two northern-most posts could only scrape up thirty-four cars. He needed forty-one. Seven short!

Still, he reflected, even if that were all they managed to get, they could be put at the most likely intersections leading through the barrier of the Tollway, leaving open the roads that were least heavily traveled or had poor connections with roads downstate.

However, he didn't like it. He'd rather post cars at all forty-one places. For a fleeting moment, he debated calling police from the Chicago metropolitan area in on the blockade. However, he realized immediately there was no hope of getting effective co-operation for his plan of sealing off the Tollway in the scant time that was left. It would take two days to go through the chain of personalities that would be involved in something like this.

The whole state had received the broadcasts they'd put out. He had to let it go at that.

As a hedge, in case they were not able to get together enough cars to patrol all intersections on the Tollway, they would need to know which ones to omit. He picked up a phone and put in a call downstate to the statistics branch for information.

He spoke directly to the point.

"We plan to put in a blockade covering all possible intersections on the Tri-State Tollway between Roosevelt Road and the Indiana line. We may not have enough cars to cover it. In case we have to set up priorities and leave some of them unmanned, I'd like to have the traffic count for each of them. As quickly as you can, please."

The Sergeant stuck his head in the door again, saying, "Sir, a farmer just called in. A green car answering the fugitives' descriptions just wrecked a farm tractor and wagon, about fifteen miles west and twenty miles north of Bucola, on a country road. The car kept going."

Franklin walked quickly out to the radio room and said, "Turn Eight and Ten back east." Then, realizing that for the moment matters were out of his hands, he sat down to listen tensely.

CHAPTER THIRTY-THREE

UNKNOWN to Rayder, Post Seven had put out its release of the farmer's report shortly after the near-wreck with the pickup truck —one of the intervals when Rayder had not been listening to the radio. Now, a few minutes after they had slowed down, he was suddenly startled to hear a message coming in loud and clear, from a transmitter obviously no more than a few miles away.

"Post Seven, this is Car Twenty."

"Come in."

"I just passed the dumped hay wagon and tractor, and am proceeding north on the same road."

Rayder stared in disbelief. That man couldn't be more than six or seven miles behind, and on the same road! He had a sudden vision of being trapped. They were now only about four miles south of Route 10 and remained fifteen miles west of Post Seven. There were two cars just recently turned south from 10, but he didn't know whether they were between him and the city or out beyond.

He couldn't run toward the city. He was afraid to run up against Route 10. It was heavily traveled, and they probably would have to stop to cross it. Maybe even get tied up. The only thing he could see to do was run—west.

Just in time he yelled, "Turn left."

The other man, whose eyes were beginning to look frightened again, braked heavily, then swung the car neatly to the left at the intersection that had come up.

"Sonofabitch," he said softly.

"Run, goddamit," said Rayder, "but keep your marbles this time."

The driver punched the throttle—just a little too hard. Under the force of the engine, the back wheels broke traction and began to spin. He let off on the gas till it settled down. Then he ran it up to one hundred, the needle on 10.

This was risky as hell, Rayder reflected, and also he didn't like running back up to speed when he'd just had a run-in with Grozzo over going fast, but he had had a sudden feeling of coming close to being trapped, and he wanted no part of that.

Besides, they were going only a hundred right now. That was a lot different than one-forty. They had been going almost this fast when they skidded by the pickup, and had not gone out of control.

However, despite his efforts to reassure himself, he knew they were taking a hell of a chance again. He looked at the dark man. That one was the bright, alert, confident driver again, now that the last crisis was past.

"Goddam him," Rayder thought. "Goes up and down like a kite. You can't tell how he's going to act."

The radio squawked into life.

"Post Seven, and Car Twenty."

"This is Twenty, come in."

There was a pause. The Post did not reply. The original voice went on: "This is Ten. Bill, about where are you now?"

The voice of the man identifying as Car Twenty said, "About six miles south of Route Ten."

The other voice said, "Hank and I were on sweep about thirty miles west of the city on Route 10, when the Post dispatched us south. When your message about the wreck came over, the Post turned us east. We're running parallel to Ten. I'm four miles south of it, and Hank's two miles further south and a couple of miles behind. About twenty miles west, I'd say."

"Yeah, so?"

"They oughta be close in here somewhere. Why don't you slow down? We're headed right toward you now. We'll try to flush them out, like quail, with you at the end."

"Yeah, sounds good. Shall we check the Post?"

"No time."

"Okay, come on through."

"Okay, I'm gonna open up." His engine noise increased. "Hank?"

"Yeah, I gotcha. Me, too."

Rayder felt a clammy feeling on his forehead. He leaned over the front seat.

"Open it up. All the way!" he said. His nostrils were pinched. "I'd rather die than go back in that crummy tank. Keep it open."

Again the car surged up to its dizzying top speed. The sensation was like flying at a very low altitude.

The car ran evenly. There were no tremors. The engine was smooth. Apparently, it had suffered no ill effects from its spin and brush with the tractor.

A dust cloud appeared down the road, and then grew. It mushroomed as the distance between the cars telescoped like a TV zoom shot. The cars closed at a combined speed of over two hundred sixty.

For a split fraction, as they rocketed past, there was the clear image of a trooper driving, sun goggles on, Sam Browne belt flashing in the sun. The radio exploded with the excited trooper's voice: *"They just passed me; they passed me,"* he shrilled. "Cut 'em off, Hank, cut 'em off."

"Okay, I'm turning north," came the tight-voiced reply.

"Hurry. Try to stay with 'em. I'll try to catch up. I'm turning around, they're going like hell," the voice stumbled rapidly.

An instant later, the reply came in: "I turned, I'm running."

The voice coming in was beginning to sound strained as excitement mounted:

". . . north. I can see dust raising from a car going west—awful fast—must be them. They're gonna beat me to the intersection." After a short pause, he said, "I've turned west after them. They beat me to the intersection."

The other trooper's voice cut in: "I've turned around, Hank. I can't see any dust ahead. You must be three or four miles in front of me. Can you see my dust in your mirror?"

"Goin' too fast. Can't see in mirror, I'm flat out. Gonna try to catch 'em. They're about a mile ahead."

A different voice came in. "This is Post Seven. We are monitoring you. Cars Five and Twenty, if you are reading these transmissions turn west and give any help you can."

Without waiting for acknowledgment, the dispatcher's voice went on: "Car Eight, how are you doing?"

"Okay, I guess. I'm still flat out. That's an awful fast car they got. I don't know if I'm gaining or not."

"Okay, close them if you can, but don't try to overhaul them. Try to plink their tires, and don't take any unnecessary risks. They may be armed."

"Okay."

"This is Car Five. Roger on that last transmission, I have turned west."

"Car Twenty, me, too."

"Hank, I've had it floored all this time, but I still can't see anything. You think maybe they could have switched roads after they passed me?"

"No, because I was two miles south of you and I came back up two miles to where I am now. You just can't catch up, 'cause we're going as fast as you are."

"How *fast* are you going? I'm hitting one thirty-five. I still think I ought to be catching up."

"Well, it's getting a little rough. I'm floatin' off these bumps half the time now. The needle bounces around; about the same as I was, I guess, about one thirty-five. This guy's got the fastest car I ever chased."

The Post voice came back on: "If it gets too rough, back off on it. Don't kill yourself."

The reply was an inaudible mumble that might have been: "If he can do it, I can, too."

After the warning from the Post, the trooper in Car Eight stopped transmitting. He was young, and he had been challenged. No one had ever outrun him yet. He had one of the newest cruisers, supposed to be capable of matching, if not topping, any production car in the country. To him, this chase was now a matter of professional pride. He couldn't let the other driver simply walk away from him on a clear road. If he did, he figured, he might as well turn in his shield and go drive a truck.

He knew the dispatcher was probably aware of all this, but he also knew that if the chase got much more hairy—at least, if he told them about it—the dispatcher would do his duty and tell him to back off. And if he did, that would be the end of it. In that case, he would have a face-saving excuse. But he didn't want to be saddled with a failure, excuse or no. He wanted to catch them.

Carefully letting go with his right hand, but without for a second taking his eyes from the road, he dropped his arm, undid the clasp of his holster, and transferred his service revolver to the left side, where he stuck it into his tunic belt, reversing it so that he could grasp it readily with his left hand when the time came.

CHAPTER THIRTY-FOUR

IN the radio room, the men sat like statues, hardly breathing. Franklin said nothing, letting the Sergeant continue to handle the dispatch.

The trooper had stopped transmitting messages as he concentrated on his driving, but he had left his transmitting equipment on.

Not wanting to interfere with his man, the Sergeant did not say anything for a few minutes. Finally, deciding it was time for a check, he thumbed the mike switch and said, "Car Eight."

The sensitive receiver in the Post picked up, not only the return transmission, but the sound of the car's engine, laboring at extreme speed.

"This is Car Eight." The excitement was still in his voice. "I'm still on 'em. I think I'm gainin' on 'em."

There was a sudden rise and fall in the motor's crescendo. Then it settled down again to the steady, high-pitched roar.

"What was that?" asked the Sergeant.

There was a pause, then the somewhat reluctant reply: "Well, it's gettin' just a little bit rough. The back wheels get bounced up every once in a while, and the motor revs up." He said it half-apologetically, then rushed on. "But the bumps are slowin' them down. I can see it. I'm cuttin' down on them."

The Sergeant knew that his man was taking an awful chance, pursuing at that speed on any kind of surface, let alone on a gravel road, but he could sympathize with the boy. It was hard to give up in a chase. If he were forced out of it now, the young man would sulk for months. Moreover, there was the morale of the other men to consider.

Reluctantly, the Sergeant bit his lip and said into the mike: "Okay, stick with it. Anybody else in sight?"

"No, but I can't see much out of the rear view."

"Car Ten, can you see anything of him?"

The other voice came on quickly.

"Still no sign. I've got her wound clear up."

"All right, keep at it. You can't be very far behind. Car Twenty, where are you?"

"Heading west, too."

"Are you on the same road they are?"

"I'm not sure. I'm three or four miles south of Route Ten."

"Car Ten, what do you think?" the dispatcher asked.

"I don't think so. We're four miles down from Route Ten, I don't think Twenty got up this far."

"Okay, Car Twenty, you're probably on the wrong road. Cut up to Route Ten and head west. You might be able to head 'em off."

"Yes, sir. On the way."

As he listened to the chase, and the desperate effort of the young man in Car Eight to catch the fugitives, the Superintendent felt a pang of dismay at not being able to help. Worse, he had qualms of guilt over the way he had directed the chase.

Perhaps he had guessed wrong on the best way to use his forces. The thing had happened which he had predicted would not happen. The car had been located on an open hunt, and was being chased, within a few miles of the city where the robbery had taken place. Of course, it was luck that the trail had been picked up.

The fugitives had almost wrecked their own car. But there was always the element of luck to be reckoned on.

He started back to the teletype room to call off the blockade, but as he sat down and got set to type, he had a second thought. Maybe he had better wait.

They were not caught yet. If he stopped the machinery of setting up a blockade now, there would not be time to set it up again if the criminals gave the cars from Post Seven the slip. These men were tricky. They had already eluded a helicopter earlier today.

He typed only "WAIT MIN," and again walked back to the radio room to follow the chase.

He stood behind the Sergeant and listened to him query Car Eight, which appeared to be gaining slowly. Then he scribbled on a piece of paper and pushed it in front of the Sergeant, who glanced down at it, nodded and then dispatched Car Twenty up to Route 10 to try to outflank the fleeing men.

Franklin, fighting down his urge to stay and listen, walked quickly over to his map, studied it intently for a minute, then went into the teletype room. Interrupting a message, he belled Peoria's signal, then typed: "PRIORITY PEORIA DISPATCHER THIS SUPER."

"PEORIA GA," the machine chattered.

He typed, "ARE U MONITORING CHAS POST 7 CARS?"

"YES" appeared on the sheet.

"HAV ALL UNITS BEEN DISPATCHED NORTH TO TOLLWAY BOCKADE"

"ALL BUT 2" was the reply.

"CHANGE DISPATCH FOR THESE 2. START THEM DOWN ROUTE 121 TOWARD LINCOLN NOW FOR INTERCEPT TRY. BE SURE U GIVE DISPATCH CONTROL OVER TO POST 7. HAVE CARS USE POST 7 COMM. FREQ SO CAN TALK TO CARS NOW IN CHAS. ANY QUEST," he typed.

"ROGER WILL DO NO QUEST," appeared on the paper before him.

He leaned back a minute in thought, resisting the impulse to make a quick dash to the radio room to see how it was going.

Leaning forward again, he belled the upstate Post to which he had given local dispatch control for establishing the blockade.

"POST 7 CARS HOT PURSUIT FELONS AM SUPER-MARKET ROBBERY. PROCEED WITH TOLLWAY

BLOCKADE AS PLANNED UNLESS THIS CHASE ENDS
WITH POSITV CAPTURE. ACK AND CONFIRM."

"CONFIRM TO PROCEED WITH TOLLWAY
BLOCKADE AS PLANNED UNLESS CHASE ENDS POSI-
TIVE CAPTURE," was the reply.

He rang off and went back out to the other room to plan how to
use the two units now moving down from Peoria toward Lincoln.

CHAPTER THIRTY-FIVE

RAYDER hunched in the rear of the plunging machine. His face
was not pleasant. It was contorted, animal-like. He alternated
between crouching, listening to the radio over the whistling rush
of air, and peering back at the rocketing cruiser as it gradually
closed in on them.

He had made a couple of mistakes, and he was a man who
neither liked to make mistakes nor liked to admit them. And there
was no one he could blame for his errors. There was no alibi. The
whole caper had been his from start to finish. The driver, who was
tensed in front, fighting his duel with their pursuer, was little
more than a chauffeur. Rayder was the brains.

Not that he would have alibied anyway. Making excuses was
not one of his weaknesses. Basically, he was too proud, too strong,
to make even that slight gesture toward weakness which looking
for an excuse implied.

His first mistake had been in accepting Grozzo's assurance that
this machine would outclass the police cruisers. When the chunky
driver had told him this car was uncatchable, he had simply
accepted it uncritically as the statement of an expert. He should
have checked.

He glanced up again. The police car was drawing noticeably
closer. It was no more than a quarter-mile behind now, pitching
as they were from the slight changes in grade, and sometimes
taking small, sharp upleaps on small bumps.

His second mistake had been not to bring a gun. Rayder had a
horror of dying. He was young, and he felt that he had a lot of
living to do, especially since he had lost so much time in prison.
He had felt that if they brought guns, there was always a good
chance of something going wrong and somebody getting shot. He
knew that if anyone was shot during the commission of a felony,

even accidentally, even if killed by police fire, the *felons* were automatically guilty of murder.

He could think of no worse death than electrocution. The feeling that had pervaded the Big House when there was an electrocution was impossible to describe. Toughened as he was, the memory still made his stomach knot. Better—he had thought at the time—better a thousand times to be captured than to be electrocuted.

But that was then, and this was now, and he was alive and free, and he wanted to keep his freedom. He realized that, more than anything else, he simply wanted to stay free. He would risk death for it now, if he had the chance.

Slowly the young trooper edged up.

The large windshield of the pursuing car gave almost a complete view of the interior. The trooper had whipped off his hat, but left his sun goggles on. Now, switching hands so as to leave his right hand on the wheel, he dropped the left into his lap. It came up with his service revolver.

Working slowly, as if he had all the time in the world, he deliberately put the gun out the window—only to have it sent flying viciously back, straight up in the air. It looked as though it bucked once, shooting harmlessly into the air as he fought to control it in the slipstream. He had completely misjudged the rushing force of the wind; at this speed it was sufficient to support heavy jet aircraft.

He worked the weapon back inside, then dropped everything while he damped down the slow, sidewise oscillation he had set up in his car by his actions. Rayder watched the man going through this deliberate ritual, bringing the car back under full control.

Without any conscious effort on his part, Rayder suddenly relaxed. The tension and hatred drained from him. He felt somehow detached. This had happened to him before in tight places. At a point where other men lost their nerve, got hysterical or went to pieces, he suddenly became cold and objective. He was aware of this trait in himself and he valued it. He was aware that he had no control over it. It was just something that happened to him.

With this rush of cool reason to his hot brain, there came the realization that the trooper could not hurt them. At least, not with the gun. It might as well be a BB pistol.

He would be shooting with his left hand while driving with his right, from a jolting auto going over one hundred thirty miles an hour, at another pitching machine going the same speed. These things made his shot difficult, but what made it impossible, Rayder knew, was the wind. It was far too strong for him to be able to hold a gun steady.

He watched coolly as the gun inched out again. Sure enough, as soon as it was extended sufficiently out the window to hit the main blast of air, it began to wobble and shake, as if it were held by an old man with palsied hands. In a few seconds it discharged. He neither saw a flash nor heard a report, but the weapon and the hand holding it leaped back and were caught fully by the wind, whipping back with a vicious snap into the doorpost.

Two down and four to go.

Rayder began to try to think of a way to get this guy off their backs. True, he could not shoot them, and at this speed he would hardly be silly enough to try to wreck them, but as long as he sat there on their tails with his radio going, it would not be too long till a roadblock would be set up ahead.

He wanted to wait until the man was out of ammunition. He was pretty sure Grozzo didn't know they were being shot at. Of course, he could see in the mirror that the cruiser was fairly close, but all he would be likely to see at this speed would be a dancing, blurred image of a car, not the driver, or the gun. And he couldn't take his eyes off the road and look around.

Rayder was afraid of the volatile Latin's reaction if he found out the cop was shooting. He plotted for a minute. To shake the cop, they would almost certainly have to slow down and maneuver, and maybe throw stuff out. But they would almost surely have to slow down just to pitch something out the window. If they slowed while the cop had shells left, he might just get one into them. They would have to keep going like this till he used up the other four shots.

Again the gun came out the window. Apparently, the trooper had not hurt his hand. This time as he pulled the trigger, he seemed to pull the pistol down, too, and it was again caught by the full force of the air blast and whipped back.

Rayder was almost sure that the man did not actually get the shot squeezed off until the gun was pointed almost straight down. He got a distinct impression of a splatter in the road near the front of the pursuing car.

"He's liable to shoot out his own tire," he muttered, with a sudden surge of elation.

It had become apparent to the trooper by this time that he did not have much chance of using the gun effectively. Each time, as he shot and his left arm was flung back, his whole body was jostled so that his right hand, tightly gripping the wheel, caused it to jerk. Even though he tried to avoid this, he could not do so entirely, and every time it happened, his car started to sway. Slightly, it was true, but at top speed a slight sway could build rapidly, so that it would be necessary each time for him to stop and concentrate on damping out the dangerous rocking.

Once more the gun appeared. The hand was weaker this time. The gun wobbled more. The slaps against the window frame were taking their toll. This time he did not try as hard to aim. Again the hand slapped back.

"That should make five," Rayder thought. "One more, you bastard."

Again the dogged trooper tamed the swaying machine. Then, instead of trying to aim deliberately and squeeze off the round, he tried a snapshot.

Probably by nothing more than blind luck, he got a hit with his last bullet. Almost before Rayder was aware he was taking another shot, the hand had flashed out. A small neat hole, starred with cracks, opened up in the side of the rear window opposite the watcher. The bullet, deflected upward, buried itself harmlessly in the headliner.

For a second the policeman seemed to be waiting expectantly. Then realizing his defeat, he dropped the gun and whipped off his sunglasses. He stared his impotent fury at the figure looking coldly back at him, now harmlessly out of his reach.

Grozzo was trying to look over his shoulder. His eyes were wide. "Is he shootin' at us?" he asked.

"No, he's not, not now," replied the hawk-nosed man harshly. "You know any tricks to throw him off? He's gonna sit back there and sing like a canary over that radio. We gotta get rid of him."

"Yeah, okay," replied the other, nodding his head emphatically. "I been waitin' for you to gimme the word. Better hold on."

He was confident. This was his specialty. Also, he felt put on the spot. He had claimed to have the fastest car, and it had been caught. He *had* to shake the cop.

Without visibly changing his position in the seat, he simultaneously made two moves. He pushed in the clutch and with his left hand gave one swift tug on the hand brake, then released it. He did not pull it hard enough to break the rear wheels loose. He wanted to kill some of their speed quickly, but not too much, and he wanted to do it without telegraphing this to the other driver.

The hand brake did not connect to the stop lights, as did the foot brakes, so there was no warning flash. By disengaging the clutch, he eliminated the telltale puff of exhaust smoke which would tell an experienced driver that the car ahead had changed engine speeds.

It almost worked.

Without warning, the startled trooper found the green car suddenly in his lap. Reflexively, he hit the brakes.

Grozzo had made his moves in the hope that his pursuer would be taken by surprise and would reflexively slam on his brakes. If he locked all four wheels, at this speed, even for an instant, there was a good chance he would go into an uncontrollable slide.

But the trooper was a good driver, too. Even as his foot hit the pedal, he realized what was going on. He rode the brakes, just a touch; just enough to dump sufficient speed to keep from hitting the other machine. Then, smarting, and wanting to show that he could play, too, he let his car glide up to the other, closer and closer until they almost touched.

Down between the endless banks of shimmering green corn they flew—bumpers less than six inches apart—the trooper looking quietly into Rayder's cold, hard eyes. There was no more than eight feet between them. Each would have shot the other without hesitation if given the chance. But for all the damage they could do to each other, they might as well have been on separate planets.

Cooling off a bit, the officer slowed and let his car fall back a couple of hundred yards. Readjusting his sunglasses, he settled back in his seat like a man getting ready for a long ride. Then he reached over for his radio mike.

His voice came in very loud in the fleeing car, over the road noise, so that both driver and passenger could hear it.

"Post Seven, this is Car Eight."

The reply was immediate, but sounded weaker than before. They had traveled some distance.

"Car Eight, this is Post Seven, we were getting worried. How are you doing?"

"Still on their tail. I put a bullet hole in the back window, but no damage I can see. Out of shells now. Can't reload, with one hand."

"Okay, any sign of Car Ten?"

Another voice broke in. "This is Car Ten. I can't see a thing. Any idea where you are, Hank?"

The voice was petulant; the reply was irritating.

"I'm right here, baby, waiting for you to catch up. Better crank it up."

The dispatcher's voice said, "Knock it off. Car Twenty, come in."

"This is Car Twenty. I'm heading east on Route Ten."

"Are you making good time?"

"Well, I am when the road's clear, but I'm running into traffic, off and on."

"Okay, stay with it. Now listen. Peoria has two units moving down Route One Twenty-one to intersect Route Sixty-six at Lincoln. There's a loop in Sixty-six south of Lincoln. The road these men are on runs up to but does not cross Sixty-six at the loop. It was cut off when the loop was put in. It is a dead-end road for the last mile. We'll try to run them into it. The cars from Peoria should be there by that time. Any questions?" There were none, and he said, "Okay. Acknowledge."

"Twenty, okay."

"Ten, okay."

"Eight, okay."

"Car Eight."

"Yes, sir."

"Crowd 'em. Keep it up tight enough so they don't get a chance to turn. Have they fired at you?"

"Not that I can tell."

"That's good, but don't press too close. They might just be waiting for you to get close enough for a good shot."

There was a short pause before the reply came. The voice sounded a little different. "Yes, sir."

It was all audible in the arrowing green car, just as it was to those in conversation.

"Sonofabitch!" Grozzo's lip curled. He half-turned. "How far back is he?"

"Two, maybe three hundred yards."

The cars' relative positions had not changed.

"We gotta get out of this box. Right?"

"What do you have in mind?"

"We're gonna have to take a chance."

Rayder became faintly annoyed. "Okay, get on with it," he snapped. He did not like the implied question about his courage. "Hold on."

Grozzo lifted his hands free of the wheel, pushed in the clutch, and braked hard. All four wheels froze and slid. He kept his hands off the steering wheel, letting the car track itself. If it were perfectly balanced, he thought, it might just track straight; if not—well, that was just the chance they had to take.

It went straight as an arrow, locked wheels scrubbing, thumping and pounding over the slight corrugations in the road.

This time the driver following had no chance to slow with fancy footwork. He had to lock his wheels, too.

But this action on his part alone could not prevent a collision. It took him a second, during which his machine traveled a full two hundred feet, just to apply the brakes. Two hundred feet was about a third of the distance separating the cars.

Even after his brakes were on full, the gap continued to narrow. Since the lead car had braked first, it was decelerating at a faster rate, and would continue to do so as long as the brakes were left on, until the second caught and hit it.

As his machine slid helplessly toward the other sliding car, the trooper braced, and cursed himself for a fool for not allowing more gap, and for setting himself up so that the other man could deliberately wreck him. But Grozzo had no intention of risking a rear-end collision. He watched the dancing image—they were still going over ninety—in the mirror until it was almost on them, then, still holding in the clutch and brake, he twisted his right foot and floored the throttle.

The rugged engine, now without load, over-revved, shrieking and bucking in its mounts. When it peaked, he slid his foot off the clutch so that it popped out, simultaneously taking his foot off the brakes.

With a whipping jerk, under the blast of power he had poured into them, the back wheels broke traction and spun madly, their high-speed rubbery scream suddenly filling the car.

A geyser of rocks fountained from the rear wheels out and back, straight at the face of the surprised policeman. While the forward surge carried the leading car away from the danger of collision, the cruiser's windshield disintegrated under a storm of flying stones striking with an impact equal to a dozen shotgun blasts.

Rayder, braced in the back seat, spun around to look as the officer threw up his hands in a last reflexive attempt to save his eyes.

Momentarily, the police cruiser continued in a straight line, then it began to veer slightly to the left. There was no corrective movement of the wheel, and the veer increased.

At this part of the road, there was no ditch, the bordering field being on a level with the running surface. The cruiser continued turning until, still at high speed, it was next to the cornfield. Abruptly it simply disappeared, swallowed up in the corn field like a pebble dropped into water.

There was no hint as to what happened after it left the road. The radio was silent.

Rayder leaned back in his seat and took a couple of deep breaths. Then he leaned forward and said, "Good going, Groz." He was impressed with the driver's skill.

The other had regained some of his self-confidence.

"The sonofabitch," he said.

The dispatcher's voice came back on. "Car Eight, what was all that racket?" When there was no response, the voice took on a more urgent tone. "Car Eight." Then it said, "Car Ten, can you read me?"

"Loud and clear."

"Any sign of Eight?"

"No."

"Keep your eyes peeled," it said, then went on in a not very convincing tone. "Maybe his radio went out."

"Yeah," Rayder said, his lip curled.

He turned now from the radio. "There's still another one somewhere behind us on this road, and one up on Route Ten about four miles north of here, heading west," he said.

"Yeah? Well, you wanna go south a couple of miles and let 'em go by, then turn around and go north?"

"Balls on that. We're ahead of 'em, and we're goin' to stay ahead. Cool it at the next corner, and go on north now. If we get across Route Ten and they don't spot us, we can go north while that whole mess of bastards are chasing each other around Lincoln where they got that trap set."

A sudden flicker of caution made him ask, "What do you think of the one we just dumped? Any chance he got out of that field?"

"Hell, no! That sonofabitch got corn rammed clear out his ass. He ain't goin' nowhere till they go in and get him."

The car slowed and cornered, turning right at a fairly slow speed, but still sending up a spray of rocks. Rayder then maintained a close watch out the back, keeping his eye on the intersection until it was out of sight, watching that the other pursuing car didn't pass it and see them.

Presently a stop sign in the distance indicated that they were at Route Ten.

"Shall I stop?" the driver asked.

"Yes, that's a busy road. It won't prove anything getting killed," Rayder said.

With all the prudence of a Sunday driver, Grozzo eased up to the highway. It was a good thing they had stopped. The highway was alive with traffic, going both ways.

They sat a few minutes. No openings appeared in the steady line of cars. The dark man quickly got restless.

"That sonofabitchin' cop's gonna come here any minute." His voice sounded tense.

"You're right," the other replied, leaning over the back of the seat. "Can you turn right here into this traffic without getting in a wreck? If we do that, we can turn left up the road somewhere. We won't have to wait for a hole to cross both lanes at once."

"Okay."

Turning the wheel right, the driver pulled out into the line of traffic, accelerating violently. He was greeted by the screech of tortured rubber as the car behind braked desperately to avoid the smash.

Immediately they became a part of the traffic flow, one of the multitude of cars on the busy road. They cruised steadily, ignoring the fuming driver behind them.

Ahead, a flicker caught their eyes. It resolved itself into the blinking, red rotating light on a cruiser desperately snaking through traffic toward them but headed in the other direction. They watched tensely as it went past, without even a glance from the driver.

After that the traffic seemed to loosen up. They made their left turn without difficulty and found themselves again on a now-familiar smooth gravel road.

Again, with the immediate source of tension gone, Grozzo was relaxed and confident. He turned around.

"How we gonna take it, boss, hot or cool?"

"What's the best you can do and still stop if some yahoo comes out of a cornfield again?"

The other's face took on a sulky look. The lip curled. "Well, hell, uh, maybe only fifty or so on these loose rocks, you know," he finished weakly.

"Christ, they could catch us with dogs. We're just gonna have to take a chance on these farmers. Run it up to about ninety. I want out of here."

The other nodded and complied, again bending over the wheel and concentrating keenly on the road ahead, his whole attention absorbed in his driving, leaving it to the man in back to do whatever thinking and worrying had to be done.

CHAPTER THIRTY-SIX

Superintendent Franklin sat off to one side of the transmitter, quietly but intently listening to the flow of radio conversation. His face was a study in emotions.

His stomach would have made a more violent study. It churned and burned. He was frustrated and unhappy. Now there came a lull in the transmissions, and he slipped into thought.

For all his theorizing about the chances against intercepting the robbers in open country, the men from Post Seven had managed to do just that. They had not only found them in full flight, but had given chase, and as they raced westward in pursuit, it seemed there was a good chance they could run the quarry into a trap south of Lincoln. He was glad they almost had their men trapped. Catching them was their job—and his.

But he felt sorry that they were being trapped in a way he had thought could not happen, a way that made him and his ideas look slightly foolish.

"Maybe a really big man wouldn't react like this," he told himself. "Maybe I should be able to swallow my mistake and congratulate these men with a clear conscience and no regrets."

He knew he could not, not yet, anyway. It made him feel guilty toward his men and put him in conflict with himself. It was a sticky feeling. He wished something would break, something would happen to get him off this hook on which his conscience had put him.

Then the pursuing car fell silent. He sat forward, listening with a curious mixture of disappointment and fear, as the Sergeant tried desperately to contact the car, then the one following it, and the one going west on Route Ten, trying to get information.

There was fear in the dispatcher's voice, too.

"Car Ten," the Post repeated. The voice was tense.

"Yes, sir."

"Any sign of Eight?"

"No."

"Car Five, come in."

"Yes, sir."

"You haven't been transmitting. Where are you now?"

"I'm not just sure. You dispatched me west at the same time as Car Twenty, only he went on up to Route Ten. I'm still going west on the gravel road, but I'm not sure how far south I——"

"Post Seven, Post Seven, this is Car Ten," an excited voice broke in. "I just passed a bunch of glass, and a little farther on a hole in a cornfield. Looks like somebody went in."

Franklin was on his feet and taking the mike from the Sergeant. "Car Ten, continue as you are—straight west in pursuit. Car Five, find out where you are, then get on the road that runs four miles south of Route Ten. Find out what that hole is that Car Ten's talking about. Check it out and report. Any questions?"

"Well, uh, I don't know whether he's east or west of me now."

Franklin's voice took on the cold, oily edge of a man impatient with a stupid child.

"We'll just leave that up to you to find out."

There was no reply.

A few seconds later, Franklin said, calmly, "Car Ten."

"Yes, sir," was the instant reply.

"Keep going as you are until you run into a dead end at Route Sixty-six. We are going to assume that Car Eight is still on their tail, unless or until we hear otherwise. The cars from Peoria are still on the way down. The plan is just the same."

"Yes, sir."

With the lead car out of communication, no one knew at this point whether they actually had a chase going or not. It might be that Car Eight was still on the felons' tail, chasing them toward the cul-de-sac south of Lincoln, but, at any rate, the car's radio was broken. This had been his reasoning when he had directed Car Ten to proceed on west with the chase. It was only a few minutes behind Car Eight and the culprits, on the same road.

He hoped he had done the right thing. Just because Car Eight had stopped transmitting, he reasoned, he was not justified in jumping to conclusions. He had no actual knowledge that Eight was out of commission. It was best to proceed on the assumption he was still running.

On the other hand, there was at least a good chance—better than even, in the Super's opinion—that something had happened to Car Eight. Especially after that business of the glass in the road, and the swath cut in the cornfield. It didn't look good. He had a familiar sick feeling now in the pit of his stomach. He had had it during the war whenever one of the Hellcats under his direction had been splashed by Zeros.

The minutes dragged on as he waited for the report to come in from Car Five's investigation. He was afraid it might be a long wait. The man had not sounded very intelligent. He checked his watch. Twelve-eighteen.

He need not have worried.

After fourteen lead-dragging minutes, a sudden voice, high-pitched with excitement, filled the room.

"I found him, I found him. He went all the way across a cornfield. The windshield's out and the car's all jam-fulla corn stalks. I can hear him moanin' under there. Send an ambulance."

Immediately, the Superintendent replied, "Can you give us your position? Where are you?"

There was no reply. He had apparently gone back to aid the other man.

Franklin did not keep trying to contact him. The air was dead except for the background hum of the set. Franklin handed the mike back to the Sergeant and, hands in pockets, without saying anything to anyone, walked back to the teletype room.

Things were again as they had been before. There was no use now pretending these men were going to run into the trap south of Lincoln. They might by some blind piece of luck run into it, but he knew he could not count on luck of that sort.

No, they were out again—free—loose once more in the maze of secondary roads. Only now they would be more alert, harder to jump. They were like animals that had been flushed—wary and keen. It would be harder to get near to them a second time.

And he had lost a man!

He felt more strongly than ever that their only real chance now was to bag the pair at the Tollway. This interception down-state, with its tragic ending, had been only a statistical fluke. He had to count on staking everything at the blockade ring. He forced himself to think.

Was there anything he had overlooked? Any source, any avenue of aid or assistance? Chin in hand, he thought for a moment, then went to the phone and picked it up. After dialing, he said, "Operator, this is the Superintendent of State Police. I want a person-to-person call to the head of Air Traffic Control at Chicago Municipal Airport. Will you give this call priority, please!"

After less than a minute's pause, he said, "Hello, this is Franklin, head of State Police." He went on to explain in some detail the situation that they faced, and the fact that they hoped to use the Tollway as a blockade. "I called you," he finished, "to see whether it is possible that you might alert the pilots flying over that area in the next three or four hours to be on the watch for the car we are looking for."

"I, uh, well, that's a pretty unusual request, sir. I don't know," the man said. "I don't, uh, think I have enough authority to pass on it, actually. Let me call the FAA. I'll call you back."

"Okay, thanks," Franklin said, but his hopes sank. The request had started its upward bureaucratic spiral. He'd probably get a letter next week asking him to put it in writing.

He dismissed it from his mind and went back to the teletype.

CHAPTER THIRTY-SEVEN

THEY had been lucky. During the thirty-mile chase there had not been a sign of a car other than the one chasing them. Now they were out of the jaws of the trap, and headed north once more. Without the pressure and tension of pursuit, the old pattern of the intersections came to haunt them again.

It was worse for the man in the back seat. He had nothing to do. At least the driver was kept busy driving, and did not have as much opportunity to sit back and imagine things, like a tractor emerging in front of them at every crossroad. Perhaps it was just as well that their positions were not reversed, for the man in the back seat was stronger. He could take more.

Yet, for all his cold nerve and intelligence, Rayder was not psychic. He could not know that the man in charge of the police apparatus had—for the second time that day—decided that they could not be intercepted and chased down in open country and had elected to concentrate on trying to catch them at the approaches to Chicago.

Rayder's foresight in bringing along the short-wave receiver had not made him privy to the wired teletype messages being used to set up the defenses to the north. For all the men in the car knew, the whole State Police force was on its way to the area they were in now. In fact, the only solid information that they had pointed to just this possibility.

The dispatcher had mentioned cars coming down from Peoria to set a trap at Lincoln. Rayder felt that he and Grozzo had no choice but to continue their high-speed run. Their experience with the hay wagon showed a speed of a hundred thirty or forty would be suicide if anything showed up in their path. They had to go slower than that. He had told the driver ninety, because he figured they needed to go at least that fast to get out of the area. Also, despite the dark man's protests that he could not stop at anything less than fifty, Rayder knew that he had real ability at the wheel and was sure that, like most skilled people, Grozzo could do better than he thought.

Rayder sat, immobile, his arms on the back of the front seat, concentrating just as intently as the driver. The only break in the rhythm of their flight was the very occasional slowing down to cross the hump of a railroad track at grade.

They came to a small town, passed through it carefully at the legal limit, then, at the direction of the man in the rear, accelerated back to their regular speed.

"There's going to be more of these damn little towns as we get closer in," Rayder said, his mouth hard. He didn't like it. He didn't want to lose a second.

Another crossroad loomed as they bore down on it. At the last possible second, in what would have been a classic scene from an old movie, a self-propelled corn picker clanked across in front of them. They missed it by inches.

Rayder's face went chalk white, but he said nothing.

The green Chevrolet hurtled on through the early-afternoon heat.

CHAPTER THIRTY-EIGHT

THE SUPERINTENDENT stooped over the clacking teletype and glanced at his watch. It was approaching two, almost two hours since he had listened to the last message in the radio room.

The defensive ring of cars—he hoped it would turn out to be a noose—was drawing tight around Chicago's South-west Side. Backing them up, an integral part of the defensive wall almost like some ancient, massive earthwork, was the physical bulk of the Tollway. This modern concrete dike, built to carry traffic rapidly around the South Side, would now be made to serve a different function: as a dam to keep the culprits out of the city.

But this dam had holes in it. Forty-one holes between the Indiana line going south and Roosevelt Road, running west: the area where the men would most likely try to penetrate.

The teletype came to life.

"WE WILL HAV 39 CARS," it stuttered onto the unwinding roll.

"HOW MANY IN PLAS NOW?" he pecked back.

"THIRTY ON STATION. FIVE MORE DISPATCHT. FOUR LEFT TO GO. LOOKS LIKE WE'LL HAVE TO LEAVE TWO HOLES."

"O.K. LEAVE TWO NEAREST INDIANA LINE."

"O.K."

He had a thought. "WAIT MIN," he typed. He wanted a strategic reserve. His defense line was entirely static. He wanted at least two cars mobile, held back centrally someplace, even at the risk of uncovering two more of the less heavily traveled routes.

He went back to the other room and looked at his map, then returned to the teletype and spelled out: DISPATCH CORRECTION. PULL CARS OFF INTERSECTIONS AT TORRENCE AND BLUE ISLAND FOR MOBILE RESERVE. ONE AT JCT RTS 50 AND 7 OTHER AT 34 AND 42A."

"YES SIR," was the reply.

He bent over again and typed. "THIS IMPORTANT. VERIFY YOUR DISPATCH THEN TELETYPE ALL CAR NUMBERS WITH INTERSECTIONS ASSIGNED. I WILL HANDLE THE DIRECT DISPATCH FROM HERE ROUTED THROUGH YOUR TRANSMITTER FOR EXTRA POWER. DO YOU HAVE ANY QUEST."

In a minute the reply came. "NO QUEST. SIGNAL WHEN U ARE READY TO ASSUME CONTROL."

"O.K.," he typed, then walked out toward the other room. As he got to the door the bell rang the Post Seven signal again, and he walked back to the teletype. He acknowledged, and the machine spelled out: "WE HAVE CALL FROM CIVIL AIR PATROL. PRIVATE TRI-PACER AIRCRAFT ALERTED BY FAA, MIDWAY AIRPORT, WAITING ORDERS."

"Why, bless their cotton-pickin' hearts," he mumbled to himself. It was only one little plane, and air spotting in a situation like this was chancy, but he was glad to have it. It made him feel good that they had come through for him. It was the first lift he had had all day.

"GIV HIM DESCRIPTION AND HAVE HIM ORBIT BLOCKADED SECTION TOLLWAY," he pecked.

"YES SIR," was the reply.

CHAPTER THIRTY-NINE

THE red needle stuck to 90 as if pasted there.

Their luck was holding. It had been almost an hour since they had passed the corn picker, and there had been no more close calls since then. It was 1:35.

The monotonous cornfields kept going by as if they would last forever. The deadly crossroads appeared just as regularly as the second hands went two-thirds of the way around the dials on their wrist watches.

Both men were tired now. Beat. The chases and near-misses had stirred them each time to a high pitch of excitement; their blood was saturated with adrenalin and loaded with sugar. Their bodies could not take supercharging indefinitely, and they were beginning to feel the strain. They were both in the early stages of auto-intoxication: tense, jumpy, irritable and mean. Ready to fight!

Both had sensed that something like this had happened, and by unspoken mutual consent they had stopped talking.

Then something came up which demanded communication. Grozzo noticed that they were almost out of gas. He waited until the needle was almost on "E," then reached over and tapped the gauge with his finger to attract the other man's attention.

"Goddam," said Rayder tensely. "How much farther will it go?"

"Twenty miles, maybe thirty. I wouldn't risk more'n twenty."

"I make it, we're still forty or forty-five miles out. We may have to stop and hit one of these farmers," said Rayder.

Silently he cursed himself again for not bringing guns.

They peeled off another five miles; then the clump of trees that usually signified a town showed above the green fields ahead.

"Here comes a town."

"Go all the way through and stop at the last station on the other side. Leave the motor running."

It was a village of a few thousand, about the size of Bucola, at the fringe of the metropolitan build-up. They watched with cat's eyes for anything suspicious.

Nothing! Just a drowsing country town. They idled through.

A block from where the cornfields started up again, the driver swung into a station.

"Fill it," he said to the uniformed man who walked out.

Rayder kept watch out the back as the attendant set the hose into the opening and left it running while he went around to wipe the windshield.

Ahead of them, a block away, a black car pulled up at the side street entering the highway, paused, then turned in their direction and came slowly down the street. It had a big, bronze star on the side and the legend GRAPE CREEK POLICE DEPARTMENT.

Grozzo made a peculiar noise in his throat. The attendant was right at his open window, leaning across, wiping the windshield.

Rayder instantly swung around. Smoothly, appearing not to hurry, he completed the turn and nonchalantly rested his chin on the back of the front seat. His head pointed towards the dashboard, but his eyes, like a hawk's, followed the black sedan. Its driver, a young-looking man without a hat, was not in any apparent hurry. He came easily down the street, eyes casually taking in the scene on both sides. As he came by, his eyes flickered over them quickly, then stuck for just a minute. They shifted away again. As they did so, Rayder touched the driver's sleeve. There was a barely perceptible nod.

As soon as the police car was a few feet past them, its driver quickly spun his head for a fast look at the rear window. Almost instantly he was jamming on his brakes and turning.

Rayder shouted, "Hit it!"

Grozzo had had the car in gear with the engine running and clutch depressed. He let it out and floored the gas. The tires screamed as the car rocketed out, spilling the attendant sideways and pulling the hose from the pump. They were a hundred yards down the street before the police car was fairly on to the station apron.

But, once past the sprawled attendant and back out into the street, he came charging—siren, lights and all. And from his back bumper waved the twenty-foot, spring-mounted fishpole that meant he was radio-equipped.

Both cars accelerated flat out until the men found that they were once again tempting fate in a hundred-thirty-mile-an-hour chase. The road was dry and powdery. The lead car raised a plume of dust which soon obscured the pursuing machine.

Rayder immediately got on the radio, just on the chance the man might slow or turn rather than chase them blindly at high speed through the dust cloud they were raising.

"Not all cops are brave," he said, half-aloud.

For a few minutes he got nothing, then he realized that this would be a local outfit, not on the state frequency. He shifted to the other wave band and picked him up. The cop was young. His voice was excited, and he sounded inexperienced.

"This is Grape Creek police. I am chasing a green Chevrolet with a bullet hole in his rear window. We are north of Grape Creek. There was a call out on a car like this. Can anybody help?"

In a minute an authoritative voice said, "Grape Creek police, this is State Police Post Two. Where are you now?"

"Several miles north of Grape Creek. We should be getting close to the canal and the Des Plaines River. I'm in his dust and can't see very well."

"We are searching for a car that fits your description. The men in it hit a supermarket downstate this morning. I am going to feed your transmission into our communications net here so the cars we have out will be able to help you. It is very important that you let us know where you are at all times so we can move in. Do you understand?"

"Yes, okay, I'll do my best, but I can't see much in this dust."

Sweat broke out on Rayder's brow as he listened to the noose again being tightened about them.

The dispatcher carefully began to inform the men in the blockade of the status of the chase. He was interrupted by a shout from the young officer.

"We just crossed the bridge over the river. They're heading for Route Sixty-six. That's just about five miles north of here. It looks like they're going to take Sixty-six to Chi."

A babble of voices broke loose as cars announced themselves ready to join the chase, asked questions or said they were ready to leave their posts. This sudden scrambling rush was not at all according to the Super's plans, but men in action rarely conform to carefully prelaid schedules.

An angry voice cut through the babble and mounting confusion. "This is Superintendent Franklin. I am assuming dispatch control. I want total radio silence. *NOW!*"

In a few seconds the air became silent, and Franklin continued in a calmer voice. "All units maintain position unless dispatched otherwise. Cars Four-One, Eight-Three, and One-Nine, proceed south on Route Sixty-six. Try to intercept the car now being chased. You are authorized to use your radios; acknowledge."

They did, and Franklin stopped transmitting.

The chase car came on again. "We ought to be getting pretty close to Sixty-six. I can't tell if he's slowing down yet. I'll let you know as he turns."

In the lead car there was no plan, nor apparently any resources left for forming one. The two men were scared and tired, not far from panic. Even Rayder's strength seemed to desert him. He appeared to be capable of nothing but a hypnotic concentration on the radio, as if by some act of will he could do something about the relentless pursuer, unseen but broadcasting loudly from the dust cloud boiling behind the fleeing car.

Grozzo appeared oblivious to everything except concentrating on just keeping them on the road.

At the break in the transmissions, Rayder looked blankly up

at the road ahead. It curved, ever so slightly, not enough to slow them, but just enough so that he could see only a few hundred feet ahead.

Presently, to one side, he saw a smoking factory chimney rising into the air. His subconscious mind was about to dismiss this as of absolutely no consequence when the impression stopped being subconscious. Something was wrong with the picture!

Something was really wrong! It all rushed to the front of his mind. That chimney was moving—*toward him*—only it wasn't a chimney. It was the exhaust pipe of a diesel truck rising above the corn.

Even as his mind was registering the fact, they came into the open at an angling crossing. A bare hundred feet ahead lay the two concrete ribbons of a superhighway. There was a truck, only a few feet away and approaching them at an acute angle, looking like an ocean liner. The massive grill loomed over Rayder like a big square cliff. Then the car squirted past, saved only by its great speed.

Neither of the drivers had any time to react. In an instant, the car was across both lanes of the divided highway. It was safe, blasting down the gravel road again on the other side.

Rayder watched the huge tanker as it crossed his field of vision out of the rear window. It looked like a great blunt-ended sausage. Just as it came squarely behind him, he saw a flash of wheels under its belly, approaching from the other side.

Suddenly, the monster jumped four feet into air. He was sure he saw a seam in the middle of the tank opening and a wash of liquid starting out. Before it could touch the ground, there was a huge yellow flash followed by a great white and red ball of fire that mushroomed, grew and tumbled as it coiled in upon itself, churning skyward.

Simultaneously came a clap like an exploding artillery shell. Then a huge *whoof* nudged his own car, as it sped down the road. He felt the skin on his face singe.

Incongruously, there came jumping, bumping and flipping, chasing straight down the road after them and looking almost like a glittering football, the egg-shaped siren-*cum*-red light mounting from the police car. It gave a last mighty bounce high into the air and disintegrated, a small silver part twinkling in the sunlight as it spun up and up into the air, then down and over into the field.

Stunned, they slowed the car and drove along slowly for a moment. Then Grozzo turned to look at his companion.

"That was Sixty-six," he said. "You wanna go back and go into the city on it? It's the quickest way."

Rayder looked at him with dull, vague eyes. Finally, he said, "No, we couldn't get by the wreck."

"What do you wanna do?"

Again there was a pause, while Rayder stared with dead, unfocused eyes. Eventually, he said simply, "You do it."

The driver gave him a long look, then turned back around without speaking. He turned right at 55th Street, which ran into Chicago on an angling course north.

The Tollway was ten miles ahead.

CHAPTER FORTY

Superintendent Franklin had been pacing the floor like a man outside a hospital delivery room. It was time now, it must be time. The climax of their frantic, pushing, day-long effort was bound to come within the next few minutes.

He had known that he shouldn't react as he did, but he had felt somehow responsible. If the intercept failed, he would consider the blame and humiliation to be his alone.

Then the speaker had squawked into life with the report from the Grape Creek policeman that he had brought the men to a chase again.

Franklin had walked over and gripped the edge of the radio console with both hands. He felt like a football coach on Saturday afternoon. He had created the team and directed its strategy. Now, he must direct it in action.

Taking the mike, he had ordered the upstate transmitter run up to maximum power, then had taken charge of the dispatch and gotten the situation under control again. As soon as things were stabilized he had pulled three cars off the blockade and sent them down Route 66 to try an intercept at the junction of the county road and 66.

He had had a desk moved up near the transmitter with the large Chicago area map atop it. Each car he had at his disposal had been marked with a numbered pin so that he could see the whole situation at a glance.

The pursuing car had come on again, saying, "We're almost . . ." Then the voice had stopped suddenly and the air had gone dead. There was not even transmitter hum. It was the second time today this had happened, and Franklin felt a chill of apprehension.

The tension in the radio room started to rise. Somebody broke in. "This is Unit Four One proceeding south on Sixty-six. There's a big ball of fire, about two miles ahead of me on the highway. Must be a tank truck, to be that big. I'm about six miles south of the Tollway intersection now. Shall I stop and assist?"

"You'll have to," Franklin said instantly. "But keep your eyes peeled till you get there. The Chevrolet should be up to Sixty-six by now. Can you see the two cars we pulled in from either side of you to go down Sixty-six?"

"This is Eighty-three," said a voice. "I was at the Plainfield interchange. I'm about two miles behind him."

He was followed by another. "Nineteen. I can see Eighty-three."

"Okay," said the dispatcher. "You two keep going."

There was silence for a few moments. The Super began squeezing the mike, and his hand began to vibrate.

A trooper's voice filled the room. "I'm at the fire! Lemont Road. That was a police car that hit a tank truck. They said it was chasing a car."

Franklin jumped erect. This meant the fugitives had crossed 66. They were north of it somewhere! They had got past the interception point!

As the significance sank in he expected, somewhere in the back of his mind, to become emotional again, to feel as before the bitter disappointment and hurt. Instead his emotions dropped away like a garment, and he was suddenly coldly analytical.

Faster than he could have articulated them, his thoughts sped through his brain. He was in serious trouble. He had breached his static defense line to send three units down 66 to try for an intercept. Because of the explosion and wreck of the pursuing police car, contact with the quarry was now lost. They were free, loose in the maze again, and there was a gap in his line at Route 66.

The explosion had occurred at Lemont Road and Route 66, ten miles down 66 from the point where 66 bisected the Tollway. The static defense, the blockade on the Tollway to the south and east of that line, was already obsolete. The cars there could be pulled out and used offensively, provided there was time to use them. Could they be brought up and used to reinforce the arc of cars stretching north of 66, and plug the hole?

Most of the cars were farther away from the blockade points on the Tollway than were the fugitives. The idea of bringing them up as reinforcements was useless unless he could gain time. How?

Freeze it! He could freeze time by having the units already in position to the north of 66 pull out and physically block the inbound lanes. Stop all traffic through their intersections into Chicago. If the fugitives went around the stalled lines they would be giving themselves away. They would have to wait in line immobilized, while he moved his forces. Then his men from the south end could come up to reinforce them.

He realized that his greatest weakness was still the hole at 66 and the two adjoining intersections which he had stripped for the abortive intercept try. These intersections had to be sealed first. They must have first priority.

He had started to reach for the mike when a thought from a deeper level hit him. According to games theory, the safest optimum assumption was that the pursued knew the pursuer's strategy.

Something in him rebelled at the concept. They couldn't know about the Tollway blockade. He had used the teletype! Besides, nothing that had happened had indicated that the men had a radio.

But, using the games theory assumption, if they did have a radio, the minute he started to broadcast, his whole strategy would be compromised. They would know about the blockade and all its elements.

The first thing he had intended to do was to plug the three holes directly north of 66. If the fugitives were listening they could beat his cars—drive right through.

Impasse! There was no way out for him.

Then it hit him—a double-win strategy, a fail-safe maneuver.

He would use the games theory assumption, use it as a lever, on a forcing gambit, and then, if the assumption failed, he would still have the original reinforcement strategy intact.

He said into the mike, "Civil Air Patrol, this is Franklin, State Police. How far are you from the intersection of the Tollway and Route Sixty-six?"

"Uh, about five or six miles."

That was good enough. That left one absolute condition, about which he could do nothing but hope. He decided to risk it.

He said, "Civil Air Patrol, head for Tollway and Route Sixty-six junction. Do not transmit until I call you."

He said slowly and succinctly, "This is Franklin to all cars north of Route Sixty-six on the Tollway blockade. Pull out and block traffic inbound. Do not allow any cars into Chicago through your intersection. Do it now!"

He continued slowly, without pause, "Civil Air Patrol, three intersections on the Tollway, the one at Route Sixty-six and the intersections at either side—Plainfield and Archer—are unguarded. Get there as quickly as you can and maintain a patrol. Our quarry is a green Chevrolet, two men, bullet hole in the back window. Do you read the transmission?"

"Roger," came the reply, "on the way, but——"

"Do not transmit unless you sight them," Franklin almost shouted. "That's an order. I have priority."

Deliberately he began to pull the cars from the south half of the blockade and dispatch them north, to reinforce the units now blocking traffic. He was careful to dispatch them only by number and to refer to the units being reinforced only by number, giving neither the street location nor direction.

He finished with an admonition: "Cars Seven-Eight and Three-Four, keep your engines turning. Be ready to move out without notice."

CHAPTER FORTY-ONE

THE green car tooled up 55th Street toward the Tollway, observing the speed laws. The driver was clear-headed and alert. Once more, as soon as the immediate danger was past, he had relaxed.

The tightly controlled man in the back seat was having a little harder time of it. For the first time in his adult life, he was feeling in less than complete control of himself. His cold poise was wearing away, abrading under the repeated cycle of excitement and danger. He wasn't completely out of action by any means; but he was profoundly shaken.

The radio boomed out the trooper's announcement that he was at the scene of the fire. Rayder half listened. So what?

As Franklin's voice came on, directing the cars in the north segment of the blockade to pull out and seal the intersections, Rayder snapped to alertness. He spun the dial, flooding the car with volume.

"Did he say blockade on the Tollway?" Grozzo's fear-tightened voice sounded louder than the radio.

"Shut up," roared Rayder, straining to catch everything that was coming in.

Franklin's direction to the plane and then his clear exposition of the three unguarded streets brought them to violent action.

"We gotta beat that plane!" yelled Rayder. "Plainfield is the closest. Go! Open up!!!"

The husky driver needed no urging. He pulled into the left lane, turned on his lights and, dropping the car into second, charged the oncoming traffic at seventy miles an hour.

Deftly, like a swivel-hipped quarterback going downfield, he danced the high-powered machine through the knots of cars approaching them. The quick and the bright yielded to him, getting out of the way. The uncomprehending or frightened, or those with slow reflexes, he maneuvered around, matching and balancing his car's speed against his own reflexes, surely and deliberately using the power from the big engine and the racing brakes to maneuver the sedan like a sports car.

They turned south on Madison and raced the two miles to the junction with Plainfield. Coming into the intersection they had a green light. His hands a blur of motion, Grozzo cribbed the wheel, hit the gas, then the brakes, then the gas again, and sent them through the turn in a sixty-mile-an-hour racing drift. Two miles straight ahead, barely visible, was the Tollway interchange.

The luck was holding.

CHAPTER FORTY-TWO

A TRANSMITTER came in. It carried a different background sound from those of the police cars. The aircraft engine was much noisier. The pilot was excited.

"State Police, this is Civil Air Patrol. I am over the junction of Route Sixty-six and Tollway at about three thousand feet. About a mile north of me and a mile and a half west, on Plainfield, there is a green car headed in toward the city going like blazes. He is driving against traffic most of the time and keeps his lights on. Shall I——"

"Can you stay with him? Can you keep him in sight?"

"No sweat."

"Stay with him. Stay on the air. Give us a continuing broadcast of where he is and whether he turns."

"Roger."

Franklin turned the volume up high, and said, "This is the Superintendent to all units. This is it! Our quarry is on Plainfield now, approaching the Tollway from the southwest, about a mile out. Anyone who thinks he is close enough to get into it, get down there. Some of you dispatched north as reinforcements should be at or near the Plainfield intersection now. You should be in the best position to give chase. Units Seven-Eight and Three-Four, you are released from reserve. Move out. Seven-Eight, you are almost directly in their path. Move up three blocks to the intersection of Plainfield and First. Commandeer a truck and block the road."

CHAPTER FORTY-THREE

THE airplane wheeled over and fell in behind the fleeing car. With each dispatch order that came over the transmitter, the car spurted ahead, until it was traveling the city street at over a hundred miles an hour.

As the car finished under the Tollway interchange, a blue police car, looking from the air oddly like a toy, came rapidly up the Tollway from the southwest. Without slowing, it turned into the parabolic curve of the exit ramp and went around it in a full-power, tire-smoking drift, emerging from the exit chute like a stone from a slingshot. It was only two blocks behind the madly plunging green machine. A minute later, another one completed the same maneuver.

The sight of the cruiser seemed to unhinge the driver of the first car. His maneuvers became less precise, almost as if his reflexes had gone bad. The crisp authority with which he had controlled his machine seemed to give way to sluggishness, to uncertainty, perhaps to fear. His responses became exaggerated. The car began to wallow and slip in its desperate maneuvers. But it did not slow down.

When the roadblock became visible ahead, the driver of the green car hit his brakes to kill speed, then turned and braked more to set up his drift for a turn.

And the long string of luck ran out!

He overcontrolled. Instead of a drift, the car went into a wild slide, out of control. It slid around once, glanced from a taxi, then went head-on into a utility pole.

The crash was so loud that the pilot heard it plainly. His quiet words, "Oh, my God," came back over the air.

His observer, sitting alongside, was not so reverent. He took the mike and said, "It's all over. They ran into a post, but good." He paused a minute, then said, "Say, you know it's a good thing they were driving fast enough to draw attention to themselves. We'd never have picked them out otherwise. There's hundreds of green cars, and you can't tell one from the other from the air. We have to fly at least a thousand feet high over towns. Whattya suppose they were driving so fast for? Nothing was chasing them!"

At the Post, Franklin leaned against the radio and said softly, "Oh yes there was. It's something called the Safest Optimum Assumption. We *made* them race you for that hole."